FARMING IN LINCOLNSHIRE
1850–1945

STUDIES IN THE HISTORY OF LINCOLNSHIRE 2

FARMING IN LINCOLNSHIRE
1850–1945

JONATHAN BROWN

Lincoln

HISTORY OF LINCOLNSHIRE COMMITTEE

2005

Published 2005 by
The History of Lincolnshire Committee, Jews' Court, Steep Hill, Lincoln, LN2 1LS

ISBN   hard back   0 902668 22 X

ISBN   paperback   0 902668 23 8

Cover illustrations:

Top: Robin Wheeldon, *Marshall Threshing Set* (detail), painting reproduced by kind permission of the artist

Bottom: 'Planting Majestic potatoes near Spalding', photo reproduced by kind permission of Lady Nevile

Cover design by Max Marschner Graphics, Lincoln LN5 8 PN

Typeset and produced for the publisher by Yard Publishing Services, Sudbury CO10 2AG

Printed in England by the Cambridge Printing House, Cambridge CB2 2BS

British Cataloguing-in-Publication Data

A catalogue record for this book is obtainable from the British Library

CONTENTS

FIGURES

Photograph acknowledgements

Museum of English Rural Life, University of Reading: 2–5, 7, 11–16, 22–24, 26–30, 32–36, 38–43. North East Lincolnshire Libraries: 6, 8–10, 17–21, 25. Mr G. H. Brown: 37. Lady Nevile: 31.

TABLES

FOREWORD

Jonathan Brown's study of Lincolnshire farming from 1850 to 1945 is the second in the Studies in the History of Lincolnshire series. This is a series of substantial works which supplement the authoritative chronological account presented in the first History of Lincolnshire series, with scholarly studies of particular aspects of the county's history at various periods. In this volume Dr Brown examines almost a hundred years of farming in Lincolnshire from the 'Golden Age' of the first half of Queen Victoria's reign to the dawning of the new era ushered in by the exigencies of the Second World War. Meticulous study of the 'June returns' of cropping and livestock numbers underpins this peroration of the ups and downs of a century of animal husbandry and cultivation of the diverse soils of the county. The book considers the extent to which the renowned, mid 19th-century 'high farming' of Lincolnshire was maintained in the periods of depression and recovery which followed. The story is enriched with abundant references to the experiences of individual farmers, landowners and labourers. It draws on a wide range of sources: farm accounts, diaries, estate records, government figures, newspaper reports and a body of literature which embraces local studies as well as erudite academic works. From this narrative a clear picture emerges of the distinctiveness of the different farming regions of the county and the diversity of human experience. Dr Brown's position at the University of Reading has enabled him to illustrate his account with photographs from the Museum of English Rural Life as well as from local collections.

Shirley Brook
Lincoln, October 2005

PREFACE

I count it a great honour to have been invited to contribute to the History of Lincolnshire series. I have admired the series from its inception, bought and enjoyed all the volumes. To become part of the project has been, therefore, a considerable pleasure.

Fulfilling my side of the bargain has proved to have taken rather longer than expected. Hardly had I been asked to write this volume than the demands of my day job grew to eat up much of the time that should have been free for this book. However, I had promised, the history of Lincolnshire I think is important, and besides, I have generally enjoyed writing this. So, eventually the time pressures eased, and I have been able to reach a full stop. Inevitably there are lines of inquiry that I could have, indeed would have liked to pursue, but it is definitely time to allow others to take up those causes.

In view of what I have just written, of course, my first debt of gratitude is to Professor John Beckett and his fellow members of the History of Lincolnshire Committee for inviting me to write in the first place, and then for being so patient as I continually overshot the deadlines I was setting myself. There are numerous archivists and librarians in Lincolnshire and elsewhere who have helped me with books, documents, newspapers, and illustrations ever since I first started doing research on the county and its agriculture in the mid 1970s. Several people have read drafts of the book and passed valuable comment, and spotted some slips. Most of these readers were anonymous to me, being chosen by the committee, others I asked to read. Perhaps it is best if I do not single out those I know to name: I am grateful to all these readers. There is one exception to this anonymity, and that is my wife Patricia, who has lived with this book for rather a long time, has read the draft, noted corrections, and been the greatest possible support.

INTRODUCTION

Farming has been for centuries, and to a considerable extent remains, the lifeblood of Lincolnshire. Because of that the course of change in agriculture assumes major importance in the history of the county. The century covered by this volume saw the transformation of Lincolnshire's agriculture. This was a counterpart to the industrialization of other parts of the nation, for Lincolnshire agriculture came to supply the urban markets with potatoes and suburban gardens with bulbs, two characteristic products of the county that became established during this period.

Change in Lincolnshire's agriculture was already gathering pace by the middle of the 19th century. The county had experienced its agricultural revolution, through which had come increased cultivation of root crops and rotation grasses, and the process of improving livestock to produce the improved Lincoln sheep and Lincoln Red cattle. Much of the land had been enclosed by Acts of Parliament.[1] At first these changes proceeded at a gentlemanly pace, perhaps, and did not gather momentum until the Napoleonic wars and after. It was usual for commentators on agriculture to emphasize how considerable the progress had been in the decades since Arthur Young's mixed reports on Lincolnshire agriculture following his visits at the turn of the 19th century.[2] Land that had been unenclosed waste was turned into first-class farm land in only a few decades. Local farmers themselves were coming to agree: 'Other counties, both in England and Scotland, may have entered earlier into the field of agricultural improvement, but in none has it been cultivated with greater energy and with more marked results than in this county in the half century just concluded.'[3]

That agricultural revolution was drawing to a close by the middle of the 19th century, and in Lincolnshire, in common with the rest of the country, agriculture was entering new phases of development. Most of British agriculture had gone into recession during the 1820s and 1830s, but the 1840s had seen strong recovery.[4] Markets and prices seemed now to be turning in the farmers' favour. Farming was in relatively high spirits. The repeal of the corn laws had been expected to have dire consequences for British farming but, apart from a brief pause at mid century, progress seemed to continue. Farmers were encouraged by these conditions to invest in, for example, some of the implements produced at the new engineering works at Lincoln and Gainsborough. 'High farming' was a term coined at the time to describe the type of husbandry now being adopted which depended on strong investment by farmers. 'Golden Age' was a description that came in retrospect, as many came to regard this mid-century period as a high point for British agriculture. The effect of free trade in grain proved to have been deferred. In the 1870s imports of wheat reached such a scale that prices fell sharply. Most other agricultural commodities were affected by a similar, though lesser, downward trend in prices. This 'Great Depression' lasted until the 1890s, and was one of the severest tests British agriculture had so far had to face. Recovery came slowly until the demands to feed a nation at war gave agriculture a much-needed fillip. Hope that these conditions would continue were dashed as a return to peace-time free trade brought agricultural prices down again and a renewed recession. Recovery began again in the 1930s leading up to the Second World War, helped by some support from government, acting partly in anticipation of war. So the period covered by this volume ends with farmers a second time producing as much as possible in wartime conditions and hoping that, this time, peace would look more favourably upon them.

Alongside these fluctuations in the cycle of prosperity there was the longer-term trend, the diminution of agriculture's place of importance in the economy. The effects of industrialization meant that already by the 1850s agriculture's share of economic production had fallen to about twenty per cent, compared with more than thirty per cent at the beginning of the 19th century. By 1914 the share had fallen further to no more than seven per cent of gross domestic product. The proportion of the working population engaged in farming had fallen by similar degrees and had dropped to eight per cent by 1914. The actual numbers were falling as well, and this would gather pace after the First

World War. At the same time the quantity of food imported had increased to the extent that by 1914 British farming produced only about forty per cent of the nation's food. These changes were a natural consequence of a growing, industrial economy, but there were consequences, not least the fact that government came to take less account of agriculture than in earlier ages.

Agriculture had lost its position of primacy in the national economy and society, but the same was far from true in the more rural parts of the nation. Lincolnshire was a prime example of that, and the substance of this book is the ways in which the farming of Lincolnshire experienced these vicissitudes. This is the story of how those who worked the land in Lincolnshire dealt with all these economic changes, whether in reaction to the external trends or by shaping their own fortune. Essentially, the story told here is that of the farmers and their farming. The other main sections of rural society, the landowners and labourers, have lesser roles. Landed society is the subject of another volume in the History of Lincolnshire series, *Rural Society and County Government in Nineteenth-Century Lincolnshire* by R. J. Olney, while the farm workers await their volume. Both landowners and labourers are featured by Charles Rawding, in *The Lincolnshire Wolds in the Nineteenth Century*.

There are two parts to the book. In Part I, Chapters 1–5, there is an outline of the nature and structure of the agricultural county of Lincolnshire, with chapters on its physical character and the rural infrastructure, the people who farmed and husbanded the land, and the structure and organization of the farming. These chapters tend to be weighted towards the 19th century, setting the scene for the chapters in Part II, which take us through the course of agricultural change in the county, starting with the High Farming of the Golden Age in the mid-19th century and closing with the Second World War. The concluding chapter offers a retrospect and prospect.

Notes to Introduction

1   The details of the agricultural revolution in Lincolnshire are to be found
     in T. W. Beastall, *Agricultural Revolution in Lincolnshire* (History of
     Lincolnshire v. 8, 1978) and David Grigg, *The Agricultural Revolution in
     South Lincolnshire* (1966).
2   There were two reports produced by Arthur Young for the Board of
     Agriculture: *General View of the Agriculture of Lincolnshire* (1799), and *General
     View of the Agriculture of Lincolnshire* (1813).
3   Report of the committee of the North Lincolnshire Agricultural Society,
     1851, quoted in James Obelkevitch, *Religion and Rural Society in South
     Lindsey 1825–1875* (1976) p. 14.
4   B. A. Holderness, Rural Society in South East Lindsey, unpublished PhD
     thesis, University of Nottingham, 1968, pp. 581–2.

PART I

The Land and its Cultivators

1
LINCOLNSHIRE: THE AGRICULTURAL COUNTY

Lincolnshire lies within the eastern, lowland, arable zone of England. James Caird drew this distinction between an arable zone and the pastoral and livestock farming of the western counties of England and Wales in 1851, and its validity has held ever since. In other forms of regional analysis Lincolnshire has been counted variously as part of the Midlands, the East Midlands, treated along with parts of Yorkshire, or left as a county to itself. The Board of Agriculture grouped Lincolnshire along with Norfolk and the East Riding of Yorkshire into one of the subsections of its eastern counties division. Whatever form of regional grouping one takes, however, Lincolnshire is firmly within the arable and mixed farming tradition.

That does not make Lincolnshire a county of uniformity. The contrasts within its boundaries are in many ways as strong as those with other counties and regions, for the county contains a remarkable variety of distinct physical and agricultural landscapes. Although three-quarters of the county is below 100ft, and there are some significant areas of fenland below sea level, it is by no means uniformly low lying.[1] The uplands of Wold and Heath stand out from the low-lying lands around them, the flat expanse of the Fens and Marsh, and the undulating hills of south-west Kesteven. The distinctiveness of the regions within Lincolnshire have been sufficiently marked to affect not only types of farming but also patterns of life and outlook. They can be strong enough to make moving from one area of Lincolnshire to another difficult. Charles Kightly tells of 'George', a waggoner from Walmsgate in the Wolds, who after the First World War moved to a new job in the Fens. The higher pay, £80 a year compared with £50 back home, enticed him. He could not settle, either in the job or in the flat lands and open skies of the Fens. He went back to Walmsgate as soon as he could.[2] It was common likewise for landowners to seek tenant farmers who would be familiar with their district of the county.

Figure 1 shows in simplified outline the principal regions within Lincolnshire, based upon the underlying geomorphology. The Wolds, running parallel to the coastline, are of chalk, reaching 450 feet at their highest. There is a steep escarpment to the west, and a gentle falling away to the east, but within this range, the hills are undulating, often quite steeply so. Between the Wolds and the sea lies the plain of the Marsh. The Inner Marsh, or Middle Marsh, from Barton in the north to Firsby in the south, is mainly heavy boulder clays, while the Outer Marsh is an open landscape on marine silts and clays. Below the western scarp of the Wolds is a broad vale drained by the River Ancholme flowing north to the Humber, and which is formed of Jurassic clays of the Oxford and Kimmeridge series. The second upland range in the county is of Jurassic limestone. To the north of Lincoln it is known as the Cliff; to the south it is the Heath. Like the Wolds, this range slopes away to the east, with a steep west-facing escarpment, a prominent feature as one comes into Lincolnshire from the west. Below that escarpment is the Western Clay Vale, or Vale of Trent, of deep Lias clays. The southern part of the Jurassic upland broadens out into the Kesteven plateau, overlain with clays, mainly boulder clays. The Fens, the open, flat landscape of artificially drained low-lying clays and silts, take up the whole of the south-eastern third of Lincolnshire, and extend into the neighbouring counties around the Wash. The final segment of Lincolnshire is the Isle of Axholme in the north-west, a distinctive district of alluvial silts and peats, bound by the River Trent to the east and the Humber to the north. Like the Fens, much of this district has needed artificial drainage to secure it from flooding.

Soils vary considerably. The Fens have peat fens and silt fens. The Inner Marsh has soils of clay and loam ranging in depth from 4 to 15 feet which are suitable for pasture and tillage, while on the Outer Marsh soils are thinner and poorer, less suited to the plough. The clay vales include boulder clays, greensands, and gravels. Alan Straw identified eighteen broad types of soil in Lincolnshire. Other studies go

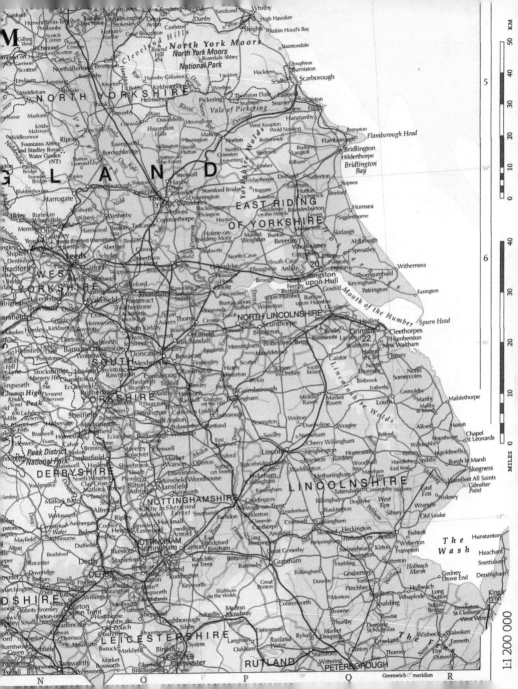

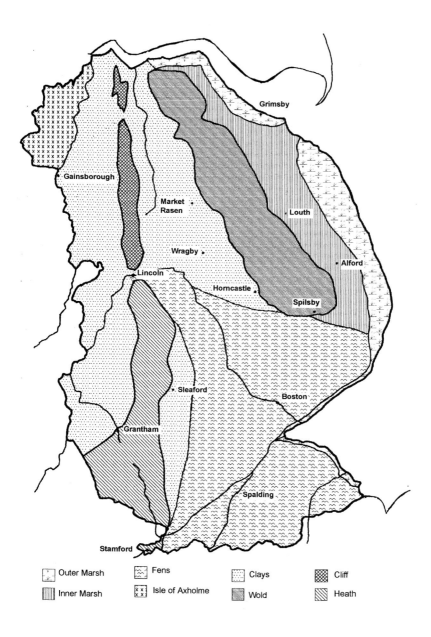

Fig. 1   Main physical regions of Lincolnshire

into greater detail: in Kesteven there are at least fourteen distinct soil types, ranging from fen-edge soils through Oxford and boulder clays to light soils of the limestone, and it is reckoned that only one parish in this division is entirely on one soil formation. These soils range in quality even within short distances. Barrowby, in south-west Kesteven, was described by J. A. Clarke as 'probably... the most fertile parish in Lincolnshire', but only a few miles away were places where the clays were more intractable, others with sandy soils that failed to hold moisture.[3] The most naturally fertile soils in the county are the alluvial and silty soils of the Fens and Isle of Axholme. At the other end of the scale, the chalk and limestone of the Heath and the Wolds can produce very thin soils with little innate fertility, short of organic matter and quick to dry out. The extent to which clays and other soils overlay or mixed with these soils could be significant for the nature of the farming. Thus the Wolds range from the 'good wold' of the north, which has deeper, more fertile soils, to the 'poor wold' in the south of this district from Caistor to Spilsby, where the hills are steeper, occasionally quite difficult to cultivate. Along the eastern edge of the region is an area of 'heavy wold', where the chalk meets the clays. Although soil quality has varied greatly, very little land has proved incapable of cultivation.[4] Local variations in soil and landscape have been exploited historically in the development of patterns of settlement and farming. Farm boundaries and layouts created to include the full range of soils available locally continued to have influence into the 20th century.

The climate in Lincolnshire has on the whole been a benefit for agriculture. In common with all of eastern England, rainfall is fairly low. Few areas in the county receive more than 25 inches of rain a year. Its distribution through the year has generally been favourable for the germination and ripening of cereal crops, although for potatoes additional irrigation has often become necessary. Cold easterly winds can be a problem in the open agricultural landscape, but for the most part temperatures have been kind to the county's agriculture.

Economic and agricultural change

Lincolnshire in the mid-19th century was, if not isolated, at least on the periphery of England. The Great North Road skirted the south-western corner of the county on its way to York. The main line of the Great Northern Railway followed suit, even missing out Stamford, which the road went through. The industrial revolution, too, was almost entirely by-passing the county. Not until late in the 19th century, with the arrival of the iron and steel industry at Scunthorpe, was there much to suggest that Lincolnshire was other than rural. Most of the industry that had been established before that had its foundations in agriculture, processing the products of farming in mills and maltings. Even the new engineering firms founded their success on manufacturing implements and machines for farming.[5] The 20th century introduced new industries, such as canning, while the engineering firms steadily moved away from agricultural roots into other branches of heavy engineering. Fishing and the holiday trades of the coast both expanded. Even so, these developments were not sufficient to turn Lincolnshire into an industrial or commercial county by 1939.

   With neither coal nor major industry to attract them, railways came relatively late to Lincolnshire. The first line, from Lincoln to Newark, was opened in 1846. The main railways were opened between 1848 and 1852, including the Manchester, Sheffield & Lincolnshire Railway serving the north of the county, and the East Lincolnshire line from Grimsby to Boston and Peterborough. Grantham was the only Lincolnshire town served directly by the main line of the Great Northern Railway on its route from London to Doncaster, although junctions with other lines did offer many other places better connections to London. Branches and cross-country lines in the county were still being built in the 1870s, some even later, and people in many parts of Lincolnshire felt their isolation keenly. The Wolds was one area particularly affected, for this is not good terrain for railway construction, and the one line that crossed the region, from Louth to Bardney, was not opened until 1876.[6]

   Once the railways had arrived they had an immediate impact on local transport. Traffic on turnpike roads declined. Although the county was not blessed with the extensive network of navigable rivers and small coastal ports that East Anglia had, there were some useful waterways. The River Witham was navigable from Boston to Lincoln. Improvements to this and to other waterways in the Fens, including the River Glen, the Fossdyke and the South Forty Foot Drain, had enabled goods and passenger services to develop in south Lincolnshire. The River Trent through Gainsborough linked the western part of the county with waterway networks of the Midlands. Connections to the Trent via the Grantham Canal and to Lincoln via Torksey were also established. All of these, however, soon declined as the railways established their dominance in the transport of Lincolnshire's barley and malt to Burton upon Trent, wool to Bradford, potatoes to Manchester and London. With many parts of the county still at a distance from a railway and without good communications, proposals for new branch lines and light railways continued to be put forward until the early 20th century, when the petrol lorry began to offer a way out of transport difficulties.[7]

Lincolnshire, then, was primarily an agricultural county. At the 1871 census nearly a third of the working male population in the county was enumerated under the agricultural class of occupations. If one removes those such as fishermen, grooms, and jockeys to get a more purely agricultural class, the figure is still almost 30 per cent. In villages the occupational balance was tipped even more heavily towards agriculture. Four examples demonstrate this, taking male occupations only: Pinchbeck had 70.2 per cent in the agricultural group (1871), Heckington 64.2 per cent (1871), Barnetby 63.2 per cent (1881), Welbourn 69.6 per cent (1881). To those who worked the land can be added many more who were dependent directly or indirectly upon farming. There were the landowners, the processors of the produce of farming, and those who supplied goods to farming. Craftsmen, such as blacksmiths, were among the largest occupational groups after agriculture, and to those could be added all those who made and mended things for farmers, constructed their buildings, transported their goods, banked their money and wrote their wills.[8]

The market towns in Lincolnshire were an integral part of this agricultural structure. Their closeness to the surrounding country was such that into the 1850s and 1860s directories record farmers with addresses quite near the centre of such towns as Grantham and Sleaford. The small markets were already disappearing as transport was improved. Caistor, Folkingham, and Wainfleet were among the places whose markets were described as of little consequence by the 1850s. Sometimes fairs continued to function at these smaller towns for some years. In the larger towns the markets were maintaining their vigour, and there was much activity in improving their conditions and facilities. As might be expected in a strongly arable county new market halls and corn exchanges were among the principal improvements of the mid-19th century. Stamford had a new market hall built in 1839. Lincoln corn exchange was opened in 1847, and nearly all the other towns had their exchanges built during the next ten years. Sometimes there were two, as at Grantham. The largest corn markets were in Lincoln, Gainsborough, Grantham, and Boston. Prices recorded in the *London Gazette* tended to be higher in the markets on the western side of the county, closer to the main routes to London and the Midlands. The differential could be as great as five shillings a quarter between Lincoln and Louth, for example. Long before the railways came, there were many farmers who found it worth carting their barley twenty or more miles to Lincoln to take advantage of higher prices. There were several fairs held in the county. By far the greatest and most renowned were the Boston May sheep fair and the Horncastle horse fair in August.[9] The railway brought more buyers and sellers from a distance into Horncastle fair, at least for a couple of decades, but it was also opening up new patterns of marketing for Lincolnshire farmers. They could travel or send their produce to markets further away. The railway companies, for example, encouraged the development of Retford livestock market as a regional centre for the eastern counties.[10] By the end of the century direct sales of potatoes and wool to merchants travelling out from London and the industrial towns were becoming more common.

While industrialization was yet to have serious effect upon Lincolnshire, agricultural revolution had already had considerable impact. Here, too, the county was something of a late developer, lagging some way behind the pioneers of agrarian change to be found in Norfolk in the 18th century. Those problems of isolation and poor transport were reckoned to be among the primary contributory influences behind the slow pace of agricultural change in Lincolnshire before the Napoleonic wars.[11] Among the features of laggardliness compared with East Anglia was the late enclosure of some tracts of land. Parliamentary enclosure got under way in Lincolnshire between the 1750s and the 1780s, but several places remained to be enclosed after 1815. The waste character of the Heath had a certain notoriety. The last major enclosure here was not until 1823, when 2,500 acres of Blankney Heath were brought into cultivation. Some pockets were still not enclosed until later in the 1820s and 1830s, and gorse was a common feature of the landscape into the 1840s.[12] Most of the Wolds had been enclosed by 1780, but a few parts were still rabbit warrens as late as 1800, and in some parishes enclosure was not completed until well into the 19th century. Enclosure of North Kelsey and Grasby was not finished until the 1830s–40s. Much of the Marsh and clay vales had been enclosed from the 18th century onwards in order to provide for the expansion of grazing land. Even here, though, there were parishes where enclosure was still being undertaken after 1820. North Thoresby and Marshchapel were among the last, not completed until 1846. Late though some of these enclosures had been, by 1850 the process was effectively over, and agricultural Lincolnshire presented a landscape of hedged and fenced order. Many of the farmsteads, especially on the Wolds and Heath, were scattered and isolated.[13]

The Fens were also subject to continuing change during the early 19th century. Securing the low-lying land from flooding by controlling the surface drainage had begun in the 17th century and was still going on in the early 19th century. East, West, and Wildmore Fens were being drained during the Napoleonic wars. In the years after the wars some of the main drainage channels of the Fens were deepened. Steam-powered drainage pumps were introduced at this time, the first in the Isle of Ely in 1819–20. By the late 1840s there were sufficient steam pumps at work to give the region much greater assurance of freedom from flooding. There was room for some further improvement, but at last the drainage of the Fens was drawing to a close.[14] The Fens now had become a largely artificial landscape. Those parts that remained liable to flooding were left as unimproved pastures; elsewhere improved methods of husbandry were rapidly being adopted. The recentness of these developments meant that much of the eastern fens continued to have the air of a frontier settlement.

The Isle of Axholme also needed artificial drainage and flood control, and here again the first major works had come in the 17th century, followed by a long process of securing the land. With the watercourses secure, farmers on land adjoining the Trent and its tributaries developed the practice of warping, the controlled flooding of land to gain additional deposits of river silts. Warping was well established by the end of the 18th century and common by the 1850s. It was expensive. Arthur Young quotes some high figures for building sluices on the Trent, and in 1918 £50 per acre was reckoned to be the going rate. Farmers were satisfied that increased yields more than paid for it, until the inter-war years. Then rising costs sent warping into decline.[15]

The change that had come to Lincolnshire's agriculture and landscape by the 1840s was attracting comment. Philip Pusey was struck most forcibly when he visited the Heath in the early 1840s. 'For miles', he wrote, 'we passed on through fields of turnips without a blank or a weed, on which thousands after thousands of long-woolled sheep were feeding in netted folds…. Every stubble field was clean and bright; all the hedges kept low, and neatly trimmed; every farm-house well built, with spacious courts, and surrounded by such rows of high, long, saddle-backed ricks as showed that the land did not forget to return in August what it had received from the fold in December….' Pusey was clearly enthused by the more observable and dramatic changes. He added, 'It is not until you reach Northumberland that superior farming is found'.[16] The farming of the light-soiled lands such as the Heath especially attracted him, and he contrasted them favourably with similar areas in southern England. In 1851 James Caird was of the opinion that Lincolnshire farmers still fell below the best in the country, to be found in East Anglia, and especially Norfolk. In general, however, later comment on the county returned to the theme of high standards of upkeep of the land. Many commentators on agriculture were in general agreement that Lincolnshire was now one of the foremost of English counties. A report on the farm prize competition of the Royal Agricultural Society in 1888 emphasized the 'trim and highly-farmed enclosures, productive as a garden' to be found on the Heath, while the farms of the Wolds were 'celebrated examples of high and skilful cultivation'. Later, Rider Haggard wrote, 'To those who are concerned with the land and agriculture this is perhaps the most deeply interesting county in all England.'[17]

The healthy state of the agricultural land and its husbandry was owing to the care of those who tended it, and they form the subject of the next chapter.

Notes to Chapter 1

1   L. Dudley Stamp, *Land Utilization Survey of England, parts 76–77* (1942) p. 425. K. C. Edwards, 'Lincolnshire', in J. Mitchell (ed.), *Great Britain: geographical essays* (1962) pp. 308–15.

2   Charles Kightly, *Country Voices: life and lore in farm and village* (1984) p. 49.

3   J. A. Clarke, 'On the Farming of Lincolnshire', *JRASE,* v. 12 (1851) p. 267.

4   G. B. Wells, 'Some Aspects of East Midland Agriculture: 5 Lincolnshire (Kesteven)', *JRASE* (1954) p. 16. Alan Straw, *The Soils of Lincolnshire* (1969).

5   See Neil R. Wright, *Lincolnshire Towns and Industry* (1982).

6   J. G. Ruddock and R. E. Pearson, *The Railway History of Lincoln* (1974) chapters 3–4. J. V. Beckett, 'Lincolnshire and the East Midlands: a historian's perspective', *Lincolnshire History and Archaeology,* v. 27 (1992) p. 25.

7   David Grigg, *The Agricultural Revolution in South Lincolnshire* (1966) pp. 41–6. J. G. Ruddock and R. E. Pearson, *The Railway History of Lincoln* (1974) pp. 18–28. Wright, *Lincolnshire Towns and Industry,* pp. 119–36.

8   Census Returns, 1871, vol. iii, Occupational Tables, pp. 374–81. The total population of Lincolnshire in 1871 was 436,599. Dennis Mills (ed.), *Twentieth Century Lincolnshire,* History of Lincolnshire v. 12 (1989) pp. 27, 321.

9   D. N. Robinson, *The Book of Horncastle and Woodhall Spa* (1983) pp. 89–99, gives a full description of Horncastle horse fair.

10   Roger Scola, *Feeding the Victorian City: the food supply of Manchester 1770–1870* (1992) pp. 56–7.

11   Grigg, *The Agricultural Revolution in South Lincolnshire*, p. 69.

12   *Ibid.*, p. 156.

13   G. E. Collins, 'Agriculture', *Victoria County History, Lincolnshire*, v. 2 (1906) pp. 399–401. E. & R. C. Russell, *Making New Landscapes in North Lincolnshire* (1983). E. & R. C. Russell, *Parliamentary Enclosure and New Lincolnshire Landscapes* (1987). T. W. Beastall, *Agricultural Revolution in Lincolnshire* (History of Lincolnshire v. 8, 1978) pp. 22–4, 30–2,42–3.

14   H. C. Darby, *The Drainage of the Fens* (2nd ed. 1956). J. A. Clarke, 'On the Great Level of the Fens, including the Fens of South Lincolnshire', *JRASE,* v. 8 (1847) pp. 80–133. Grigg, *The Agricultural Revolution in South Lincolnshire*, pp. 23–32, 137–41.

15   Beastall, *Agricultural Revolution in Lincolnshire* pp. 71ff, has a full description of the process of warping at the end of the 18th century. *Agricultural Gazette,* 21 October 1918. V. Cory, 'The Development of Farming in the Isle of Axholme', *JRASE,* v. 147 (1986) p. 59.

16   Philip Pusey, 'On the Agricultural Improvements of Lincolnshire', *JRASE,* v. 4 (1843) pp. 287, 289.

17   James Caird, *English Agriculture in 1850–51* (1852) pp. 187, 189, 193–7. F. I. Cooke, 'Report on the Farm Prize Competition in Nottinghamshire and Lincolnshire in 1888, class I', *JRASE,* v. 49 (1888) pp. 510, 521–2. H. Rider Haggard, *Rural England* (1902) v. 2, p. 144.

2
FARMING SOCIETY: FARMERS

By the mid-19th century the farmers of Lincolnshire were beginning to enjoy the reputation of being among the best in the country. The Lincolnshire farmer 'belongs to the aristocracy of his race', wrote a contributor to the *Farmer's Magazine* in 1855.[1] This eminence had grown during the preceding half century. Excepting a few, Arthur Young had not been at all impressed with Lincolnshire's farmers.[2] A hundred years after his time the standing of the elite of the county's farmers, socially and economically, was widely recognized. In many farming families generation had succeeded generation, if not always on the same farm, at least on the estate. The tale of a Lord Yarborough (which one varied according to the telling) replying to an enquiry as to where he found such good tenants that he 'bred them' became something of a chestnut.[3] However, it demonstrated the mutual convenience that owner and farmer found in encouraging stability, so that investment in the land might be made and recouped. The result of this and of the progress of farming in Lincolnshire was that many of the leading farmers achieved some prominence and renown beyond their locality. John Evens of Burton by Lincoln, a breeder of Lincoln Red Shorthorns, was one. William Frankish, farmer of 2,000 acres at Great Limber on the Wolds, was a member of the council of the Royal Agricultural Society of England, and witness to Royal Commissions. William Torr of Riby merited a lengthy memorial in the journal of the Royal Agricultural Society when he died, while his successor on the farm, Henry Dudding, was equally renowned.

There were about 11,000 farmers in Lincolnshire during the second half of the 19th century (Table 1). Numbers declined sharply during the Great Depression, but had recovered nearly all the loss by the First World War. Changes in employment categories had much to do with a sharp increase recorded by the census of 1921, although some of the change did result from increased numbers of smallholdings now available. The downward trend was resumed as renewed depression hit agriculture in the 1920s.

The farmers were not a homogeneous group. Some farmed, for the time, enormous farms of several hundred acres, and a few had more than a thousand. There were many more farmers who had only a few acres, smallholdings of between ten and fifty acres. In between were the farmers with their 'ordinary' farms of one or two hundred acres. Their businesses turned over thousands of pounds a year, and usually earned them enough to live a life of frugal respectability that set them firmly in the middle ranks of village society.

Table 1 Numbers of farmers 1851–1931

Year	Number of farmers	Year	Number of farmers
1851	11,048	1901	11,357
1861	11,112	1911	11,255
1871	11,788	1921	12,944
1881	10,048	1931	12,158

Source: Census Reports

Lincolnshire farmers were regarded as wealthy in contemporary eyes. The National Agricultural Labourers' Union claimed in 1876 that 'in no county in England are farmers so well off as in Lincolnshire; for proof of which see how many of them have from two to six or seven farms…'.[4] Those who were really well off were, however, few in number. The agricultural returns for 1875 recorded 1,215 holdings greater than 300 acres. The number of farmers involved will have been less than that, for multiple occupation was quite common even at this scale. Of the total number of farmers, therefore, fewer than ten per cent were likely to be farming on a scale that gave them an income on a par with members of the professional and business classes. These farmers of the large acreages did tend to form a distinct group. With their wealth went social standing. They were not gentry, but were able to associate with the landowning class on terms of reasonable comfort. They might in their own parishes be called 'squire' in lieu of the actual proprietor living elsewhere. The line dividing them from the gentry might occasionally be crossed. The Dixon family of Holton were tenant farmers in the 18th century. By the mid-19th century they had joined the ranks of the squirearchy, owning about 3,500 acres, although they continued to farm some land.

These farmers lived a life of comfort and respectability. G. E. Collins said they 'drove to market in a carriage, dined every evening and hunted in scarlet'. Their conversation at rent audit dinners was often of 'shooting, hunting, game, landlords and landed estates and racing'.[5]

Fig. 2 Mr J. Popple, of Hallington, near Louth, farmer of 2000 acres, on his favourite hunter, 1935
Source: Museum of English Rural Life

They were likely to be leaders in social affairs in their villages, and, like
Cornelius Stovin, in the churches. They were sufficiently well off by the
late 19th century for the womenfolk of the family to reduce the amount
they contributed to the business of farming. They were linked by
friendship, often by marriage. Cornelius Stovin, who farmed at
Binbrook, had relationships by marriage with the Riggalls, Sharpleys,
and Atkinsons, all leading farming families in north Lincolnshire.[6]
Their sons, brothers, and nephews who did not go into farming were
likely to enter the county's professional classes, as land agents, lawyers,
clergymen. The great farmers were investing some of their wealth in
other activities such as mills, feed and fertilizer companies, and local
railways. The exclusivity of the farming elite of Lincolnshire was made
more pronounced by the fact that they were concentrated in a few areas.
By far the most prominent were the great farmers of the Wolds. Not
even on the Blankney estate on the Heath or the Ancaster estates of
south Kesteven did the farming grandees stand out quite so much.
Their rise to wealth and status had taken a short time. At the beginning
of the 19th century farmers on the Wolds were still of modest fortune.[7]
Their fortunes were inextricably linked to the late flowering of the
agricultural revolution in Lincolnshire that saw the pace of
development increase from the Napoleonic wars onwards. As
agriculture entered its Great Depression in the late 1870s, they found
themselves under pressure. Some outsiders said the great farmers lived
a life of too-great luxury. Richard Jefferies, for example, in some of the
essays that were published in *Hodge and his Masters* (1880), was a writer
nationally known for such views, but there was correspondence along
the same lines in the county newspapers. The depth of the successive
depressions of the 1880s and 1920s dealt a double blow to the
prominence of these farmers of the Wolds and Heath. The next
generations of great farmers were likely to come from a wider range of
locality, men such as William Dennis with his vast acreages of potatoes
in south Lincolnshire.

The great majority of farmers was nothing like so wealthy or
grand. Professor Collins, calculating from the income tax schedules for
the 1850s, suggests that fewer than half of the farmers in England had a
net income as high as £100 per year.[8] As a county with a large number

of smallholders, this would be true of Lincolnshire. The farmer in the middle, with 100 to 300 acres, seems likely to have been earning perhaps £150 or so per year. In contemporary urban terms this was similar to a good clerk. In village society it was enough to afford good local standing and respectability.

There was a social and economic gulf between the great farmers of the Wolds and Heath and the smallholders. Indeed, the gap was quite wide between the farmers on the really large scale and those with middling farms. Social outlooks and business reactions differed greatly. They all had in common the name of farmer, but not much else. The gap between highest and lowest was quite unbridgeable. To many 19th-century observers the holders of the smallest farms were barely distinguishable from labourers. Indeed, many of them did spring from the ranks of the labourers, taking on a few acres as a part-time holding,

Fig. 3   Some notable farmers at the sale of Lincoln Red cattle at Lincoln, in 1926. Among them are John Evens in the centre, and to his left Robert Chatterton, T. W. Cartwright, and Fred Scorer
Source: Museum of English Rural Life

and, with luck, building up from that to a full-time occupation of something like 50 to 100 acres. Their way of life was in contrast to that of the large farmers as well. Whereas the farmer on the Wolds had the air of leisure, was an employer of many hands and leader of village society, the smallholder seemed to work all hours, reliant upon his own and his family's labour. William Paddison, who started with a small holding on the Marsh, building up to a farm of about 150 acres, has been described as existing on 'parsimony bordering on poverty'. Another small tenant farmer himself wrote, 'I've not known great luxury, only constant work.'[9] By this combination of strict economy and hard work most farmers managed to keep a balance in the bank.

Just as many of the really large farms were concentrated in certain districts, so too were the smallholders. They were found mostly in the Fens and the Isle of Axholme, along with some of the mixed fen-clay soils of the parishes below the limestone heath, such as Rippingale and Aslackby. Farming society here could show patterns of family relationships just as complex as those on the Wolds, though on a much lesser scale of wealth. In a village where nearly all were farming on a small scale it took relatively little to raise some of the more successful to local eminence. This tended to be quite a mobile society as well, as farmers gave up some parcels of land to take on new fields. They might be tenants of various small parcels of land, often rented from two or three different owners, while themselves also owning a few acres.[10]

Farm tenure

Nearly all farmers, great and small, in the 19th century were tenants. When in 1887 the annual agricultural returns started to make the distinction between the acreage of farmland rented and that farmed by its owner, 16 per cent of the land of Lincolnshire was 'owned and occupied'. This included home farms and other estate land held in hand by the landlord. Since this was in the middle of the Great Depression, when many farmers were giving up and leaving the estates with farms on their hands, the proportion of land recorded as farmed by its owner was high. By 1900, with the return of calmer times, the proportion was down to 10.5 per cent, and remained at about that figure for the next decade. It might reasonably be inferred that the proportion of land in the hands of its owners was about this figure for much of the period from the 1850s to the 1870s.

Perhaps it was a rationalization of a relatively static market in land, but there was always reckoned to be a mutual convenience about these tenurial arrangements. Landowners did not wish to have direct involvement with farming and, on the whole, wanted farms to be in hand only temporarily. Farmers, equally, were content to remain tenants, leaving the estates the responsibilities and capital burdens that came with ownership. They did not wish to tie their capital into the ownership of land, especially if this involved inflexible mortgage payments, but to be free to invest in the practice of farming. So, when Lord Monson offered to sell one of his farms to its occupier in 1876 he found that 'he prefers being a tenant at his present rent to borrowing money at £4 or £4½ per cent.' That turned out to have been a sensible decision on the tenant's part, for land prices fell during the next two decades. It was not until after the First World War that farmers seriously entered the market to purchase land.[11]

This is not to say that there were not farmers who owned land before the First World War. There were many, and some owned a thousand acres or more, enough to set themselves up as minor gentry. Some did make the transition into the gentry class. The Dixons and the Skipworths, two families who had begun to build up landholdings during the 18th century, were examples. On the whole, however, the farmer of the 19th century neither established himself as a small squire nor became a true owner-farmer. Essentially, he was interested in the land from a practical, agricultural point of view, rather than in the matters of social or dynastic status to which the gentry were drawn. As likely as not, a farmer who owned land would carry on farming the land he rented and let the land he had bought to somebody else.[12] Farmers might buy some grazing land to work alongside their main rented farm, as Wolds farmers did with land in the Marsh, and the ramifications of ownership and tenancy among the small farmers of the Fens were complex. The numbers of fully owner-occupied farms, however, remained small until the 1920s.

Lincolnshire's tenant farmers nearly all held their farms by annual tenancy. Their occupation was thus assured only for twelve months rather than a set number of years that a lease would prescribe. Usually the tenure commenced from Lady Day, by the old calendar that is, 6 April in 19th-century terms. In most other parts of the country Michaelmas was the usual date for starting tenancies. Lincolnshire tenure was also commonly under a six-months' notice, compared with the twelve months of other regions. These practices drew a lot of criticism from agriculturalists who thought that farmers should seek the security of a lease lasting for seven or more years, as the custom was in Norfolk. James Caird could not understand why farmers should accept annual tenancy; nor had Arthur Young before him. Caird and S. B. L. Druce, among others, were similarly dismayed at the short term of notice. Two years' notice was a minimum requirement if farmers must accept annual tenancy, they thought, if there was to be any feeling of security.[13] None of this made any impression in Lincolnshire. Indeed, leases became even less usual during the late 19th century. Even institutional landowners, who had been more inclined to use longer-term leases, renewed very few from the 1880s onwards. Those leases that were agreed were for short terms, rarely for more than three years. In a falling market, the farmer was not prepared to be tied for a long period. Neither was the landlord willing to have a lease that fixed rents at low rates for 21 years.[14]

'There is no such thing as insecurity of tenure in Lincolnshire', Charles Scorer of Sudbrooke declared to the local investigator for the Royal Commission in 1895.[15] The answer to the apparent incompatibility between a statement such as this and the weaknesses of annual tenancy emphasized by Caird and others lay in two things. The first was the Lincolnshire custom of tenant right, by which farmers set great store. Second, the tenurial relationship in its practice offered greater security than many of the pundits thought. The proprietor who saw it as his job to make sure that his land was fully tenanted would evict only in exceptional circumstances. Farmers generally had confidence in their landlords over security, even in those who otherwise were not especially attentive to their estates or supportive of their tenants, while they also appreciated the flexibility to give up their tenancy.

On most estates there was a fair amount of support and nurture of the tenantry. The Yarborough quip about breeding tenants had foundation in the general practice among landowners of favouring the existing families when letting farms. Son would succeed father. Brothers, nephews, and other family connections with the estate would be looked on with favour. Widows would often take on the farm, perhaps in trust for a young son. On the Dixons' Searby and Holton estates in 1901, three out of the fifteen tenancies were of this nature. This pursuit of stability, of decency to established families, meant that rent rolls seemed to have a familiar air to them from year to year. Lord Ancaster still had Grummitts farming on his Kesteven estate in 1900 just as he had in the 1870s, and up at Hainton members of the Drake family were tenants throughout this period. At Searby in 1901 William Coates and William Bainbridge were tenants, as they had been twenty years previously, while John Lingard had succeeded William in the rent roll.[16]

Mobility in the farming population

The long continuance of farming families on an estate, of course, tells only part of the story. Farmers also moved, from place to place, and up and down the farming ladder. Farming families did disappear from the rent rolls. They had run out of heirs, capital, or inclination. New people came in their place.

Most farmers did not move far. A common step was to move to another farm on the estate. This was especially true of the larger estates, which could offer more choice. New tenants on the Ancaster estates in Kesteven were nearly always from the parishes of south-west Kesteven or neighbouring Rutland, where more of the estate lay.[17] Familiarity with the local soils and farming practices was perhaps as strong a determinant as any: Wolds farmers tended to keep to the Wolds and so on. Many agents and landowners also preferred local knowledge when making their choice of tenants. Lord Heneage received a memorandum from his agent that a certain applicant should be given first refusal 'as he is a native and much more likely to know what he is taking', whereas the second-choice candidate was from Holbeach Marsh.[18] There was good reason in this approach. Cornelius Stovin retired from his farm at Binbrook to a smaller place on the Marsh, but this proved to be an unhappy move. There were those who moved further afield.

Lincolnshire could attract farmers from other parts of the country. In 1889, during the Great Depression, one agent was receiving enquiries about a vacant farm from Sussex, Chester, and East Lothian. All mentioned the *Stamford Mercury* as the source of their information. This was not untypical. Although Lincolnshire was not among the destinations for those large numbers of farmers from Scotland and western England who moved to the English lowlands to take farms at low rents at the end of the 19th century, there were some incomers. One of these exceptions was Colin Campbell, a Scotsman who moved to Stapleford at the turn of the 20th century, and achieved fame as president first of the Lincolnshire Farmers' Union, then of its successor the National Farmers' Union.

Opportunities for farmers to expand their holdings and their businesses varied from time to time and place to place. Where small farms prevailed mobility was marked. Men were able to add to their holdings piecemeal to build up respectable farms from small beginnings. The extent to which it was possible to move into farming from the life of a labourer was limited, but it could happen. Robert Tasker, after thirteen years' service as a labourer in the Marsh, entered farming in the 1850s. At the census of 1861 he was renting 147 acres. The ability to build up capital was the main determinant of a labourer's chances of moving into farming. Determination, thriftiness, and taking any opportunities for additional earnings were essential. Fred Gresswell's parents at Digby in the late 19th century saved mainly from his mother's work milking until they had enough to buy a pig. The proceeds from the first litter were invested in a cottage with a half-acre paddock, and from there they progressed to a two-acre field and eventually to larger holdings.[19]

In areas of large farms the opportunities to expand might seem fewer, except that landlords were willing to detach fields from one holding and let a neighbouring tenant take them. This was happening quite a lot during the Great Depression, when owners were more willing to take almost any measures to keep their land tenanted. By this means a tenant could alter considerably the holding that he farmed.

There was movement down the ladder as well, of course. John Maltby, who farmed 400 acres at Louth Park in the 1850s, died leaving a very small estate in 1864. He was unusual in that he seems to have given much of his wealth away, in support of his church, the Primitive Methodist. Many another farmer reduced his holdings as a result of losing money. Some farmers were forced to give up. An example is one in south Lincolnshire who entered farming in 1860, and held more than 1,000 acres by 1874. Flooding in 1880 caused him to lose £2,000. Further losses in subsequent years took their toll, though he managed to keep going until 1894, when he was declared bankrupt.[20]

The depression at the end of the 19th century increased the turnover in the farming population compared with the years before 1879. The number of farmers in the county fell (Table 1), as many gave up the business, including some from the prominent, large-farming families. Landlords and their agents were commonly reporting in the 1880s increased numbers of farms being given up. However, the upheaval was not so great as it might perhaps have been, and not so great as some of the bleak assessments presented to the Royal Commission's investigators. Lord Monson's agent observed in 1879 that there were 'farms being given up in every direction, but it is certain that in many cases the outgoing tenants will be looking for farms elsewhere'.[21] Tenants were not necessarily leaving farming, but might be taking the opportunity to escape from areas of poor land. James Banks Stanhope told the Richmond Commission that he was experiencing few changes at Revesby. Farmers did all they could to hang on, and landlords were anxious to avoid having land without a tenant. A newspaper report on conditions in the Marsh in 1882 said that there had been fewer changes of tenancy than might have been expected because landowners were making efforts to retain sitting tenants.[22] Bankruptcy was an unusual reason for leaving farming. Even at their peak in 1881–3, when they were more than three times greater than they had been in 1875, bankruptcies were no more than 0.4 per cent of the agricultural population.[23] More farmers, of course, got out before matters were so bad as to result in bankruptcy. Even so, the changes in lists of tenants on most estates had as much to do with the passage of generations as with widespread abandonment of farming. Some of those who did leave their farms retained a farming life, as farm managers and bailiffs, whose numbers were up in the 1891 census.

The turnover might not have risen dramatically, but during the late 19th century, and again in the depression of the inter-war years, some of the names that had been most prominent began to disappear. Henry Dudding died in 1912 with no successor from his family. New blood was drawn into farming, attracted by the low rents and relatively slight competition for tenancies. Herbert Carter was an example, who began farming at Holbeach in 1885. His accounts do not tell us how big a farm he had, either at the start or subsequently, but success in his farming enabled him to add to the acreage he held. He became one of the largest farmers in Holbeach. William Dennis built up a large farming enterprise from small beginnings. Not all these new farmers were new either to farming or to Lincolnshire. Clifford Nicholson came from an old Lincolnshire farming family that in previous generations had controlled thousands of acres. During the 1920s and 1930s Clifford succeeded in building the holdings back up again. E. W. Howard was another from an old farming family of the county who became a leading light in his generation of farmers.

Farmers old and new

Among the poems in the Lincolnshire dialect that Tennyson wrote were two about farmers. In 'Lincolnshire Farmer, Old Style' an aged farmer looks back over his life and recalls how he had tried to do right by the land, and right by the landlord, even though that might not have made him wealthy. The 'Lincolnshire Farmer, New Style' had 'proputty, proputty' as his watchword, the increase of his assets, and was disgusted that his son could contemplate marriage for love to the daughter of a poor clergyman rather than finding someone who would bring some money into the partnership.[24] The inference, that a new school of hard-headed businessmen-farmers was taking over, has frequently been drawn. G. E. Collins had similar thoughts when he lamented the decline of the old yeoman farmers, and the hereditary tenant families in his part of north Lincolnshire. Bishop Hicks in 1915 wrote of new farmers in the Fens, 'They are very modern businessmen ... wealthy and sterling men, but "near" with their money.' Rider Haggard, a few years before, had found many of the farmers who were most dispirited were so, not simply because prices were low, but because they felt that an old order was passing. The 'old-fashioned, hard-working tenant farmer' was not a success in the new conditions, while the way was open for 'land-skinners' and others who generally farmed with costs as low as possible.[25]

It is a recurring theme, and one that might be put down to the way one generation views the next. For, while G. E. Collins mourned the passing of the old types of independent gentleman tenant, with his carriage and hunting, the diaries of the daughter of a farmer in the Wolds continue to reveal a leisured social life among this class into the 1890s.[26] There was not a simple change from non-businesslike farming to businesslike, and this is apparent in Tennyson's poems. The attitude of the new-style farmer's son to his approaching marriage goes against a universal triumph of hard-headedness. Nor was there anything about the old-style farmer to suggest that he was not a man of business. Farmers of his generation and before knew very well what their business was. The land was their livelihood, not a means of social or dynastic benefits, though those might well accrue. This was what distinguished the farmer from the gentry, and can explain much of the attitude of even the wealthiest farmers to the merits of buying or renting land.

Even so, there were changes in the way farmers looked upon their lives and businesses. The demands of the farming business, especially the financing of it, were likely to change from generation to generation, and this was the type of thing that the social commentators picked up. From the mid-19th century onwards farmers were investing more of their own money in capital-intensive high farming, and this was bound to have an influence on the way they managed their activities. The Great Depression reinforced this, making farmers pay more attention to their costs and the return on their capital. Their accounts began to be more purely business records, as they were less likely now to mix general household expenses with those of running the farm. To an older generation and to many an outside observer, of course, this indicated that the farmers were becoming more 'hard-headed'. They were seeing opportunities to make money from the land, in ways that the preceding generations had not, as those who came into the Fens to grow bulbs and potatoes did. This is perhaps hardly surprising, for by the 1880s farming was already being widely referred to as an industry. The incorporation of farms into limited liability businesses was but a logical step. The first to do this, at the turn of the century, were bulb growers, as befitted a business for which marketing counted as much as the growing. In 1919 William Dennis & Sons became a limited company with a share capital of nearly £2m, and by the 1930s several more farming businesses, especially potato growers and dairy farmers had made the move to limited liability.[27] Lord Londesborough's Farms Ltd was an example of the way a few estates were beginning to organize their business activities. A further step in corporate farming came in 1936 when Smiths Potato Crisps Ltd bought the Dennis estates at Nocton.

Alongside the comment about the new business-like farmers there was another strong stream of complaint. Farmers were often held to be lacking in enterprise and managerial skills, of not changing their ways to suit the times, of not being businesslike at all. This argument surfaced especially at times of difficulty for agriculture. Giving evidence to the Royal Commission on the Depressed State of the Agricultural Interest in 1881, the Hon. Charles Gore, for the Crown Estates, said, 'It is only within recent years that farming has become a mercantile operation: farmers were bad accountants....' This theme of poor management ran through much of the comment during the Great Depression.[28] It continued into the 20th century. Two bankrupt farmers were admonished by the judge at Lincoln County Court in 1936 for not having kept accounts. One said he had been too tired to do accounts after working all day in the fields. 'I'm beginning to think that farmers don't keep accounts because they don't want their position to become known,' said the judge.[29]

Each succeeding generation, then, brought with it new farmers with new ideas and new approaches to their business. While some lamented with good reason the passing of the old-style farmer, it was the new men, who saw and exploited business opportunities, who tended to prosper. They gave the character to the changing patterns of agriculture, often providing inspiration to other farmers around them. Without them farming itself would have found difficulty contending with a changing world.

Notes to Chapter 2

1   Quoted in Sir Francis Hill, *Victorian Lincoln* (1974) p. 88. The
     anonymous writer was most likely Philip Pusey.
2   Arthur Young, *General View of the Agriculture of Lincolnshire* (1799)
     pp. 39–40. David Grigg, *The Agricultural Revolution in South Lincolnshire*
     (1966) pp. 62–3.
3   It was repeated down the years, appearing, for example, in *Farmer's
     Magazine*, 2nd ser. v. 20 (July 1849), p. 5 and Wilson Fox's report for
     the Royal Commission on agriculture in the 1890s (p. 178).
4   Quoted in Rex Russell, *The 'Revolt of the Field' in Lincolnshire* (1956)
     p. 102.
5   G. E. Collins, 'Agriculture', *Victoria County History, Lincolnshire*, v. 2
     (1906), p. 406. J. Stovin, *Journals of a Methodist Farmer, 1871–1875*
     (1982) p. 175. R. J. Olney, *Rural Society and County Government in
     Nineteenth–century Lincolnshire* (1979) pp. 56–7.
6   Charles K. Rawding, *The Lincolnshire Wolds in the Nineteenth Century*
     (2001) p. 119.
7   *Ibid.*, p. 58.
8   *The Agrarian History of England and Wales, vol. VII, 1850–1914,* ed. E. J.
     T. Collins (2000) p. 123.
9   Linda Crust, 'William Paddison: marsh farmer and survivor of the
     agricultural depression, 1873–96', *Agricultural History Review*, v. 43
     (1995) p. 195. *SM,* 13 December 1878, a letter from a small tenant
     farmer contributing to a debate in the newspaper's correspondence
     about the economies that farmers might make to fend off depression.
10   The structure and nature of smallholding agriculture are treated in
     greater detail in Chapter 4.
11   LAO, MON25/13/18, 7 April 1876. For conditions that militated
     against farmers moving into ownership see Avner Offer, 'Farm
     Tenure and Land Values in England c1750–1950', *EcHR*, v. 44 (1991)
     pp. 1–20.
12   Olney, *Rural Society and County Government in Nineteenth-century
     Lincolnshire*. pp. 58–9.
13   RC1879, Second Report of S. B. L. Druce, p. 52; Minutes of
     Evidence, QQ. 4990, 49208–11, 56209, 56246, 62767–8, 68618–20.
     RC1893, Wilson Fox, p. 17.

14 RC1893, QQ. 458–65, 1668–71. Thomas Stirton,'Report on the Farm Prize Competition in Nottinghamshire and Lincolnshire, classes 2 and 3', *JRASE*, v. 50 (1889) p. 48.

15 RC1893, Wilson Fox, p. 17.

16 LAO, DIXON 6/1/12/3, 6/1/5/12; 9ANC 1A, Kesteven estate surveys, 9ANC 2/C/1, Kesteven farm agreements; 2HEN 2/4/5, 2/5/71.

17 LAO 9ANC 2/C/1.

18 LAO, 2HEN 2/10/1/8, 13 August 1901.

19 Fred Gresswell, *Bright Boots* (1956) pp. 18ff.

20 James Obelkevitch, *Religion and Rural Society in South Lindsey 1825–1875* (1976) pp. 247–8. *Agricultural Gazette*, 24 December 1894.

21 LAO, MON 25/11/13, 8 October 1879.

22 RC1879, Q56249. *Mark Lane Express*, 24 April 1882.

23 P. J. Perry, 'Where was the "Great Agricultural Depression"? A geography of agricultural bankruptcy in late Victorian England and Wales', *AgHR*, v. 20 (1972), reprinted in P. J. Perry (ed.), *British Agriculture 1875–1914* (1973) pp. 129–48.

24 Tennyson, *In Memoriam, Maud and other poems*, ed. John D. Jump (1974) pp. 191–4 (and see Obelkevitch, *Religion and Rural Society in South Lindsey 1825–1875*, p 46–61).

25 See R. J. Olney, *Lincolnshire Politics 1832–1885* (1973) p. 245. Sir Francis Hill, *Victorian Lincoln* (1974) p. 217. H. Rider Haggard *Rural England* (1902) v. 2, p. 160.

26 G. E. Collins, 'Agriculture', *Victoria County History, Lincolnshire*, v. 2 (1906) pp. 405–6. LAO, Misc. Dep. 265.

27 *Agricultural Gazette*, 25 August 1919, p. 198.

28 RC1879, Minutes of Evidence, Q.370. And see E. J. T. Collins in *The Agrarian History of England and Wales, vol. VII, 1850–1914* (2000) p. 167f.

29 *Lincolnshire Chronicle*, 10 October 1936.

3
FARMING SOCIETY: LANDOWNERS AND WORKERS

Landowners

The tenant farmers of the 19th century held their farms from a variety of landowners, great and small. Those that set the tone of landed society, naturally enough, were the larger proprietors. Lincolnshire was not the most fashionable county, perhaps, and had never attracted the greatest of landed magnates. Even so, it could boast some very large estates; indeed, the return of owners of land in 1873 showed that the county had slightly more than the national average of estates of more than 10,000 acres (28 per cent of its area compared with 24 per cent for England). By far the largest estate was the Earl of Yarborough's, with its seat at Brocklesby, extending over 55,000 acres of north Lincolnshire, much of it in the Wolds.[1] There was no other estate comparable in size until the late 1880s when the Willoughby and Heathcote estates were united under the twenty-fourth Lord Willoughby de Eresby (created Earl of Ancaster in 1892). The combined estates, mainly in south-west Kesteven, totalled 42,000 acres.

There were some other large estates, such as the 23,000 acres of the Chaplin estates. These were in two parts, based on Blankney, on the Heath, and Tathwell, in the southern Wolds, respectively. However, these estates were broken up in the 1890s after Henry Chaplin's finances disintegrated.[2] Another estate with its territory split, between the Wragby area in the north and Stoke Rochford in south Kesteven, was the estate of the Turnor family, who possessed 21,000 acres. The Heneage family had 11,000 acres, mainly around the seat at Hainton, but with a substantial part of Grimsby and its neighbourhood.

The Crown holdings in Lincolnshire, of 12,700 acres, were the largest of the institutional estates. The Ecclesiastical Commissioners held 8,800 acres in the county. Estates of medium size, between 3,000 and 10,000 acres, were a little under-represented in Lincolnshire, occupying 13 per cent of the area compared with a national average of 17 per cent. Among estates in this category were the 6,800 acres of Lord Monson's, mainly on the Cliff around the seat at Burton north of Lincoln, the Stanhope estate of 7,000 acres at Revesby and the Dixon family's 3,600 acres around Holton-le Moor.

Distribution of large and medium estates within the county was uneven. The larger estates were concentrated in the Wolds, Heath, and south Kesteven uplands. By contrast landownership in the Fens, Marsh, and Isle of Axholme was more diverse, and quite modest estates could give their owners local status. There were large estates here, but they were mainly outlying parts of greater estates, such as the 9,600 acres of fen and marsh belonging to Lord Carrington, whose main estate was in Buckinghamshire.

Landowners and their tenants

The relationship between landlord and tenant was based upon mutual interest and a good deal of collaboration, all with unwritten understandings of the social position of the two classes. The landlord expected to take primacy, even though the owner of a smaller estate might be far less wealthy than the greater farmers. This did mean deference on the part of the tenant, and dependence on the landlord's goodwill. Ecclesiastical and political loyalties could influence a farmer's preferment. In 1871 Lord Monson sought the opinion of the vicar of Croft on a prospective tenant and received the reply that he was a good farmer, but 'he is a rabid Baptist, for which reason I should prefer his not being tenant of the Manor Farm'.[3] Whether or not this was the reason, he did not get the farm. The forms of deference continued throughout the 19th century. Many farmers continued to address their landlords in the tones adopted by one of Lord Ancaster's when asking permission to shoot: 'I hope I may respectfully remind you that I have done something for the Conservative cause which might possibly receive some small consideration at your hands.'[4]

Fig. 4   The Earl of Yarborough, portrayed in the *Farmers' Magazine*
of 1849. 'The breeder, perhaps, of farm tenants.'
Source: Farmers' Magazine

The landlord for his part also needed the goodwill of his tenants. Much of his political and social standing depended on it. Sometimes he manifestly lost that goodwill, as on the occasion when the tenants refused to toast William Angerstein at the rent audit dinner. Angerstein was a non-resident owner, his main estate being in Norfolk, which did not help his cause. Independent-minded tenants were to be found in the mid-19th century, farmers confident both in their investments of capital in their farms and of their local social relations. These were almost always occupiers of very large farms, especially those in the Wolds who were tenants of more land than many a landlord owned. They were able to adopt quite independent attitudes, such as William Frankish's open opposition to the Yarborough political interest.[5]

In terms of practical agricultural business, the landlord's place was to invest in and maintain the estate. Landlords spent heavily on their estates. Throughout much of the second half of the 19th century many landlords were spending between a fifth and a quarter of their rentals on improvements and repairs. On the Ancaster estates, for example, the proportion was 21 per cent between 1860 and 1895. In a quarter of a century, from the 1840s onwards, G. F. Heneage invested more than £100,000. The landlord also retained a place as an encourager of his tenants and of agricultural improvement. Sir John Thorold, of Syston, was one who took this seriously, maintaining his home farm as a place for experimental work, especially in the testing of new agricultural seeds.[6]

The Great Depression at the end of the 19th century put the relationships between landlord and tenant under strain, from which they did not fully recover. There was the tradition that in times of difficulty farmers could look to their landlords for help. Landlords generally looked upon it as their duty to help their tenants. However, the pressure on their finances, together with the ebbing away of political and social advantages from land, began to erode that old understanding between landlord and tenant.

The poor seasons and prices of the 1870s soon had tenants invoking tradition: 'the seasons have of late been so very unpropitious that I am terribly perplexed and who am I to look to but my landlord', wrote one of Henry Chaplin's tenants in 1881.[7] Landlords met their tenants with rebates of rent, followed by permanent reductions, at the same time trying to maintain expenditure on improvements and repairs. However, when this became never ending, or so it seemed, landlords began to weary. 'These are very difficult times for agents,' wrote Lord Monson's agent, feeling pressure both from the landlord wanting to protect his income and from the tenant wanting relief. 'I fear the result may be that I am unable to give satisfaction to either.'[8] The relationship between tenant and landlord, or at least his agent, had now become a continuous round of negotiations over rents, buildings, landlord's responsibilities, and all with the pressure mainly upon the landlord to make concessions. The files of correspondence from every estate are filled with letters from tenants asking for their rents to be reduced, with varying amounts of special pleading. Robert Toynbee, Lord Monson's agent, summed things up again: 'I fear gratitude no longer enters into the relations between landlord and tenant, which are now reduced to mere matters of bargain.'[9] This could work both ways, of course, with the landlord taking a more cold-hearted approach to such matters as repairs and arrears. Several tenants on the Grimsthorpe estate were given up as hopelessly insolvent by the 1880s and served notice to quit.[10]

Of course, this was nothing more than market forces giving the tenant the edge. Ease of reletting a farm at a rack rent in the 1860s and 1870s was followed by farms taking longer to let in the 1880s and 1890s, and often only after a resort to advertising in the local press. Hardly a rent audit passed without agents being confronted by at least some of the tenants stating bluntly that they would not be able to continue without a reduction in rent. The outcome, however, was a permanent change in the relationship between landlord and tenant. Resentment began to surface against landowners. Agricultural writers regularly argued that farmers had to bear nearly all the burden of low prices, while landlords continued to collect high rents. Here is one expression of that, from the North Lincolnshire notes in the *Agricultural Gazette*: 'Times are dreadful here still…. It is true rents cannot be paid in the corn-growing districts and must come even further down, for the burden has not fallen equally on landlord, tenant and labourer.'[11] Landlords also found themselves the targets of political attack from those who advocated 'fair rents' and from those who regarded the landlord and tenant system as unjust in itself.[12] By the end of the century farmers were more independent of their landlords and striking for leadership of rural society. They were finding a new political voice, with the emergence of the Lincolnshire Farmers' Union and its rapid development into the National Farmers' Union. The greatest pressure on the landlord, however, was the simple economic fact that maintaining the rents of the 1870s into the 1880s would have left him with all his farms untenanted.

From landlord to owner-occupier

The basic balance between tenancy and ownership described earlier continued throughout the 19th century. The Great Depression did not induce any Lincolnshire landowner to emulate Lord Wantage in Berkshire or the Hon. Edward Strutt in Essex, who took large acreages into direct control of their estates to be farmed by efficient large-scale methods. Rather, farming by the estate was regarded as an evil brought on by the necessity of the times: 'the universal experience of landlords is that it is better to let land almost at a nominal rent than to farm', wrote Robert Toynbee. Profit and efficiency were secondary considerations to economy when it came to managing farms in hand. Farming was not a worthwhile occupation for the landowner. Robert Toynbee wrote again: 'the tenant right has to be paid for and the land must be kept in cultivation, and to do this a capital of £7 or £8 an acre would have to be found. I see no reason why that capital should not yield a fair return with ordinary times and average seasons, but there is necessarily some risk attending it which I imagine your Lordship would be glad to avoid if you can do so without submitting to too great a reduction in rents for the next few years.' Rather than risk their capital most landlords preferred to play safe and keep their tenants.[13]

The amount of land farmed in hand remained small throughout the late 19th century. The agricultural returns offer a rough and ready means of assessing this through their record of the land returned as owned as opposed to that which was occupied. In 1888 17.3 per cent of the total in the county was in the 'owned' category, and in 1900 this figure was down to 10.5 per cent. Wilson Fox, in his investigations for the Royal Commission of the 1890s reported that, on six of the largest estates, 27,690 acres out of 174,636 were unlet, 15.9 per cent of the total. Experience varied from estate to estate. Lord Yarborough never had more than two farms in hand during the years from 1885–86 to 1893–94. Both on this estate and on that of Heneage, farms never stayed in hand for more than two years. Elsewhere, however, Edmund Turnor had 3,600 acres out of 21,000 in hand at the time of Wilson Fox's enquiry, and the Ancaster estates had 7,000 acres out of 57,000.[14]

In this respect landowners weathered the depression successfully. However, the falling rent rolls coincided with a decline in the political and social returns from landownership. Heneage commented in 1886 that if he had known how much his rental income was going to fall he would not have taken on the expensive occupation of Member of Parliament. As such disadvantages to landowning began to become apparent during this period, owners began to contemplate the more radical course of selling land. This represented a major change from the position a few decades previously, for in the mid-19th century several estates were still expanding and consolidating. Land prices continued to rise into the 1870s, boosted by demand from purchasers, great and small. Few estates added land from the 1880s onwards. Instead, they were more likely to sell outlying holdings. The small landholding at Corby of Lord Petre, whose home estate was in Essex, was sold in the early 1890s. Lord Ancaster started selling his land in Wales in 1894. Landowners based in Lincolnshire began to look at the possibility of sales of land within the county. Edward Heneage was one. From 1887 he was considering the sale of some farms in order to plough the proceeds back into the main estate. In 1891 he did sell Ludford Farm. Henry Chaplin was unable to keep his estates when a combination of accumulated debt and falling rentals became too much for him. The Earl of Londesborough, his principal creditor, foreclosed in 1896 and became the possessor of one of the largest estates in the county.[15]

Sales of land were starting to increase in the years leading up to the First World War. Acreages involved were still fairly small. The agricultural returns show an increase of 16,000 acres in owner-occupied land between 1910 and 1914, most, it may be surmised, coming from land sales. This brought the proportion of land in the hands of its owner up to 11.4 per cent. A bigger change came immediately after the war. In common with many in other parts of the country, Lincolnshire landowners took advantage of high land prices to sell. Even before war ended more land was beginning to come to market. Among these sales was the Nocton estate in July 1918, to William Dennis & Sons, who, reported the *Agricultural Gazette,* 'intend to develop the estate on their well-known system of improved cultivation'. After the war the Earl of Lindsey was among the first of the established landowners to sell, bringing his estates of 1,728 acres at Uffington and Tallington to market in 1919. All sizes and natures of estates were affected. Large owners sold parts of their estates. The Londesboroughs sold portions of the Blankney estate in the 1920s and 1930s. Owners of smaller estates often sold the whole. Institutional owners included Guy's Hospital, sellers of 6,300 acres at Sutton Bridge for £400,000 to the Board of Agriculture in 1919, which used the land as smallholdings for ex-servicemen. Although prices fell back in the 1920s, reducing the volume, sales continued throughout the inter-war period.[16]

A large proportion of the buyers now were farmers. During the Great Depression few had been in a position to buy land even at low prices. After the First World War farmers had good balances, and spent some on buying their land. Some perhaps felt forced to buy in order to safeguard their interests in the land, but most, especially in the first few years, were very willing. By 1927, when the agricultural statistics gave a reasonably accurate return of tenancy and ownership, the effects could be seen. More than a third of the farmland of England and Wales was now cultivated by its owners, and in this Lincolnshire was not out of line. No further statistics were collected until the National Farm Survey in 1941. The figures presented there suggested that the percentage of land owner-occupied was now 39 per cent in Holland, 28 per cent in Kesteven and 32 per cent in Lindsey. They were open to interpretation, however, and the Department of Agriculture at Cambridge University in a survey suggested that owner-occupation in Holland was 43.8 per cent. In the course of this land transfer many smaller estates disappeared altogether, broken up for sale as individual farms and the large estates were drastically reduced in size. The comparison of three of the largest estates a century apart demonstrates the long-term effect. Between 1876 and 1976 the Yarborough estate declined from 55,000 acres to 30,000, Ancaster from 67,638 acres to 22,680 acres, and Brownlow from 57,798 acres to 10,000. While these changes were important, they are not to be exaggerated: estates were still very active at the end of our century as at its beginning.[17]

New entrants to farming after 1918 were more likely to have to invest in buying their farms. At the same time estate owners who continued to hold on to their land began to change from being squires in the old sense to more active land managers, often farmers of their own land. G. H. Nevile, whose family had been major landowners of Wellingore, was one example. By 1940 the gap between landowner and farmer had narrowed considerably. Leaders of the agricultural world were no longer drawn almost exclusively from the landowners, but were now more likely to come from the farmers, usually those with larger farms. The National Farmers' Union was already establishing itself as the dominant agricultural pressure group. This affected local political and social affairs as much as farming matters. Some of the old landowners, such as the Earl of Ancaster, continued to take an active part as county and district councillors, and as lords lieutenant, but farmers had grown in prominence as members of school boards, boards of guardians, and councillors ever since these were established as elected bodies.[18]

Labour

The first people employed on most farms were the farmer's wife and children. For a sizeable minority, they were the only people employed. The general report to the 1851 census noted that a third of all farmers in the country employed no labour. Employment was not really the term to use of family labour for the 19th and well into the 20th century, for wages rarely entered into the equation. Even so, being a farmer's wife was a full-time job, and the same was true for a large number of adult sons and daughters. This was recognized in effect by the 19th-century censuses, which had separate entries for farmers' wives and children in the occupational sections. The numbers of farmers' wives in the census for Lincolnshire were nearly three-quarters the total returned for farmers. It is likely that there were a few more working wives who, for one reason or another, escaped entry in that column of the census. Only the wealthiest of farming families could afford to let the wife withdraw from the business of the farm. To use another slight anachronism, farming marriages for the majority were very much partnerships, and business partnerships at that. This was part of the complaint of Tennyson's 'new farmer', that his son was putting love before the business needs of the farm. The importance of the wife's contribution to the management was such that it was unusual for a single man to take a farm. Most single male farmers were widowers. Conversely, the experience gained by the wife meant that it was not uncommon for widows to take on the running of the farm. At each census there were in the region of 570 to 700 female farmers in Lincolnshire. Nearly all of them will have been widows, for social custom and property law militated against a single woman taking on a farm.

Very small holdings depended on family labour for almost all aspects of the farm's work. Going up the scale of farming a simple division of labour took the farmer's wife and daughters away from field work, except perhaps at peak times, to concentrate on keeping the hens, dairy cows for domestic needs and local markets, and managing the household for living-in servants. The convention of this arrangement was that the wife, who arranged the sale of milk, butter, and eggs, would keep the earnings for her domestic accounts.

Table 2 Numbers of agricultural workers 1851–1931

Year	Number of workers	Year	Number of workers
1851	52,046	1901	36,341
1861	57,027	1911	39,463
1871	48,676	1921	38,932
1881	44,640	1931	38,142
1891	41,259		

Source: Census Returns

While small farmers could meet most of their needs for labour from within their families and from casual employment of neighbours and friends, other farmers on a larger scale needed labour on a more regular footing. The fluctuations in the total numbers of labourers in Lincolnshire are shown in Table 2. The strength of demand for labour in the mid-19th century was followed by a marked downward trend, as workers found better prospects elsewhere, and agricultural depression reduced demand. The one counter trend was the effect of intensifying agriculture in the Fens in the early 20th century, which caused numbers of male workers to rise slightly in the 1920s. Nearly all the workers returned in the censuses were male. The numbers of women were small, and fluctuated greatly from census to census. Women were working on the land, but their employment was casual and seasonal rather than of the regular nature that censuses registered. After the First World War the annual agricultural returns gave figures for employment that included casual workers. In 1935, according to these figures, 19 per cent of all agricultural workers in the county were in casual employment, 40 per cent of whom were women.

In Lincolnshire the practice of hiring male workers by the year was common in the mid-19th century. In some parts of the county it was dominant. The isolation of areas such as the Wolds made this form of employment both attractive and necessary. Horsemen, shepherds, and cowmen were all likely to be employed in this way. The census returns for 1851 record totals of 'indoor' servants rather under a third of the figure for other labourers. Other calculations put the proportion higher, as much as 49 per cent of male workers as living-in servants in 1871. These were mostly young men: 76 per cent of them were aged between 15 and 24. Numbers of 'indoor' servants were falling, however. Between 1861 and 1871 they fell by 13 per cent compared with a 10 per cent fall in the numbers of other labourers. That this trend continued is clear from the reports each year of reduced business at hiring fairs. Even so, many of the fairs remained very active throughout the late 19th century. Several were still functioning at the beginning of the 20th century. A combination of changes in labour requirements, farmers and their wives ceasing to want labourers living in their house, and the workers themselves wanting independence brought about the decline of this type of contract. It was a lingering death, however. In not a few places hiring for the year continued for as long as horses were used. Between the wars there were still numbers of horsemen living in. Near Boston, for example, there were young men being lodged with the farm foreman in the 1920s. Sometimes this continued beyond 1945. In most neighbouring counties the decline both of hiring by the year, and of the fairs, had proceeded more rapidly.[19]

Many of the agricultural workers were skilled specialists, in particular those who worked with livestock. Those working with horses were the elite among them. Waggoner was the most common term by which they were called in Lincolnshire, though carter was also to be found. The training and skills required for the handling of horse and plough were reflected in the strict hierarchy, almost ritualistic in its application, that existed among the horsemen. The waggoner was head, taking the lead in all things, great and small, followed in strict order by the 'second chap' and 'third chap'. The horseman's work was exacting, rising at 4.00 in the morning to prepare and feed the horses before going out to work at 6.00. There was a break for a meal at 9.30, work continuing then until 2.30 pm. The horses were led back, unharnessed and cleaned. The men had a break before coming back in the early evening to feed the horses for the night.[20]

Agricultural wages in Lincolnshire were relatively high, not as good as in the industrial northern counties, but far better than wages in southern England. The county's isolation and small population were held to be among the reasons for the relative prosperity of the farm labourers. Clarke noted a couple of areas on clay soils in the north and the south-west of the county where labour was over-supplied in 1851, but in most areas the reverse was the case. Shortage and the high price of labour on the Wolds was one of the reasons for the practice of leaving turnips to be fed off in the fields. Wages at mid century were mostly, in summer, 12s to 13s 6d a week, occasionally up to 15s. In winter the rate dropped to 10s a week. There were many tasks, including turnip singling and ditching, paid at piece rates. Women, boys, and girls could be employed on weeding, stone-picking, driving pigs, and other tasks at rates ranging from 4d to 1s a day.[21]

The reporter on Kesteven for the report on the Wages and Conditions of Employment in 1919 commented that 'the weekly cash rate of wages, especially in the case of the hired man, in no sense fully represents the total earnings'.[22] Additional payments principally for harvest and haytime added cash to the worker's income. Then there were payments in kind, such as subsidized housing and coal. The provision of allotments was becoming well established during the early 19th century. 'There is a practice in the marsh lands in the neighbourhood of Louth and Grimsby', reported one witness to the Select Committee on Agriculture in 1833, 'of allowing the agricultural labourer to keep a cow, to give a carter so much and the keep of a cow.' In some parishes the labourer had a cottage and garden rent-free, a rood of land for potatoes, and the keep of a pig. Some were able to pasture a cow in return for a deduction from the money wage. All of this made a great difference to the labourer's diet and standard of living.[23]

Wages were rising during the mid-19th century. The day labourer's wage of 13s 6d to 15s a week in 1872 became 16s 6d to 18s by 1874. The new agricultural labourers' unions, which attracted much support in these years, especially the county's 'own' Lincolnshire Labour League, played a large part in campaigning for these increases. The unions put forward a demand for three shillings a day, and the rate of 18s per week largely fulfilled that.[24] Farmers, however, were acting not only in response to pressure from labourers' unions, but also to a general scarcity of labour, the result of men leaving the land for the towns or to emigrate.[25] Because of this the earnings of labourers had been tending to rise before the unions were established. Thus the weekly earnings of the men employed by one farmer near Spalding, which were 15s in 1863, had become 15s 6d to 16s 6d by 1868–69. From 1872 to 1874 they were 18s 6d per week.[26]

This shortage of labour became of much concern to farmers in the early 1870s. In the Fens it was ascribed to the development of potato farming, with its high demand for labour, as well as to emigration. Evidence was given to the Royal Commission on the Employment of Children, Young Persons and Women in Agriculture in 1867 that Lincolnshire farmers were having difficulty in finding labourers. The provision of more and better cottages, gardens, and allotments to entice men into staying in the country was suggested on this occasion. Speakers at the annual general meeting of the Lincolnshire Chamber of Agriculture in 1872 repeated this suggestion. In 1875 on Lord Monson's estate shortage of accommodation was such that 'scarcely a week passes without either Mr. Brown, or Mr. Evens or some other tenant in Burton or Carlton telling me that they are coming to a standstill for want of labourers.' Some landlords sought the solution to this problem by providing more cottages. An agent wrote in 1879 of the Marsh: 'Since the difficulty has arisen within the last ten years in obtaining a good supply of skilled labour, it has been the practice of the landlords in this district to attach Cottages to the Farms in proportion to their size.' Labour for harvest work was also scarce in these years, and farmers, especially in the Fens, were saved from serious difficulties only by the influx of migrant Irish harvesters.[27]

Economies brought about during the Great Depression turned this labour scarcity into something of a surplus. At times men were without work, especially during the winter. By the 1890s demand for labour was again more nearly balancing the supply. Supply was now reduced because labourers had continued to leave the countryside for the relatively greater attractions elsewhere. The outflow was much reduced in the 1880s, probably because recession in industry restricted the opportunities for finding new work, but between 1891 and 1901 the farm labouring population of Lincolnshire declined by 15 per cent.[28] During the 1891 harvest scarcity of labour was reported from several parts of the county. At Heckington, for example, 'farmers have been hampered by scarcity and perversity of the men. On one farm the hands struck work three times.' The influx of Irish harvestmen again became an important means of tiding over a shortage of local labour. In the Fens farmers were now complaining of being nearly always short of labour.[29] By the turn of the century the 'drift from the land' had been elevated into a national problem. It was leaving the farmer with only the 'one-eyed, the lame, deaf, weaklings, the small and half wits', a Gainsborough farmer put it to Rider Haggard, with perhaps a little exaggeration.[30]

Meeting the need for additional seasonal labour to assist with the harvests was a long-standing problem. In the early 19th century it was still common for the residents of towns to go out to work on the local farms. Labour was also drawn from industrial towns in Yorkshire. The greatest source of additional labour came to be the groups of Irishmen who travelled around England during the summer following the course of harvest from county to county. Their numbers built up steadily from the 1830s onwards. By the 1870s, their visits were such an established part of the harvest that the local papers would report the expected time of their arrival.[31]

Other sources of irregular labour included what became the notorious fenland practice of hiring labour in gangs. Isolation, the rapid expansion of arable, and the slower rate at which settlements grew all had their part in the development of this form of employment. With demand for labour outstripping local supply, the solution adopted was to bring in workers from outside. A gang foreman would strike the bargain with the farmers over wages for the particular job. Although not the only place where gangs were employed, the Fens achieved some notoriety for their use, especially as public concern began to gather about their conditions. Their reliance on the labour of women and children, the mixing of sexes in the same gang, and the indifferent conditions in which the gangs were often billeted were among the most pressing concerns. It came to a head in the investigation of the Royal Commission on the Employment of Women and Children, and the subsequent Gangs Act of 1867. 'Public gangs', those which went from farm to farm, were now prohibited. Individual farmers could have a 'private gang', under license. Education Acts from the 1870s onwards added further limits to the employment of children. These measures could not by themselves improve working conditions in the Fens, which were still reckoned to be very poor in the 1870s. Although the intention was that gangs should decline into oblivion, the needs of fenland farming are such that they have not yet completely gone away.[32]

Among groups of itinerant contract workers who were held in greater public respect were sheep shearers. These men were highly skilled. In the 1860s they were paid three shillings a score.[33] By the late 19th century and into the 20th, shearers were often from Australia and New Zealand, coming to Britain for work during the antipodean winter.

Contractors

Some work on the farm was placed in the hands of contractors. In the 19th century contractors were employed for threshing and steam ploughing, both areas of work where the new implements and machines cost more than most farmers wished or could afford to invest. During the 20th century contracting was extended to many other types of farm work.

The introduction of portable threshing machines in the early 19th century soon led to their being shared and hired among neighbours. Some farmers bought their own machines, but most preferred to hire when needed. More specialist threshing contractors or 'machine men' took up the work, travelling from farm to farm. The application of steam power accentuated this trend. Most of the early sales of portable steam engines in Lincolnshire were to threshing contractors. The contractors employed the engine drivers and other machine operators. The farmer provided all the general labour for the threshing. By the second half of the century threshing contractors had become quite numerous. Most owned no more than one or two sets of tackle, together with perhaps an engine or lorry for road haulage. A few firms grew much larger. The Hundlebys at Chapel St Leonards had five sets. Robert Peatfield had thirteen sets of threshing tackle when his business closed. He had set up business in Ulceby, but soon had a branch at Holton le Clay, near Grimsby. Some threshing contractors were farmers who took on additional work from neighbours. Most of the contracting firms had other work, mainly to keep busy outside the threshing season. Peatfield undertook road haulage. Others took on road maintenance contracts. Some, such as Roberts of Caistor, sold out of their agricultural work to concentrate on the highway contracts. After the First World War threshing contractors went into decline. Arable farming was in recession, and many farmers decided to save on contractors' fees by doing the work themselves. Peatfield's was one of many businesses that closed down, in his instance in 1931.[34]

Few, even among large farmers and landowners, owned sets of steam ploughing tackle. The capital cost was far too high. A basic set of Fowler steam ploughing tackle, of two engines, plough, cultivator, and living van, cost at least £1,600 in the 1880s. From its introduction, therefore, steam ploughing was almost always undertaken by contracting firms. These tended to become fairly large businesses, which undertook other works, such as drainage and cleaning of watercourses, as well as ploughing. Cole Brothers, of Roxholme, was one. They were steam cultivating contractors who later moved into road rolling and haulage. The largest firm by far, indeed the largest ploughing contractor in England, was Ward & Dale, of Sleaford. The business was formed as a partnership in 1890, and converted into a limited company in 1908, at which time they owned 24 sets of steam ploughing equipment. They operated mainly within a thirty-mile radius of Sleaford, in southern Lincolnshire, and extending into neighbouring parts of Nottinghamshire, Rutland, Northamptonshire, and Leicestershire. In 1914 Ward & Dale's steam tackle cultivated 64,749 acres. After 1918 increasing use of the tractor, which farmers tended to own, reduced demand for the ploughing contractors. Ward & Dale closed in 1939.[35]

Fig. 5   Steam ploughing at Bourne, 1955
Source: Museum of English Rural Life

Notes to Chapter 3

1 Acreage figures quoted are taken from Return of Owners of Land, *PP*, 1874, lxx ii.

2 Edith, Marchioness of Londonderry, *Henry Chaplin: a memoir* (1926) pp. 115–20

3 LAO, MON25/13/18, Vicar of Croft to Monson, 23 February 1871

4 LAO, 9ANC 2/C/1/16, 19 October 1897.

5 Charles K. Rawding, *The Lincolnshire Wolds in the 19th Century* (2001) pp. 112–13. R. J. Olney, *Lincolnshire Politics 1832–1885* (1973) p. 187.

6 *The Agrarian History of England and Wales, vol. VII, 1850–1914*, ed. E. J. T. Collins (2000) p. 879. James Obelkevitch, *Religion and Rural Society in South Lindsey 1825–1875* (1976) p. 32. C. T. Parker, 'Sir John Henry Thorold, Bart.', *JRASE*, vol. 83 (1922) p. 1.

7 LAO, BS13/1/13/50, 26 December 1881.

8 LAO, MON25/13/18, 12 December 1893.

9 LAO, MON 25/13/18, 19 December 1883.

10 LAO, 9ANC 5/1/7.

11 *Agricultural Gazette*, 11 March, 29 April 1895.

12 See, for example, F. A. Channing's minority report to the second Royal Commission on Agriculture (Final Report, pp. 225–370), which concentrated much attention on rent as a cause of depression.

13 LAO, MON 25/13/18, 15 February 1880, 27 August 1880, 22, 27 February 1884; 2NEL, 5/1, 30 May 1885.

14 RC1893, Wilson Fox, p. 56. LAO, YARB5, summary rentals and accounts.

15 Essex Record Office, D/DPE179. John Davies, 'The End of the Great Estates and the Rise of Freehold Farming in Wales', *Welsh Historical Review*, v. 7 (1974) pp. 189–90. LAO, 2HEN5/14–18. Edith, Marchioness of Londonerry, *Henry Chaplin, a memoir*, pp. 115–20. Peter Baumber and Dennis Mills, eds., *Kirkby Green and Scopwick: historical sketches of two Lincolnshire parishes* (1993) p. 6.

16 LAO Misc. Dep. 145/9. G. M. Robinson, *Agricultural Change* (1988) p. 136. Baumber and Mills, *Kirkby Green and Scopwick*, pp. 6–7. *Agricultural Gazette*, 22 July 1918, p. 67.

17 D. Cannadine, *The Decline and Fall of the British Aristocracy* (1998) pp. 725–6. S. G. Sturmey, 'Owner Farming in England and Wales 1900–1950', in W. E. Minchinton, ed. *Essays in Agrarian History*, v. 2 (1968) pp. 295–301. *Agricultural Statistics, 1927. National Farm Survey of*

England and Wales (1941–43): a summary report (1946). University of
Cambridge Department of Agriculture, *Landownership in the Eastern
Counties 1941* (1941) pp. 8, 30.

18   F. M. L. Thompson, 'English Landed Society in the Twentieth
Century I', *Transactions of the Royal Historical Society*, 5th ser., v. 40 (1990)
pp. 1–24. R. J. Olney, *Rural Society and County Government in
Nineteenth–century Lincolnshire* (1979) pp. 136–8.

19   A. Hall, 'A Lincolnshire Horseman: work and class', *Oral History*, v. 5
(1977) p. 90. *The Agrarian History of England and Wales, vol. VII,
1850–1914*, pp. 839, 1317. *SM*, 16 May 1890. RC 1893, Wilson Fox,
p. 84. G. K. Nelson, *To Be A Farmer's Boy* (1991) p. 129. Len
Woodhead, *A Lincolnshire Lad Looks Back* (2003) p. 26.

20   Hall, 'A Lincolnshire Horseman: work and class', pp. 88–96.

21   J. A. Clarke, 'On the Farming of Lincolnshire', *JRASE*, v. 12 (1851)
pp. 403–5.

22   *Wages and Conditions of Employment in Agriculture. General Report*, Cmd 24,
PP, xxii (1919) p. 183.

23   *Select Committee on Agriculture* (1833) QQ. 7495–7. John Burnett, *Plenty
and Want* (1966) pp. 45–6.

24   This was an aim formulated in the early meetings of the new unions.
SM, 16, 23 February, 1 March 1872.

25   There was a slight increase in the numbers of agricultural labourers in
Lincolnshire between 1851 and 1861, but at the 1871 census numbers
were 10.7 per cent lower. Census Returns, 1851–1871, occupational
tables.

26   *Agricultural Gazette*, 19 October 1885. These figures are averages for
the year and include the extra payments at harvest time.

27   *Royal Commission on the Employment of Children, Young Persons and Women
in Agriculture*, Reports and Evidence on Lincolnshire by Edward
Stanhope, PP, 1867–8 (4088), 1868–9 (4202). Rex Russell, *The 'Revolt of
the Field' in Lincolnshire* (Lincoln, 1956) pp. 5–6. LAO, MON
25/13/18, 2 May 1875; Misc. Don. 157. *SM*, 2, 9 February 19 April, 9,
16, 23, 30 August, 13 September 1872. See also, E. L. Jones, 'The
Agricultural Labour Market in England 1793–1872', *EcHR*, 2nd ser. v.
17 (1964–5) pp. 322–38, which shows similar developments
throughout the country.

28   Census Returns 1871–1901.

29   *Royal Commission on Labour: the agricultural labourer, vol. i, part vi, Report on
Lincolnshire*, by Edward Wilkinson, C6894 (1893) pp. 42, 106. LAO,
2HEN 5/18/49, Heneage to Wintringham, 13 September 1891. *Tariff*

Commission (1906), para. 814. *SM,* 18 September, 27 November 1891, 2 September 1892.

30   H. Rider Haggard, *Rural England* (1902) v. 2, p. 234. C. S. Orwin and E. H. Whetham, *The History of British Agriculture 1846–1914* (1964) pp. 343–4. The drift from the land was the subject of exhaustive investigation by, for example, W. Ogle, 'The Alleged Depopulation of the Rural Districts', *JRSS,* v. 52 (1889) pp. 205–32; G. B. Longstaffe, 'Rural Depopulation', *JRSS,* v. 56 (1893); Lord Eversley, 'The Decline in the number of Agricultural Labourers in Great Britain', *JRSS,* v. 70 (1907).

31   J. A. Perkins, 'Harvest Technology and Labour Supply in Lincolnshire and the East Riding of Yorkshire 1750–1850, part I', *Tools and Tillage,* v. 3 (1976) pp. 51–3.

32   Richard Heath, *The English Peasant* (1893) pp. 110, 112ff. *Royal Commission on the Employment of Children, Young Persons and Women in Agriculture,* Reports by Edward Stanhope, p. 278.

33   J. A. Perkins, *Sheep Farming in Eighteenth and Nineteenth Century Lincolnshire* (1977) p. 19.

34   Ken Redmore, 'The Early Days of Steam-powered Threshing', *Lincolnshire Past & Present,* 53 (Autumn 2003) pp. 7–8. Anon, 'Some Lincolnshire Contractors', *Steaming,* v. 18 (1975) pp. 70–80.

35   Jim Procter, 'Cole Brothers, Roxholme, Sleaford', *Steaming,* v. 18 (1975) p. 109. H. Bonnett, *Saga of the Steam Plough* (1965) pp. 115–19, 176–7.

4
THE PATTERN OF FARMING IN LINCOLNSHIRE

Having been introduced to some of the people on the land, this chapter turns to their farms: the structure of farming, the distribution of large and small farms, and some of the changes experienced during these hundred years. The chapter following takes us to the types of farming practised in Lincolnshire, starting with the way contemporaries viewed the nature of farming in the middle decades of the 19th century.

The structure of Lincolnshire farming

Lincolnshire in the 19th century presented an agricultural scene of extremes: farming on a very large scale contrasting with that on a very small scale. We have encountered this feature when looking at the farmers themselves. A structural analysis of the county's agriculture shows it up again. This is how J. A. Clarke summarized the position in 1878: 'Lincolnshire is... remarkable for the distribution of its holdings; large farms prevailing on the hills, while in other parts, more particularly in the south east fen and marsh flat, and in a still more marked degree in the extreme north west, known as the "Isle of Axholme", there are among medium-sized occupations very numerous small farms often little larger than allotments.'[1]

As Table 3 shows, the very small farms of less than 50 acres and the large farms of more than 300 acres together accounted for a little over half of the agricultural acreage in the late 19th century. The remainder were the farms of small to medium size. It is easy to overlook these, the 'typical' farms. The French visitor, Leonce de Lavergne, after being smitten with the scale of the farming on the Wolds, wrote in a tone of some surprise, 'In the more naturally fertile parts of the county, again, one meets with middling-sized, and even small farming, which is rather remarkable, so close to the more brilliant model of the large.'[2] However, it was the very large and the small farms that attracted the most attention. It was also true that the large farms were among the strongest features of Lincolnshire agriculture compared with the rest of England and Wales. While the percentage of farms of fewer than 50 acres in Lincolnshire modestly exceeded the national average, the gap between county and nation was more marked where large farms were concerned. This was so, especially when measured as a proportion of total agricultural acreage. Lincolnshire remained in general a county of large farms throughout the upheavals that agriculture experienced. Holdings of 300 acres and over occupied 39.7 per cent of the agricultural acreage of Lincolnshire in 1875, compared with 30.2 per cent for England and Wales. Large farms in Lincolnshire increased both as a percentage of the total number of holdings and of total acreage between the 1870s and the 1890s, establishing a trend that continued into the 20th century. The gap between the figures for the county and the whole country widened.

Table 3 Small and large holdings 1875–1944

| | Percentage: total number of holdings | | | | Percentage: total agricultural acreage | | | |
| | 50 acres & under | | Over 300 acres | | 50 acres & under | | Over 300 acres | |
Year	Lincs	E&W	Lincs	E&W	Lincs	E&W	Lincs	E&W
1875	75.8	71.2	4.7	3.8	15.0	14.7	39.7	30.2
1895	72.4	67.8	5.4	4.1	14.4	14.3	41.3	30.0
1915	69.4		5.4		14.1		38.3	
1944					11.0	21.8	42.0	24.0

Source: Agricultural Returns

The Wolds were renowned for the scale of their farming. 'The amount of land that some of these great Lincolnshire farmers have held … and the number of farms that single families have been known to pay

rent for is perhaps unexampled in the history of British agriculture',
enthused a reporter for the *Pall Mall Gazette*. Farms were large here, few
smaller than 300 acres, reported J. A. Clarke.[3] On the Brocklesby estate
of Lord Yarborough in the 1830s there were fifteen tenants with farms
of more than 675 acres. The Chaplin estates at Tathwell were
predominantly in very large farms. In 1879 seven out of fifteen holdings
were greater than 500 acres, and several of the other holdings were not
far short of that. The Heneage estate was more mixed, containing more
land off the Wolds, but in 1879 four out of thirty farms here were larger
than 500 acres. This had dropped to one by 1903, perhaps reflecting
Edward Heneage's wish to encourage farming on a smaller scale as a
remedy for agricultural depression. Even so, plenty of farms over 300
acres in size remained on his estate.[4] Farming on the Heath was on a
similarly large scale, although they did not attract quite so much
attention. On Chaplin's southern estate at Blankney in 1879 fifteen out
of thirty-three holdings were greater than 500 acres.

The extent of large-scale farming was greater than the simple
numbers of holdings suggest because of the number of farmers who
occupied more than one farm. Although this might say as much about
the vagaries of the different statistical collections, a comparison of the
number of holdings recorded in the agricultural statistics with the
number of farmers in the population census gives a crude indication of
this phenomenon. In 1870 there were 24,500 holdings in the
agricultural returns, while the following year's census gives 11,700
farmers. The ramifications of the family ties noticed in Chapter 2 also
had their influence. The Sharpley family, for one example, farmed about
12,000 acres in the north Wolds.[5]

Multiple holdings were not a new feature. Farmers of the Heath
and Wolds, for example, had for many years taken land in the lowlands
as feeding grounds, but the occupation of several farms in multiple was
becoming more extensive during the Great Depression. Bishop
Edward Hicks commented on the increasing number of businessmen
farmers in Weston and Moulton Fens who 'accumulate farms and
manage them with foremen'. The potato-growing business of William
Dennis was a prime example of this trend, but he was not alone. John
Butler, who introduced the King Edward potato, entered farming in the

mid-1890s after being a grocer and draper at Scotter. According to his letter-heading in 1903 he was a 'celery, carrot, and seed potato grower', with four farms at Scotter, Scotton, and Messingham. The following year his list had expanded to nine farms. Further examples abound in all parts of the county. There was Robert Searby, of Edlington, who in 1881 was farming 530 acres under Mr Short of Edlington, 580 acres at Greetham and 220 acres at Croft under Lord Monson. He was applying that year to take another farm, about 700 acres, of Mr Chaplin's, although this time he was to act as trustee for the heir to the late tenant, who was a minor. One of the witnesses before the second Royal Commission held 472 acres at Belchford, 1,238 acres at Wainfleet, and sundry small farms.[6] Moves to reduce the size of holdings made by a number of estates at this time actually encouraged the holding of medium-sized farms in multiple, so that the scale of farming grew rather than diminished.[7] The reduction in the scale of farming, which some people hoped to see during the Great Depression, did not come about. The geography of farming size remained in 1914 as it had been in 1850. The Wolds and the Heath continued to have very large farms, the average size of holding in many parishes being over 200 acres.

Consolidation and enlargement of farm holdings was a strong feature of the mid-19th century. The Ancaster estate lands at Aslackby were held by fourteen tenants in 1853, eight in 1872, and seven in 1884. The estate had 368 acres at Dowsby farmed by seven tenants in the 1850s, but there were only three in 1877.[8] Consolidation was achieved mainly by the absorption of holdings of less than fifty acres into larger farms. One might expect large farmers to have been expanding their operations during the prosperity of the middle decades of the century, but not perhaps when times were hard in the Great Depression. However, that is what did happen. Farming on a larger scale was expanding and it was spreading beyond its traditional centres of the light uplands, as the examples from the Fens demonstrate. If anything, it was more apparent during the depression that farming on a large scale could offer real economies. In particular, rents per acre on large farms were lower than for smallholdings; often the difference was considerable. On Henry Chaplin's Blankney estate at the end of the 1870s farms of 75–150 acres were rented at 29s to 30s per acre, whereas

those of 700–900 acres were 25s to 26s. 9d per acre. In the 1890s
Wilson Fox found that on Lord Yarborough's estate farms of more
than 400 acres were let for 19s 3d per acre compared with 28s 9d for
farms of less than 100 acres, and on Lord Ancaster's estates there were
similar relationships between rent and size of farm.[9]

The rents on large farms were likely to have fallen by a greater
amount during the depression. Reductions of 35–40 per cent on large
farms, compared with reductions of about 30 per cent on farms of
medium size, were figures often quoted.[10] This, of course, had much to
do with the fact that farmers with capital sufficient to take on a large
farm were in shorter supply during the depression. Landlords often
complained that large farms were difficult to let. Lord Monson's agent
in 1880 reported that one of the largest farms on the estate, of more
than 800 acres, could at best attract farmers who might be prepared to
take on the 500 to 600 acres of best quality land only.[11] There were
some large farms that appeared continually in the 'Farms to let' column
of the local papers during the 1880s.[12] On the other hand, men with
capital were likely to be more resilient to the misfortunes of agriculture.
Investigators for the Royal Commissions found that large farmers
generally had more capital reserves than small farmers.[13] A newspaper
correspondent, writing of the Fens in 1888, thought that 'the larger
farmers, with sufficient capital, will take no harm: the little men, with no
stock, low price of corn and potatoes, will be left to struggle on in
difficulties'.[14] For men of capital also there were plentiful opportunities
to build up a substantial business, and that is what those such as William
Dennis did. This set the pattern for development during the 20th
century. 'The big man can make a profit, but the small man cannot,'
opined one witness to the Tariff Commission in 1906.[15]

The phenomenon of smallholdings

The economic momentum towards farming on a larger scale has
seemed inexorable, even inevitable. Even so, there has remained a
counterbalancing view in support of small-scale farming, based not only
on sentiment, but also on grounds of agricultural and economic logic.
Not surprisingly, the case for small-scale farming was argued strongly in
Lincolnshire, where it was such a feature. Smallholdings numerically

were in the majority, 74 per cent of the county's holdings being 50 acres or less in 1870. They only accounted for about fifteen per cent of the agricultural area, however, and were a slightly greater proportion than for England and Wales as a whole (see Table 3). Small farms were concentrated in the Fens and the Isle of Axholme. In fenland the average was 59 per cent of the acreage between 5 and 49 acres, with some parishes having a higher figure still.[16] In Epworth in 1885 holdings of less than 20 acres took up 21 per cent of the parish's land. The average size of holding in some of these parishes was exceptionally low: Kirton in the Fens had an average farm size of 27 acres, at Fishtoft it was 21.9 acres, and at Haxey 29.9 acres, to take some examples from 1900.

The Great Depression seemed to augur well for smallholdings. One of the leading specialists in the subject wrote, 'the year 1880 marks the revival of smallholdings'.[17] With large farms proving difficult to let the answer seemed to lie in subdividing farms. Farming on a smaller scale received some strong and enthusiastic support during this period. Farmers were often advised that one good way to counteract depressed prices would be to concentrate capital on a smaller acreage. Landlords could be attracted by this argument. Edward Heneage was one. He made a speech sympathetic to this view in 1878. In a letter to his tenants in 1886 he suggested that, in return for future reductions in rent, they should ensure that their capital was adequate for the size of holding, and they should be prepared to have less land if capital was short. He appears not to have met with a ready response from his tenants. In 1887 Heneage was writing to his agent: 'I used all my influence to induce tenants to reduce their holdings rather than capital, but none were willing to admit their inability to farm their holdings.'[18] Lord Monson's agent was similarly attracted to the possibilities of creating smaller farms, writing in 1879: 'Everything points in the direction of subdivision of estates into smaller holdings, and it will probably be necessary to adopt this policy notwithstanding the difficulty and expense of carrying it out.' While Wilson Fox reckoned that some men of capital were preferring to settle for smaller farms, and there are examples of farmers moving down the scale of farming, Heneage's experience was the more typical.[19]

When Heneage spoke of smaller farms he did not mean smallholdings, however. He, Monson and other large landlords were making very large farms slightly smaller, and by reallocating fields from one farm to another the average size of farm on some estates was reduced. On Heneage's estate in 1879 there were seven farms out of thirty that were over 400 acres, but only four in 1902.

When the experts wrote of a revival of small farming they were not looking to Edward Heneage, but to the Fens, the Isle of Axholme and the Marsh where small farming remained a characteristic feature. It was here that some of the more successful attempts to subdivide land were made. The most celebrated was Lord Carrington's creation of new, allotment-sized holdings in association with the Small Holdings Syndicate run by Richard Winfrey. This group rented 650 acres from Lord Carrington from 1904, dividing them between about two hundred tenants. These were intended mainly as part-time occupations for labourers.[20] Local authority smallholdings were established under the terms of the Smallholdings Acts from 1908 onwards. Most were in the parishes to the north of Spalding. The Ministry of Agriculture established its Holbeach Farm Colony of smallholdings in 1917.[21]

There was a more complex pattern of landholding in these districts than in most others. There were few large estates and many small landowners. The large estates, such as the Heathcote and Ancaster, which had land in the Fens or in adjacent areas, had many small tenancies, which were let variously as accommodation land to tradesmen or to small farmers. Alongside these estates were many small landowners, local tradesmen owned some land, and so did many of the farmers themselves. Hence there was a great variety of tenure: a farmer might own a few acres, and rent several parcels of land from two or three other owners, the whole of his territory perhaps amounting to no more than 50 acres. A farmer in Surfleet was a typical example. In 1887 he had 5¾ acres of his own, rented 4 acres from the Spalding Charity and another 4 acres from one of the leading estate agents of Spalding.[22]

To purchase some land was one of the main ambitions of small farmers of the Fens and Isle of Axholme. When confidence in farming was high, demand could push prices up. In the 1860s and early 1870s some land was fetching over £100 an acre. The would-be owner had usually to have about a quarter or a third of the purchase price in hand; the rest he raised by mortgage, generally from solicitors and other people of independent means. A readiness to trade in land and local inheritance customs helped maintain a supply of land on the market. On the death of an owner the land was usually either divided between the heirs or sold and the proceeds divided. The result was to maintain a high turnover of occupation in the smallholding strongholds, for each generation had to build up its holdings anew. Rate books from fenland parishes show a shifting pattern of land ownership. In Friskney at the end of the 19th century it was said there was scarcely a farm that had not changed hands during the preceding thirty years.[23]

Despite the claims of some of the more enthusiastic supporters of smallholdings, many could not be full-time occupations. Estimates varied as to the minimum needed for a full-time holding, and individual circumstances played a large part, but on the whole, the occupier of any holding smaller than 40 or 50 acres was likely to need additional sources of income. One of the most common forms of by-employment was as casual labour on larger farms. The difficulty, of course, was that demand for casual labour tended to be greatest when the smallholder most needed to be working on his own land, and in some places smallholdings were so predominant that there were few large farms on which work might be available. Those with a horse or two could hire them out to their neighbours, and if they had a cart as well there were possibilities for work as carriers and higglers. A few went outside agriculture and took jobs on the railway.[24]

Occupiers of smallholdings often pursued another trade as well. Which came first depended upon circumstance. Butchers, innkeepers, coal dealers were all likely to take on some land, sometimes as a means of entry into larger-scale farming. Equally there were those like the farmer of 30 acres at Deeping St James who turned to coal merchanting because 'I could not live on the 30 acres, nor yet three thirties without the coal trade'. Similar was the example of the farmer in the Fens who ran a pork butchery through which she could sell the farm's produce.[25]

The Great Depression at the end of the 19th century presented smallholders with severe problems, especially during the first few years, from 1879 to 1882. The Richmond Commission described the condition of the small freeholders of Lincolnshire as 'deplorable, many of them being unable to pay interest on their mortgages'. Fifteen years later Wilson Fox found evidence of some in conditions that were little different. 'I have been here 15 years,' commented one farmer of 22 acres in Wildmore Fen. 'If I were sold up tomorrow I should be much worse off than when I started.' Others told Wilson Fox that they were worse off than labourers.[26] Many of the smallholders' difficulties arose because they could not reduce their expenses as much as larger farmers. Rents remained relatively high and, for freeholders, mortgages contracted in times of higher prices and interest rates were a millstone. Freeholders were sometimes carried, unwillingly, by the mortgagees. They were slow to foreclose because they would have to find either tenants or purchasers, and neither prospect was attractive when rental and freehold values were falling. One small landowner, the Rev. Brunyee, wrote to his solicitor, 'It would be no use my taking John Sayles' lands as I have more now at Crowle than I can let at any Price'. Two years later, in 1889, he did repossess the land, a course other mortgagees and landlords were often forced to take.[27]

These difficulties did force many smallholders out of their land during the 1880s, yet small farming was still going strong at the beginning of the 20th century. While acknowledging the burden that mortgage payments could impose, Wilson Fox concluded that for most of the small freeholders in the Fens the risk and the debt were worth bearing. Rider Haggard thought the Isle of Axholme was one of the more prosperous areas of the county. Sir Daniel Hall thought the agriculture of the Isle was fundamentally inefficient, although he was referring mainly to the system of strip farming in open fields that survived in many parishes. 'Wasteful of labour' was his summary of farming here. In this he was echoing many other commentators, including the local commissioners for both Royal Commissions during the depression. Even so Daniel Hall had to accept that 'despite the smallness of the holdings and the drawbacks due to the divisions and the scattering, we were informed that the farmers were all reasonably prosperous'.[28] Alongside the sufferers Wilson Fox also found many examples of success in small farming. There was the man who rented 30 acres at Wainfleet, grew wheat, peas, potatoes, and mangolds, and kept cows, selling the butter to hucksters. 'We have always paid the rent and the wages, and keep ourselves; have lost no money since 1882.' Another at Friskney commented, 'No doubt a small freeholder can make a living in this district if he works hard. Many people here paying £4 an acre are doing fairly well.'[29] Hard work by the occupier was always emphasized as one of the attributes of success, one of the necessities, because smallholders lacked the capital of their larger neighbours. They relied to a great extent on family labour. The employment of regular labourers was rare on holdings below about sixty acres. Typically, the wife took charge of the dairy and poultry while the farmer and his sons dealt with the arable and stock-keeping. Sons might be paid wages, but not before they were adult. Where additional labour was employed, much of it was on a casual basis, at a rate of 3d or 6d a day more than the standard wage.

Fig. 6   Potato pickers at Gosberton in the Fens
Source: North East Lincolnshire Libraries

At the root of the smallholder's success was the ability to turn to good account the benefits of the rich soils of the Fens and Isle of Axholme. It was here that the smallholder could flourish. Elsewhere conditions were more difficult. On the rich soils the smallholder could quite easily diversify away from traditional patterns and into the new intensively cultivated crops coming more into demand. This was taken to its greatest extent perhaps in the Isle of Axholme where corn-growing was largely abandoned, except for stock feed, for which purpose oats were grown in preference to wheat. In place of wheat came carrots, celery, potatoes, and more stock-keeping.[30] In the Fens smallholders who did well owed their success more to the type of farming they followed than to their being smallholders. Although they grew more cereals than their counterparts on the Isle of Axholme, their main strengths lay in potatoes, celery, mustard for seed, peas, beans, clover for sale. 'If it had not been for growing early potatoes we should have given up years ago,' commented one fenlander. Most smallholders also kept cattle and one or two horses. The number of cattle in the Fens was generally greater than the average for the county. These animals consumed much of the cereals grown.[31]

   With this type of farming it was even possible for smallholders to expand their businesses. It was a traditional aim of the small farmer to

Fig. 7   Drilling seed in the Fens
Source: Museum of English Rural Life

add to his land, but most gained no more than a few acres. Now it seems that potatoes and celery were proving the foundation for the more successful to expand. William Standring of Epworth told Rider Haggard that the numbers of smallholders were no longer increasing because instead the tendency was for existing farmers to add to their holdings, and the most successful expanded well beyond the realm of small holding. This is a trend apparent from the statistics, for the average size of holding in both the Fens and the Isle of Axholme shows a marked increase in many parishes. In Epworth the average size of holding in 1875 was 26.5 acres and in 1900, 33.8 acres. In the Fens, Kirton showed an increase in average size from 27 acres in 1875 to 54 acres in 1900, and Wigtoft from 35 to 48 acres. These figures disguise the extent to which large farming had been expanding. By 1919 a report to the Board of Agriculture could describe south Holland as having 'colonies of small-holdings and little isolated occupations' existing alongside large agricultural businesses. Some were very large. Holbeach parish had three or four farmers with 'considerably over 1,000 and sometimes over 2,000 acres'. One of them was Herbert Carter, who entered farming in the 1880s. As a result the number of holdings of medium size had declined.[32] A. G. Street, writing in 1937, declared that fenland farming 'is a business of the large capitalist', citing the example of the farms of Smith's potato crisps at Nocton, which totalled 7,000 acres. A number of these large farms had been built up from smallholdings. Rider Haggard was told that the largest farm in Friskney parish, 1,100 acres, had grown in this way. In Epworth the occupiers of farms of more than 150 acres in the late 1880s were said to be mainly men who had started out as part-time farmers of a few acres.[33]

This demonstrated the dilemma for the smallholders and their political supporters, for the advantages that small farming could gain from the rich soils were available equally to large farming, and soon it was the large-scale growing of potatoes, celery, carrots, and bulbs that was to dominate. Attempts to foster smallholdings through state action had limited results. Two Smallholdings Acts, of 1892 and 1908, gave local authorities powers to buy land and let it as smallholdings. The second of these had the greater effect, in that by 1914 Holland County Council had 8,578 acres for smallholdings, Kesteven 4,628 acres,

Lindsey 3,958 acres. Even so, these totals were modest. In Lindsey, Christopher Turnor had pushed the council into taking an active role in the development and management of its smallholdings. Elsewhere enthusiasm was more muted. The First World War curtailed further expansion, and the momentum was not regained afterwards for the tide was flowing another way.[34]

Notes to Chapter 4

1   J. A. Clarke, 'Practical Agriculture', *JRASE*, v. 39 (1878) p. 611.
2   Leonce de Lavergne, *The Rural Economy of England, Scotland and Ireland* (1855) p. 232.
3   Quoted in *SM*, 18 May 1883. J. A. Clarke, 'On the Farming of Lincolnshire', *JRASE*, v. 12 (1851) pp. 330–1.
4   LAO, YARB5; BS13/1/7/6; 2HEN2/4/5, 2/5/71. R. J. Olney, *Rural Society and County Government in Nineteenth-century Lincolnshire.*(1979) p. 56.
5   *SM*, 28 October 1881.
6   H. Rider Haggard, *Rural England* (1902) v. 2, p. 160. *Report on the Decline of the Agricultural Population of Great Britain*, Cd. 3273 (1906) pp. 33–4. Sir Francis Hill, *Victorian Lincoln* (1974) p. 217. LAO, BS13/1/13/47; 2TGH 1/12. RC1893, Q.35830.
7   LAO, 9ANC 1A/1–20, 2/C/1, estate surveys and tenancy agreements; 2HEN 2/4/5, 2/5/71.
8   S. R. Haresign, Agricultural Change and Rural Society on the Lincolnshire Fenlands and Isle of Axholme 1870–1914, PhD thesis, University of East Anglia, 1980, pp. 105–6.
9   LAO, BS 13/1/7/6. RC1893, Wilson Fox, p. 19.
10   RC1893, QQ. 14298, 14300. LAO, 2HEN 2/1/4, 2/2/64.
11   LAO, MON25/13/18, 4 February 1880.
12   An example is Hagnaby Abbey Farm, 550 acres, which first appeared in 1883 and was still there in 1890. *Stamford Mercury*.
13   RC1879, First Report of S. B. L. Druce, p. 390. RC1893, Wilson Fox, p. 61.
14   *SM*, 5 October 1888.
15   *Tariff Commission*, para. 857.
16   David Grigg, *The Agricultural Revolution in South Lincolnshire* (1966) p. 170.
17   H. Levy, *Large and Small Holdings* (1911) p. 93.

18 *SM,* 13 December 1878. LAO, 2HEN 2/4/21, 2/5/16.

19 LAO, MON 25/13/18, 20 November 1879. RC1893, QQ. 49669–72.
    RC1879, QQ. 7140, 7209–13. LAO, 9ANC 2/C/1/1.

20 Rider Haggard, *Rural England* v. 2, pp. 239–42. Levy, *Large and Small
    Holdings,* pp. 94, 150–2. E. A. Pratt, *The Transition in Agriculture* (1906)
    pp. 280–7. Lord Carrington, 'The Land and the Labourers', *The Nineteenth
    Century,* v. 45 (1899) pp. 368–77.

21 RC1919, Minutes of evidence, vol. 1, QQ. 336–9.

22 LAO, Boston Sewers Parcel 26/7, Surfleet Dikereeve Assessment 1887.

23 RC1879, First Report of S. B. L. Druce, p. 387; Minutes of Evidence,
    QQ. 7126–7, 29717–21, 29731–4, 29851–4, 30582–90, 30622.
    RC1893, Wilson Fox, pp. 169ff. *SM,* 22 July 1881 *Epworth Bells,* 26
    February, 11, 25 March 1876. LAO, 2TGH1/12/13, 1/12/17; Boston
    Sewers Parcel 26/7, Surfleet Dikereeve and Poor Rate Assessments
    1879–1905.

24 RC1879, First Report of S. B. L. Druce, p. 387; Minutes of Evidence,
    QQ. 29723–4, 33218–20, 56369–70. RC1893, QQ. 8989–90; Wilson
    Fox, pp. 169ff. *Tariff Commission,* para. 857. *SM,* 22 March 1872. *Select
    Committee on Allotments and Small Holdings* (1888) QQ. 3203–9, 3268–71,
    6874–90.

25 RC1893, Wilson Fox, pp. 169–74. *Select Committee on Allotments and
    Small Holdings* (1888) QQ. 6692–6

26 RC1879, First Report of S. B. L. Druce, p. 391; Final Report, p. 10.
    RC1893, Wilson Fox, pp. 169ff.

27 LAO, 2TGH 1/12/7, 1/12/13.

28 A. D. Hall, *A Pilgrimage of British Farming* (1913) pp. 105–6.

29 Rider Haggard, *Rural England,* v. 2, p. 186. RC1893, Wilson Fox,
    pp. 70–2, 173.

30 Levy, *Large and Small Holdings,* pp. 107–10. Rider Haggard, *Rural
    England,* v. 2, pp. 193–7. RC1893, Report of Hunter Pringle, p. 16.

31 RC1893, Wilson Fox, pp. 169–74; Minutes of Evidence, QQ.
    49435–8. *Select Committee on Allotments and Small Holdings* (1888)
    Minutes of Evidence, Q. 6707. Rider Haggard, *Rural England,* v. 2,
    pp. 211–12. Joan Thirsk, *English Peasant Farming* (1957) pp. 314–20.

32 *Wages and Conditions of Employment in Agriculture.* General Report, Cmd
    24 (1919) p. 6.

33 A. G. Street, *Farming England* (1937) p. 83. Rider Haggard, *Rural
    England,* v. 2, pp. 191, 193–4, 210. *Select Committee on Allotments and
    Small Holdings* (1888) Minutes of Evidence, QQ. 3217–8, 6755–6,
    6886–8. *Agricultural Returns,* 1875, 1900, parish summaries.

34   S. R. Haresign. 'Small Farms and Allotments as a Cure for Rural
      Depopulation on the Lincolnshire Fenland 1870–1914', *Lincolnshire
      History and Archaeology*, v. 18 (1983) pp. 32–3.

5
THE NATURE AND PRACTICE OF FARMING

Almost every farmer in mid-19th century Lincolnshire practised some form of mixed farming. This remained largely true into the 1930s. Specialization was increasing with the growing of potatoes, vegetables, and bulbs on a larger scale. Even in the Fens, however, where such cultivation was expanding most rapidly, most farmers maintained at least some elements of mixed farming. This was a necessity until the wholesale adoption of artificial fertilizers together with pesticides and fungicides.

Mixed farming depended on a balance between crops and livestock. For many, both at the time and since, that balance was reaching perfection during the 19th century in the sheep–corn husbandry of the light-soiled Wolds and Heath. In this system arable had the primacy, and that was the basis of most mixed farming in Lincolnshire. Arable crops to feed livestock were the foundation of high farming in the mid-19th century, and by and large that remained true through to the 1930s. In 1875 nearly 70 per cent of the cultivated land of the county was arable. Decades of low prices for many arable crops had modest effect. In 1914 arable was still 65 per cent, and in 1935, 63 per cent of cultivated land continued in arable rotation. In Holland the proportion was even higher in 1935, at 79.8 per cent.

Rotations

In order to achieve this high proportion of arable, intensive crop rotations including roots were being adopted. This was one of the marks of agricultural progress, and Clarke and other writers paid considerable attention to it. Rotations were becoming shorter in all parts of the county. From courses extending over six or more years they were coming down to four or five years. Fallows, still quite common when Arthur Young visited the county, were rare fifty years later. At the time of the tithe surveys 7.7 per cent of the arable acreage was fallow, a lower proportion than many other arable counties, such as Cambridgeshire. Clarke in 1851 mentions fallow as playing a regular part in a rotation only once, on the clays overlying the oolite hills in the south-west, where roots were difficult to grow. In the Middle Marsh dead fallows were rapidly declining as underdrainage allowed root crops to be grown. Summer fallowing was not uncommon in preparation for autumn-sown wheat.[1] The clays and mixed soils of Scawby to the east of the Cliff were likewise on a four/five course rotation, broken only by some summer fallows. William Torr on drained clays at Aylesby was following a four-course rotation in the 1860s, with wheat sown every other year.[2]

In the 1850s a main attraction of the more intensive rotations was the fact that they offered increased production, in particular of cereal crops. They also made a contribution to improved fertility. It was not a straightforward step, because for a rotation such as the Norfolk four-course to succeed, the land needed to be reasonably fertile to start with. Arthur Young had come across some very long-drawn-out rotations on the Wolds, necessary because of the difficulty of getting enough manure on to the land. Purchased inputs helped to bridge the gap. When Clarke wrote his essay in 1850 the effect of purchased feeds and fertilizers was that the four-course was already becoming the most common rotation here, with a five-course as the main alternative. On the Heath there was still a six-course rotation in common use that included two years of seeds, but farmers here were increasingly adopting a four-course rotation on the Norfolk pattern of turnips, barley, seeds, wheat.

This basic four-course rotation was widely used throughout Lincolnshire by the 1850s. With it a high proportion of cereal crops could be achieved. It was not as universal as sometimes claimed, however, even on the Wolds. There were many variations on the standard rule. Some were introduced to overcome difficulties encountered with the pure four-course rotation, the most common being 'clover sickness', causing yields to decline. The solution was to vary the rotation. Additional breaks of oats or seeds for one or two years might be introduced, as on some of the Dixon farms at Holton in the 1860s. A typical five-course of cropping, from a farm at Thimbleby in the early 1870s, was seeds, wheat, barley, turnips, wheat. Rotations were sometimes so extended and varied that cropping in some fields followed no clear pattern. On the Kesteven plateau peas and beans often replaced seeds and turnips. This produced a course such as barley, beans, wheat, barley, beans, wheat, cole, effectively two three-year cycles with a seventh-year break crop, over the years to 1881 on a farm in Hacconby. From Ingoldsby, between 1877 and 1882, comes a six-year cycle of wheat, barley, peas, oats, barley, turnips. Whatever variation might be adopted, the aim of the rotation remained to maximize the number of cereal crops that could be taken. In the 1830s the tithe surveys recorded 49 per cent of arable land under cereals. The more intensive rotations such as those just described enabled two-thirds or more of the arable land to be under corn crops. A marshland farmer expressed the common view in 1878: 'Out of about 210 acres of arable land I find it prudent to have as high as half in corn.'[3]

The richness and natural fertility of the Fens made them stand out as a place where normal rules did not necessarily apply, to the distaste of the orthodox. According to J. A. Clarke, fenland was 'more remarkable for the productiveness of its soil than for the able manner in which it is cultivated'.[4] 'The course of husbandry pursued is not very definite,' wrote James Caird, 'most farmers being permitted to farm as they think best, or at all events according to the custom of the country; and as that custom is by no means certain, the farmers have sufficient latitude.'[5] There was not quite such a free-for-all as Caird implies, as a number of conventions were followed in the Fens. Clarke referred to a five-course on the clay fens of wheat, seeds, oats, wheat, coleseed, and a 'wold system' four-course on sandy soils of seeds, wheat, turnips, oats.[6] The expansion of the growing of potatoes and other field vegetables later in the century introduced more variations in rotation. More or less continuous cropping could successfully be practised: wheat and potatoes were often sown in alternation for long periods as the potato acreage expanded. Even this did not make for anarchy and poor standards of cropping, as some suggested.[7] Large farmers in the Fens often followed a simple three-course rotation of potatoes, oats, wheat, with beans sometimes substituted for wheat; and after running two of these courses a clover break was sown. William Dennis of Kirton used this method: of 4,000 acres he had 1,500 under potatoes, 500 under grass, and the remainder sown with corn. In the Isle of Axholme, large farms on the warplands often had similar courses of cropping, with potatoes followed by wheat and then half the land under roots, half under seeds. Mangolds, turnips, and oats were used as rotation breaks.[8] In the late 1880s some of the older rotations were still found good: 'there is no great departure from the old rotation ... of oats after a fallow, followed by seeds or pulse, and wheat again', one observer noted.[9] It was the numerous variations on the basic course of cropping that gave the impression of great eclecticism, as beans, peas, rape, barley were substituted for one of the standard courses as farmers thought fit. Farmers in the Fens also had greater freedom from restrictive covenants that proscribed some crops regarded by most landlords elsewhere as exhausting to the soil. Mustard for seed, quite extensively grown in the Fens, was most frequently prohibited by cropping covenants in other districts.[10]

Outside of the Fens the Great Depression of the late 19th century also brought about some relaxation of rotations. Many farmers, landowners, and agents thought this to be an affront to farming propriety and a lessening of standards. A farmer from the Wainfleet area told the second Royal Commission that grass was being left down for two or three years, 'but it is not the custom and it is not the fashion in Lincolnshire to lay it down for three years'. The four-course rotation was much to be preferred, he thought.[11] However, the needs of the times dictated some relaxation, and Wilson Fox, the district commissioner for the Royal Commission in the 1890s, found it was not uncommon for grass leys to be extended to three or four years. Practice varied considerably, however, with only the stronger clays being left in ley for very long. The cropping plans for a farm at Claythorpe, in the Marsh, show little change in the management of rotation grasses, which were never left for longer than two years.[12]

Arable cropping

For many a farmer in Lincolnshire corn-growing and farming were almost synonymous terms. The pattern established by the 1870s was to have as much corn as possible. Cereals were grown everywhere in Lincolnshire. They were least prominent in the Marsh, where pasture was the major land use. Of the cereals, wheat was universal until the Great Depression, when it became a minor crop over much of the Wolds and neighbouring areas, the Heath and south-west Kesteven. Oats were the crop for the stronger clay soils and for the Fens. The converse was true of barley. Crops of the best quality were produced on the light soils. Barley grown on the richer soils of the clays and Fens could be very high-yielding, but not the best malting quality. In the Fens it became a crop grown occasionally. In clay vales and on mixed soils farmers were more likely to grow it, but it was on the Wolds and Heath that it became concentrated during the late 19th century.

Wheat in the 19th and early 20th centuries was almost invariably an autumn-sown crop. Barley and oats were sown in the spring. Wheat

**Fig. 8   Young and old together harvesting
at Nettleton in 1898**
Source: North East Lincolnshire Libraries

Fig. 9   Stooking the Wheat, Cowbit Wash, 1890s
Source: North East Lincolnshire Libraries

was sown on the higher wold land as early as possible, starting by the end of October, in order to give the plants time to get established before the chill winds of winter came upon these thin-soiled lands. On heavier and lower-lying land sowing continued into November.[13] There might be some spring-sown wheat, but rarely any winter barley. Sowing of barley on the Wolds and Heath took place in late March to mid April, after the roots had been cleared and the fields ploughed and scarified. This timing was regarded as critical if a good malting sample was to result. In other areas where feed barley was more likely to be grown the sowing season could linger into April. Oats, grown almost entirely for horse feed, were sown at the same period.

In Lincolnshire roots meant turnips: 95 per cent of the roots grown on the Wolds were turnips in the 1850s.[14] Swedes and mangolds were 'too little respected by farmers' in Lincolnshire, claimed one who favoured them, but they were little grown, except in the Fens.'[15] Other root crops, such as carrots, were grown, mainly in the Fens, but they were of very minor significance before the inter-war years.

Roots accounted for 11 per cent of the land under crops and grass in Lincolnshire in 1870, and this represents more or less the greatest extent of the crop. Fodder roots declined slightly during the Great Depression, and by far more during the 20th century. The root crop was one of the main points on which development differed between districts of light and heavy land. On the Wolds and Heath roots were an important part of the four- and five-course rotations and were 15 per cent or more of the cultivated land through to the end of the 19th century. In other parts of the county roots were of far less significance, though they did maintain their value as a source of home-grown animal feed, and at times they were a source of additional income when sold to other farmers.[16] Fenland farmers also grew root crops for seeds. In common with many crops of this district, turnips for seed were highly speculative, and income varied dramatically. Herbert Carter made £1,600 from the crop in 1893, but a few years later it is barely mentioned in his accounts.[17]

In many areas the crop was usually lifted, carted, and stored for winter use. On the Wolds, though, it was more common to feed turnips in the field. Here the ordinary white turnip was grown almost exclusively, whereas Norfolk farmers preferred swede. After the turnips had been eaten by the sheep the fields were ploughed and left until seed time. About 1850 it was still common to sow the seed broadcast, but the drill was becoming more common, and by the 1860s was almost universal.[18]

Roots were among the most labour-intensive of crops. Clarke referred to farmers on stronger land in the Wolds preparing fields for turnips by ploughing three times, scarifying, and harrowing. After the stubbles had been broken up with plough and drag, manure was given to the land, both farmyard manure and artificial fertilizers, in quantities that varied according to the type of soil. Further cultivation and rolling came in spring before the seed was sown. Perennial weeds were controlled by dragging and harrowing, annual weeds by hoeing. Singling, horse-hoeing, and hand-hoeing were carried out at intervals throughout the summer until the first crops were ready in September.

While roots were a major consumer of labour, the amount of work generally applied to the land was increasing for most crops. More intensive rotations required land to be fertile and in good heart. One of the things that commentators on agriculture emphasized was the need to keep the land fit and the crops clean. As well as the use of more fertilizers and manure, and the underdraining of heavier land, the work of cultivating the land grew and was perhaps at its most intensive in the mid-19th century. On heavier and mixed soils wheat and barley stubbles were ploughed, dragged, and harrowed at least once each. Depth of ploughing increased. In the Isle of Axholme deep ploughing became the regular practice. Subsoil ploughing was being taken up by farmers on the Heath. Clarke thought this was an improvement many throughout the county should be adopting. Heavy rolling was a common precaution against wire worm in wheat. In the Fens farmers would even have people treading the land as well.[19]

The steam plough was being used for some heavy and deep ploughing by the 1860s, but by a minority of farmers. Most farm operations were horse-powered until the advent of the tractor early in the 20th century. The 62,753 horses returned in 1875 as being for agricultural use in Lincolnshire represented about three to four per hundred acres. Figures from individual farms bear this out. On the Torr farms, there were 19 horses for 610 acres of tillage at Riby, and 22 horses for 700 acres at Aylesby. Despite the importance of Lincolnshire and the Fens in the development of the Shire breed, farmers of the county used a mixed type of horse. The Lincolnshire black carthorse was 'probably too slow for agricultural purposes, except on heavy, tenacious clay soils', it was suggested in 1844. William Torr, in common with many, kept a 'light active description of cart-horse', and these he bought rather than breed them himself.[20]

Livestock

Sheep were the most important type of livestock in Lincolnshire, and farmers here generally preferred them to cattle. In the 1870s there were about 1½ million sheep in the county. After a number of years that on the whole had been good, farmers were confident that sheep were the best-paying type of livestock.[21] In 1879, Lincoln wool accounted for 17 per cent of the production of England and Wales.[22] Long wool maintained its market during the mid-19th century, and the wool of the Lincoln breed was about the longest. In prize-winning sheep the staple could be up to 22 inches and fleeces weighed on average about fifteen pounds. Even after thirty years of depression, devastating outbreaks of disease, and decline in numbers, Rider Haggard could write, 'In Lincolnshire sheep are everywhere, on the high land and the low.'[23]

Sheep husbandry in Lincolnshire was an integral part of mixed farming, but the relationship between the components was different here from the sheep–corn systems of the southern downlands. The Lincoln sheep spent more time on grass than their southern counterparts. Lambing was delayed until March, by which time the grass was growing. There was little recourse to catch crops, again in contrast to the farming further south. Instead, Lincolnshire farmers supplemented the grass with trough-feeding in the fields. Chopped roots formed the foundation of the trough feeds, with cake and other feeds being given as appropriate. William Torr added a small amount of oilcake to his troughs. Henry Dudding at Riby was giving weaned lambs a mixture of linseed cake, crushed oats and locust beans, a little bran, malt combs, and cut clover. All of this was to avoid stall-feeding as much as possible. It was a practice expensive both of capital and labour but, commented the *Farmers' Magazine* in 1849, 'as the soil is being continually enriched it is found to answer on the average of years'. Weaning was completed by the end of July. The general preference for all sheep was to feed on roots in the open. Cake was a supplement: on the Wolds it was only given to ewes with twin lambs.[24]

Most of the sheep were bred on the uplands of the Wolds and Heath. Flocks here could be very large. William Torr's total flock of 1,200 was not at all untypical, though he was unusual in having mainly pure Leicester breed. Henry Dudding, who succeeded Torr at Riby, had

350 breeding ewes. Insufficient grass on the uplands meant that it was usual to transfer stock to the lowlands of fen and marsh for fattening. J. A. Clarke referred to the Lincolnshire uplands as 'a vast repository for supplying the rich grazing grounds with sheep'. The hogs from the Torr farm at Riby were sent to the Marsh over summer, breeding ewes were given lowland grass between autumn and Christmas. Of old the breeders had sold their young stock to lowland graziers, who also bought stock in from Norfolk. The spring fairs were the markets for this trade. There were several of these, but the greatest were Caistor, on the Saturday before Palm Sunday, Lincoln in late April, and the Boston May Fair. The numbers traded were vast. The 25,000 sheep penned at Boston in 1857 were described as 'modest'. These fairs, however, were at their greatest during the mid-19th century, lasting into the 1870s. Thereafter trade fell off as disease and changes in the balance between breeding and grazing had their effect.[25]

Among the hazards to which livestock farming was liable was epidemic disease. Foot and mouth became a frequent occurrence during the middle decades of the 19th century. Losses could be heavy. The remedy of wholesale slaughter of diseased stock was not then the rule. Animals were allowed to recover from the disease, but the losses in breeding value and market value were considerable. By the mid 1870s outbreaks of foot and mouth disease were becoming so frequent as to deter many farmers from expanding their breeding.[26]

Despite the vital part that cattle played in high farming, Lincolnshire's farmers were not noted for their enthusiasm for them. A correspondent for the *Agricultural Gazette* from the north Wolds commented that 'this being such a fine corn-growing county, not much attention has been paid to stock, and farmers really do not seem to fancy feeding beef, saying it does not pay'.[27] In 1869 there were 187,861 cattle recorded in the county. Nearly all of them were for beef, and most were of the Lincoln Red Shorthorn breed. The stocking density of 13.1 per 100 acres was about four-fifths the national average, half that of nearby Leicestershire, though much greater than that of Norfolk and Suffolk. The agricultural returns, collected in June, however, did not record one of the important aspects of Lincolnshire farming, the buying in of stock for the winter. When a new tenant entered a farm at

Doddington, one of his first requests was for a shed for the wintering of twenty beasts to be built in the middle of the arable to save expense on carting manure. Clarke reckoned that many farmers in the clay vales wintered twice as many beasts as they kept over the summer. Yearling and two-year-old cattle were bought in November for winter feeding. As well as those bred locally, stock were bought in from Yorkshire, and some from further afield, including a few Irish and Scottish beasts.[28]

In a similar fashion to sheep, there was a division between upland breeding and lowland grazing, though the divide was far less sharp. Breeding of cattle was widespread throughout the county, but was an activity especially strong in the north-east. Most of the famed breeders were to be found here. The Fens and Marsh were the two areas where it was rare to breed cattle. These, along with the clay vales, were the prime grazing lands. Here, the summer density of the cattle population recorded in the annual returns was more than 20 per hundred acres in most parishes. Most of the fenland stock for summer grazing came from farms on the uplands of the Wolds and Heath. Despite the expansion of potatoes and other new arable crops in the Fens, fattening of cattle continued to be important here at least down to the First World War.[29]

The horse fair held at Horncastle in August was one of the greatest in the kingdom, attracting dealers from Europe as well as this country. Lincoln's April fair was not far behind in status by the middle of the 19th century, having the advantage of being on a more major railway route. These fairs had grown up on a local tradition of horse breeding. Lincolnshire, and especially the Fens, was one of the districts in which the Shire breed had been established. Arthur Young had written that every farmer in Holland Fen kept mares for breeding. The early stud books of the breed society record several important breeding lines coming from this county. By the third quarter of the 19th century, however, horse-breeding as a part of the farming business was, perhaps, not what it had been. Clarke commented that, although the Fens had been known for their black carthorses, since the enclosures 'comparatively few have been bred'. W. Macdonald, in a survey of the different branches of livestock farming, found no enthusiasm for horse breeding and dealing. His correspondents, mainly from north

Fig. 10 The ploughman and his horses at Swineshead
Source: North East Lincolnshire Libraries

Lincolnshire, reported that 'farmers do not care for horse-dealing in general' and that horse-breeding was not a profitable activity, although this part of the county had been an important area for the supply of horses to Horncastle fair. Most of those who did breed horses did so only for the needs of their own farm. There were still farmers breeding Shire horses for sale, and most of them were in the south of the county. Fred and Walter Ward of Quarrington or R. D. C. Shaw of Swineshead perhaps received less notice than William Torr, Henry Dudding, and other celebrated farmers of north Lincolnshire. But they and others like them were important contributors to the development of the Shire horse and its breed society, founded in 1878.[30]

All the forms and practices of farming described here were already being influenced by high farming in the mid-19th century. It is with an examination of what high farming entailed and how it was absorbed into Lincolnshire agriculture that Part II begins.

Notes to Chapter 5

1   R. J. P. Kain and H. C. Prince, *The Tithe Surveys of England and Wales* (1985). J. A. Clarke, 'On the Farming of Lincolnshire', *JRASE*, v. 12 (1851) pp. 332ff.

2   LAO, 2NEL 3/8/1/2 1870s valuations. H. M. Jenkins, 'Farm Reports 3. Aylesby, Riby and Rothwell Farms near Grimsby, Lincolnshire, in the occupation of Mr William Torr', *JRASE*, v. 30 (1869) p. 422.

3   LAO, DIXON 5/2/14; Misc Dep 2/3; HIGGINS 4/4–7; 5ANC 4/B/9. RC1879, Q. 6851. Kain and Prince, *The Tithe Surveys of England and Wales*.

4   Clarke, 'On the Farming of Lincolnshire', p. 388.

5   James Caird, *English Agriculture in 1850–51*(1851) p. 181.

6   J. A. Clarke, 'On the Great Level of the Fens, including the Fens of South Lincolnshire', *JRASE*, v. 8 (1847) pp. 129–30.

7   One Sutton Bridge farmer thought that the improvement in the land as seasons improved would be faster 'if more of it were under regular rotations, with larger proportion of fallow and seeds'. *Agricultural Gazette*, 13 July 1885.

8   *SM*, 14 October 1881, 27 July 1894. *Tariff Commission*, para. 548. Clarke, 'On the Farming of Lincolnshire', pp. 364–5. F. I. Cooke, 'Report on the Farm Prize Competition in Nottinghamshire and Lincolnshire in 1888', *JRASE*, v. 49 (1888), p. 524. A. D. Hall, *A Pilgrimage of British Farming* (1913), pp. 88, 113. W. E. Bear, *A Study of Small Holdings* (1893), p. 23.

9   Cooke, 'Report on the Farm Prize Competition', p. 524.

10   For example, in the agreements on the estates of Lord Aveland and Baroness Willoughby de Eresby; LAO, 9ANC 2/C/1/1.

11   RC1893, QQ. 36109–16, 36140.

12   RC1893, Wilson Fox, pp. 176–7, Minutes of Evidence, QQ. 14316–17. LAO, Higgins 4/5–7.

13   This and the following, see Jenkins, 'Farm Reports 3', pp. 423–7.

14   Raine Morgan, The Root Crop in English Agriculture, 1650–1870, PhD thesis, University of Reading, 1978, p. 285.

15   Cooke, 'Report on the Farm Prize Competition in Nottinghamshire and Lincolnshire in 1888', pp. 528–9.

16   Farm accounts not infrequently show small sales of roots: LAO, 2TGH 1/12/18, 3Dudding 2, Scorer Farm 2/1, 2.

17   LAO, HD65/64. W. H. Wheeler, *History of the Fens of South Lincolnshire*
      (1896) p. 404.
18   H. W. Keary, 'On the Management of Barley', *JRASE*, v. 10 (1849)
      pp. 455–6.
19   Jenkins, 'Farm Reports 3', pp. 432, 440. Clarke, 'On the Farming of
      Lincolnshire', pp. 332, 341, 354, 365. LAO, 2NEL 3/8/1.
20   Jenkins, 'Farm Reports 3', pp. 434–5. John Burke, 'Breeding and
      Management of Horses on a Farm', *JRASE*, v. 5 (1844) p. 519.
21   Numbers were, for example, 1,488,827 (1871), 1,555,090 (1875). W.
      MacDonald, 'On the Relative Profits to the Farmer from Horse, Cattle
      and Sheep Breeding, Rearing and Feeding in the United Kingdom',
      JRASE, v. 37 (1876), pp. 40, 63. RC1881, QQ. 7064–5.
22   *Agricultural Gazette*, 22 March 1880.
23   H. Rider Haggard, *Rural England* v. 2 (1902) p. 241.
24   W. J. Malden, *British Sheep and Shepherding* [1890s] pp. 165–6. W. Fream,
      The Complete Grazier (1893 edn) p. 510. *Farmers' Magazine*, 2nd ser.,
      v. 20 (1849) p. 248.
25   Jenkins, 'Farm Reports 3', p. 431. J. A. Perkins, *Sheep Farming in
      Eighteenth and Nineteenth Century Lincolnshire* (1977) pp. 35, 44.
26   MacDonald, 'On the Relative Profits to the Farmer', p. 40.
27   *Agricultural Gazette*, 28 August 1876.
28   Clarke, 'On the Farming of Lincolnshire', pp. 398–9. LAO, Misc Dep.
      265.
29   Clarke, 'On the Farming of Lincolnshire', pp. 343ff, 384ff., 400.
30   *Ibid.*, p. 412. MacDonald, 'On the Relative Profits to the Farmer',
      pp. 40, 63. Joan Thirsk, *English Peasant Farming* (1957) pp. 275, 280.
      Keith Chivers, *The Shire Horse: a history of the breed, the society and the men*
      (1976) pp. 57, 288.

PART II

The Course of Agricultural Change

6
HIGH FARMING AND
THE 'GOLDEN AGE', 1850–1875

Philip Pusey has been introduced already. He was one of those especially impressed by the generally healthy state of Lincolnshire's agriculture at the mid-19th century: in Chapter 1 we saw his reaction to the improvements on the Heath. Pusey was one of the founder members of the Royal Agricultural Society of England, and editor of its journal. As an admirer of Lincolnshire farming he did much to promote the county's cause. Through articles in the journal, written by himself and others, he commended the progress made in the county. In these articles he also promoted the concept of 'high farming', which he held to be one of the main factors in Lincolnshire's advance. 'The whole tract of Heath and Cliff has been brought into tillage farming on the pattern of high farming on inferior land, with hardly any instances of bad management,' wrote J. A. Clarke in his prize essay on the county published in the *Journal of the Royal Agricultural Society of England* in 1851.[1] Philip Pusey in 1842 remarked upon the 'high farming of the eastern side of England there so well known that it may appear superfluous to have described it at all.'[2] What precisely he meant by high farming, he did not stop to describe. For his definition of high farming it is necessary to look further into Pusey's writings, and his description, for example, of the well-ordered, well-managed farming of the Heath (above, p. 15), in which considerable investment had clearly been made in intensive cultivation of arable and in root crops and livestock.

The implication was that high farming was modern farming, farming for the new industrial age of Victorian England. Enthusiasts for new farming developments would sometimes liken farming to industry. Clarke found some of the new features of the fenland landscape much to his liking: 'It is pleasing also to view the systems of artificial drainage, where the tall smoke-breathing chimney and the massive machinery give an air of manufacturing industry to the labours of agriculture, impressing upon the mind the fact of husbandry being in effect the fabrication of meat and bread from raw inedible materials by the toil and ingenuity of man.'[3] By the early 1870s Cornelius Stovin, the Wolds farmer, could write in his diary, 'farming has become a science as well as industrial occupation'.[4] In 1872, 'A Farmer of Many Years' wrote a letter to the *Stamford Mercury* and, in terms that would not have been out of place over a hundred years later, described some of the features and results of modern, high farming:

Every good modern farmer manages upon commercial principles. His superior crops are chiefly from purchased artificial aids administered to both his stock and his crops. His farm stock are brought to early maturity by good selection, breeding, care, attention, and nutritious foods in aid of his farm resources. No modern farmer is content with the natural products of his farm. Every crop and every head of farm stock is supplemented by extraneous and the most satisfactory aids which chemical and other discoveries have opened out upon us. His crops have thus been nearly doubled in quantity, weight and volume: his farm stock have been surprisingly improved in proportions and quality, and by artificial foods and careful attention he prepares a far greater number for market and of much greater value than formerly.[5]

If high farming was modern farming, then at its heart was the development of productive mixed husbandry. This was evidently just the sort of thing that many farmers in Lincolnshire by mid century wanted to pursue: it was small wonder that Philip Pusey found the county such an inspiration. This was the farming that the 'New Style' farmer with entrepreneurship and commercial acumen was likely to adopt. High farming needed investment; to achieve the output a high volume of inputs into farming was necessary. As the illustrations already quoted show, there were several strong features of this type of farming. These included an expansion of the arable; the purchase of feed and fertilizer from off the farm; improvement to livestock; investment in buildings; improving the drainage of heavier soils; the introduction of new implements and machines. Each of these will be examined in the sections of this chapter that follow.

At the outset it should be remembered that Lincolnshire farmers were not originators of the practices associated with high farming. B. A. Holderness has traced their origins to East Norfolk, where more intensive feeding of livestock was being introduced during the second half of the 18th century.[6] During the 1820s some of the features of this farming were beginning to be incorporated into Lincolnshire agriculture. Following enclosure, farmers began to increase their acreage of fodder crops to improve the output of their stock, and thus new styles of mixed farming developed.[7] Although not the originators, Lincolnshire farmers certainly had become noted by the 1840s as being among the leading exponents of high farming. The thoroughness with which they adopted its principles was the means by which farming in the county caught up with the leaders of agricultural development.

Expanding arable

High farming as it was practised in mid-19th century Lincolnshire, and most of eastern and midland England, was based primarily upon arable. Livestock had an important, integral role within mixed farming, but not on pasture. They were fed arable crops and purchased feed. The development of high farming systems, therefore, went hand in hand with the expansion of the cultivated acreage. Several parishes, including much of the Fens, recorded more than 50 per cent of their total acreage of crops and grass as under corn crops in 1875. Figures of more than 40 per cent were common throughout the county, with few differences between regions.[8]

The Fens and the light uplands were areas where the increase was most marked. The Fens in the 18th century had been renowned for their pastures. As surface drainage improved, these pastures were turned over to cultivation from the 1820s onwards. Clarke in 1847 wrote of the 'immense plain of dark arable fields' and, looking back from 1878, he noted with approval 'the conversion of [the] region of peat and fens into some of the most productive corn-lands in the kingdom'. Typical of the change was the experience of the Guy's Hospital estate near Sutton Bridge. In 1809, 64 per cent of the land was pasture. By 1866 the positions had been reversed and 66 per cent of the land was now arable.[9] This transformation throughout fenland was greater than anything experienced in other regions, and it happened despite low prices for cereals during the 1820s and 1830s. Good yields from newly drained and cultivated land probably helped offset that disadvantage. More efficient drainage opened up the opportunities for new types of mixed farming, with livestock integrated into an arable system of husbandry rather than being kept mainly on pasture.[10]

The arable acreage on the light lands of the Wolds and Heath was also increased. These were the districts where a regime of high input, high output could most easily be applied, and it was here that many of the leading exponents of high farming in Lincolnshire were based. They attracted the attention upon which the county's growing reputation was founded. Changes in arable acreage were not quite on the same scale as the Fens, and most of the expansion came from bringing waste into cultivation. As was noted in Chapter 1, there were still some fairly extensive areas to be converted in the 1820s. As these areas were brought into cultivation the Wolds were turned into a district of arable land. Both Philip Pusey and J. A. Clarke commented that, unlike the downs of southern England, there was little waste land. 'No portion of the ground has been allowed to remain … a tract of sheepwalks in its primitive vegetation of heath and fern, but the highest parts are all in tillage,' wrote Clarke. There was very little grass land, either. In some parishes permanent pasture was no more than 15–20 per cent of the acreage by the late 1860s and the same was true of parts of the Heath. Grasses grown in rotation mostly mown for hay were also limited in extent. Hainton Walk Farm, described in detail by T. W. Beastall, exemplifies the process by which tillage was extended in these areas. Land that was almost entirely sheepwalk in 1789 had by 1814 a reasonable portion of arable, and this was increased in stages until by 1842 it was almost all arable land.[11]

Even on some of the heavier land, such as the carrs of the Ancholme valley, ploughland was increasing by the 1850s. In south Kesteven there were extensive areas of poor-quality pasture being improved or converted to tillage during the early 19th century.[12] The clay vales in general, however, retained a higher proportion of permanent grass, often about 40 per cent in 1870, and sometimes more. They were seen as a problem by the agricultural improvers. 'Drain them as we may, there are many tracts of land on which roots cannot be grown,' Philip Pusey commented. He remained the optimist, though, arguing that stall-feeding of cattle could profitably be introduced. The oilcake-enriched manure he believed would help to improve and lighten the soil.[13] Even so, it was difficult to introduce the more intensive arable rotations on these soils, the assumption being commonly made that this was what farmers all wanted to do. Whatever the aspirations, whatever the dreams behind some of the investment in drainage, the clays did not emulate the Wolds. Pasture likewise continued to dominate in much of the Marsh, although there was increasing conversion of grass to arable in this district. Clarke noted it particularly in the Middle Marsh. The later enclosures in the Marsh were often with a view to adding to the arable.[14] Wherever the change took place, the greater part of the increase in arable was sown to cereals.

Feed and fertilizers

Oilcake became one of the symbols of high farming, for it broke the old closed cycle of mixed farming whereby only inputs produced on the farm were available to improve fertility. Livestock feeds manufactured from the residue from the crushing of oil-bearing seeds were being taken up by British farmers after the Napoleonic wars. Linseed and rape were the principal sources of this feed at first, to which after 1860 cotton seed was added. A few other seeds were also used for oilcake, and by the end of the 19th century manufacturers were offering a large variety of compound feeds. Almost all of the oilseeds were imported, and these imports were growing rapidly: 76,230 tons in 1854 and 109,962 tons in 1865. By 1884 the figure had reached 269,840 tons. Two-thirds of the seed-crushing industry was based in Hull, making supplies of the feed cake very convenient for farmers in Lincolnshire, and, together with their neighbours in Nottinghamshire and the East Riding, they took full advantage of them. By 1850 the use of oilcake as feed was fairly common in almost all regions of Lincolnshire, as farmers found that this purchased feed suited them better than lifting the turnip crop for their cattle.[15] Pusey commented in 1842 that many farmers in Lincolnshire 'keep young stock in straw yards; not, however, upon straw only, as in the old system of low farming, but pushing them forward with oil-cake'.[16]

Oilcake had a high feed content, and as a result produced enriched manure. This last was the prime reason for oilcake's popularity. Livestock in the more intensive mixed farming of this period were mainly there to produce manure for the expanded acreage of arable. Lincolnshire farmers were drawing on practice already developed in Norfolk, but taking it a step further with the greater use of bought-in feed to increase the manurial value of the dung from their stock. According to Clarke, the justification for keeping cattle on the Heath and Wolds was 'simply the natural infertility of the land and the expectation of bountiful crops from the ample investment of capital in manures'.[17] One of the uses for oilcake in the Lincolnshire Heath and Wolds was in the keeping of cattle in yards over winter. The stock were fed on oilcake in order to get more manure for the arable. Pusey noted Lincolnshire farmers buying three-year-old beasts for over-wintering. Their resale in spring would, he thought, at best cover the cost of the cake, making the cattle only 'machines for converting the straw into dung'.[18] As an example of winter feeding Pusey quoted one of Mr Chaplin's tenants on the Blankney estate who bought 80 tons of cake for his 110 cattle. Caird also noticed on the Heath oilcake being fed to the cattle over winter, while the sheep had the turnips.[19]

These livestock feeding regimes led a number of commentators, Pusey included, to characterize high farming as 'high feeding', regarding the farmers of Lincolnshire as among the greatest exponents. In Lincolnshire high feeding meant oilcake. Pusey contrasted this with areas such as Norfolk, where he said chopped roots were more likely to be used. He exaggerated this difference. Lincolnshire farmers were growing and consuming roots in large quantities also; the ways in which they were used in conjunction with the cake did differ.[20]

The quantities of oilcake consumed could be large. When Clarke wrote his essay there were farmers on the Wolds spending nearly 20s per acre on oilcake for their cattle in order to produce enough manure for 10–12 cartloads to be applied to the land. The result, he added, was that 'chalk soil, in many places not more than three inches in depth, will produce 20–25 tons per acre of turnips'.[21] A farmer of 100 acres at Hareby was using from six to eight tons of cake a year 'to assist in converting my straw into manure'. By no means all farmers, even in these light-soiled districts, were using cake in such quantities. Usage varied, too, as a proportion of farming costs. Caird quoted examples of farm budgets from Lincolnshire and the East Riding. Two farms in the sample were on the Wolds, one where expenditure on purchased feeds was 5.2 per cent of total costs, the second 9.7 per cent. He also included a warp-land potato farm of 400 acres, where 9.5 per cent of costs went on purchased feed. On John West's farm, on the Cliff at Dunholme, 10.5 per cent of expenditure went on feeds in 1860–61, and 18.5 per cent in 1888–89. Great or small the amounts used, oilcake was established in the farming of Lincolnshire by the 1850s, and the farmers were few who never purchased any.

All the writers on agricultural practice stressed the importance of the purchased feeds in improving the quality and increasing the quantity of farmyard manure available for the arable crops, hence the coining of the phrase 'high feeding'. These bountiful supplies of home-produced manure were the first in importance for most farmers, and were used mainly on the wheat crop. For roots and other crops, purchased fertilizers came to assume an importance similar to that of purchased feeds. The first to achieve prominence and widespread use was ground bones applied as a top dressing to the arable. The consumption of bones increased considerably after the Napoleonic Wars, and by the 1820s farmers and landowners were investing heavily in this fertilizer. Thomas Dixon of Holton equipped himself with bone mills and hired one of them to his neighbours as well as providing himself with large quantities of crushed bones.[22]

This was a fertilizer especially efficacious for the light soils. Much of the improvement to farming in the Wolds was ascribed to the beneficial effects of bones. They were an essential component of the development of the sheep–corn husbandry of this area based on arable cultivation. The adoption of more intensive rotations, and the expansion of the barley acreage were helped by the use of these fertilizers. In the Wolds, and on the Heath, the practice of spreading bones on the turnip land was almost universal by the 1840s. Thomas Dixon was applying 12 bushels to the acre for his turnips in the 1820s, and a rate of 12 to 16 bushels per acre became common by the 1840s. Bones and oilcake together formed the basis of mid-century practice on the light lands. Mr Frankish at Temple Bruer was following the four-course rotation. He used bones on his turnip crop. His cattle were fed oilcake in the yard, and the resulting manure was spread on the clover land. His sheep were given some oilcake as well, in preparation for the barley crop.[23]

Superphosphate began to supersede bones from the 1850s onwards, but bones continued to be used in some quantity by Lincolnshire farmers. William Torr at Aylesby and Riby was applying dissolved bones at the rate of 4 cwt to the acre for swedes and white turnips in the 1860s, as well as superphosphate, guano, and farmyard manure.[24] J. A. Clarke reported in the 1870s that on the Heath and Wold farms expenditure of £5 per acre on manures for the root crop was not uncommon. On the good loamy soils farmers might apply half a ton of superphosphate or nitro-phosphate to crops of potatoes or mangolds. Of the sample budgets published by James Caird, one of the Wolds farms was spending on purchased manure an amount similar to that on the purchase of feed, the second spent only half as much. The potato farm on the warp-land spent as heavily on manure as on feed.[25]

Lincolnshire farmers led the way with the use of these new artificial fertilizers. Few farmers outside the county seem to have been using bones in the 1830s, and they were mainly in eastern Scotland. The use of bones began to spread during the 1840s, especially to neighbouring Nottinghamshire and also to East Anglia, but the continued use of grassland for sheep as a component of chalkland farming in southern England delayed the use of artificial fertilizers until superphosphate became generally available.[26]

Although not a purchased input, the practice of claying in the Fens was part of the same drive to invest in improvements to the quality and fertility of the soil. Clay, usually taken from the subsoil, was mixed into the peaty soils of the surface to add body. This was a practice that grew from the 1830s alongside the improvements to the drainage of the

Fens. It helped the advance of arable farming with shorter rotations in this district, but the cost, especially of labour, was high. By the end of the century claying was rarely undertaken.[27]

Improved livestock

Although cattle might have been regarded as a lesser part of high farming, one of the features of the developing mixed farming systems was the ability to produce good meat from a mainly arable farm. To do this attention had to be paid to the quality of the livestock, and farmers did invest heavily in raising the standards of their herds. The predominant breed was the Lincoln Red Shorthorn, kept little outside its eponymous county and almost universally within it. The breed traced its origins to the early 19th century, and especially to Charles Colling's sale at Kelton in 1810, which brought a number of shorthorns into Lincolnshire. Other strains of quality shorthorn breeding were subsequently brought in, such as William Torr's purchase of cattle from the herds of the Booth family in Yorkshire. These imports were crossed with local cattle to produce the distinctive deep red shorthorn stock. By the mid-19th century the breed was noted for its hardiness, able to withstand the rigours of the east coast climate. Clarke said the Lincoln breeders had 'achieved the feat of uniting size with constitution and quality so as to retain the merits of each'. All this made it a good type for over-wintering, especially in the early development of the practice, when yards were likely to be uncovered. It was primarily a beef breed, valued for its lean carcass and early maturity. Changes in the market for beef and in farming made this early maturity its most important feature by the 20th century. It was also useful for milk, although little-known as such because few in Lincolnshire were engaged in dairying to any extent. At the end of the 19th century, however, there were some farmers who established dairy businesses stocked with Lincoln Reds.[28]

William Torr was celebrated for holding one of the main breeding herds of shorthorns in the mid-19th century. Much of the work of improving the stock was undertaken by his bailiff, C. W. Tindall, who gained recognition in his own right and was instrumental in founding the Lincoln Red breed society in 1895. Among others active in improving the breed at this time was Thomas Turnell of

Reasby, credited with establishing the predominant colour. The Scorers of Burwell and Swinhope, the Chattertons of Brinkhill and Stenigot, the Evens of Burton by Lincoln, and Deans of Dowsby were among the leading specialist breeders of Lincoln Reds during the second half of the 19th century.[29]

Sheep, too, were subject to a steady process of improvement which went hand in hand with the development of intensive light-land farming. The introduction of turnips into the rotation encouraged farmers on the Wolds both to breed and to fatten their sheep, and this in turn prompted improvement to the sheep stock. The addition of purchased feeds reinforced this trend. This close relationship accounted for the fact that many of the leading breeders of the improved sheep farmed in the Wolds. Lincolnshire farmers maintained a preference for the Lincolnshire Longwool breed, to be found almost universally in the county. The major contribution to the breed's development was the infusion of New Leicester blood during the first half of the 19th century. The result, a heavier animal with better maturity, was becoming known as the Improved Lincoln by the 1840s. Better quality sheep offered increased production both of wool and especially of mutton. Good prices for long wool in the mid-19th century offered further encouragement. The Lincoln sheep, wrote a correspondent to *Bell's Weekly Messenger* in 1857, were 'second to none for profit'.[30] Many agricultural experts were of the opinion that the Lincoln was the best longwool breed in the country by the 1860s. A breed association and flock book were not established until 1892, then largely in reaction to the increased cross-breeding with Down breeds.

New buildings

The farmstead changed and grew with the new intensive farming methods. New and better types of building were needed. Before the 1840s little attention seems to have been paid to the buildings on most farms. J. A. Clarke's observation that buildings were both badly built and poorly arranged was typical.[31] New farming practices began to change that, and in the middle decades of the 19th century large numbers of new buildings were constructed. Few farms appear to have been untouched by this activity.

The greatest change was the provision of buildings for livestock where previously there had been few or none. Pusey complained about the number of farmsteads in which cattle were left in open yards in the depths of winter.[32] The new practices led to change. Stock being fed with oilcake needed housing: the production and collection of manure on which high farming depended was more effectively achieved in a sheltered area than out in the field. Many new buildings for cattle were constructed during the half century from the 1840s onwards. Sheltered sheds of fairly simple design were succeeded by fully-covered yards in some of the later more elaborate farmsteads. Along with the housing for the cattle came buildings for the preparation of their food: chaff houses, cake stores, root preparation rooms, in which the feed and the grinding and cutting implements might be kept, and steaming rooms where some of the feed was cooked.[33]

Barns, the oldest type of agricultural building, changed in use. Mechanized threshing, increasingly performed in the yard or even out in the field, obviated the need for the wide threshing floors. The large double-doors for through draughting were often reduced in size, usually by lowering their height. Many farmers used barns now as preparation and storage areas for animal feed. Chaff cutters, cake breakers, grinding mills, and other items of what were frequently referred to as barn machinery were placed in the building. Some were powered by hand, many by horse gear and some by steam engine. Other types of storage building were needed by the new farming: good granaries for the threshed grain, and cartsheds for the carts, wagons and other implements of the farm.

Thought now given to the layout of the farmstead demanded that all these buildings should be conveniently situated in relation to each other. Clarke had commented on the poor arrangement of buildings, and for many farms deficiencies remained. It was in this area that attempts were made to apply some of the thinking based on industrial practices. Farms were designed to be efficient in their use of labour, to accommodate new machinery and to enable a smooth flow from delivery of feed for the livestock to collection of the manure and moving the animals. Where possible, buildings were sited to minimize the distance over which manure had to be carted to the fields. The best,

most efficient results could usually be achieved by building the entire
farmstead as new. The larger estates, especially, set about the complete
rebuilding of a number of their farms. This is what the Marquis of
Exeter's estate did at Postland Farm, a relatively early example, built in
1852 and costing £1250 for a farm of 500 acres in the Fens. Christopher
Turnor's estates also started building new farmsteads and rebuilding old
ones in the 1850s. Hill Farm, Wispington, built in 1855, included two
shelter sheds for cattle facing on to open yards. Around these were
accommodation for horses, food preparation and implements. When
the new farms at the Chestnuts at Binbrook and Manor Farm, Kirmond
le Mire were built in 1868 provision was made for steam power. On
Henry Chaplin's Blankney estate the existing farmstead at Scopwick
House Farm was abandoned and replaced with a new set of buildings
on a different site in the late 1860s. The new buildings give the
impression of being a showpiece development, and included
south-facing crewyards, shelter sheds, granaries, and stables all arranged
conveniently in relation to each other.[34]

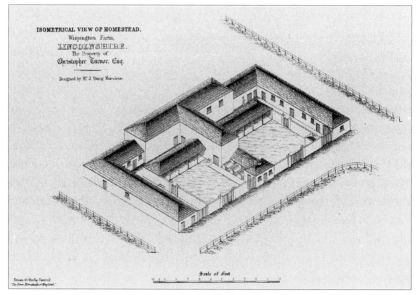

**Fig. 11 Wispington Farm, one of the new farmsteads built on
Christopher Turnor's estate, as illustrated in**
Farm Homesteads of England, **by J. Bailey Denton**

Reconstruction of farmsteads continued into the 1870s and 1880s. Coleby Grange, built probably in the 1870s, is another example of this type of planned farm, impressive architecturally as well as meeting functional needs. Hanby Lodge Farm, built in the early 1880s on the Earl of Dysart's estate, was one of the most complex examples. The majority of farmsteads were developed in piecemeal fashion and for them it was more difficult to create a smooth-flowing integrated layout. Woodside Farm at Newton was one which did achieve a good measure of integration. New cattle stalls, pigstyes, and loose boxes were added to an existing farmstead in the 1850s and arranged in a way convenient for bringing in fodder and taking out the litter and manure from the opposite side. Some of the new buildings were outside the main farmstead. Saving the cost of carting manure prompted an incoming tenant at Doddington in 1874 to request a shed for wintering twenty beasts to be built in the middle of the arable land.[35]

The legislation passed between the 1840s and 1860s, which authorized loans to landlords to finance drainage work on their estates, was extended to include farm buildings. Several Lincolnshire landowners secured loans for buildings from the finance companies set up by these Acts. C. H. Cust was one who used loan finance to build shelter sheds, feeding houses, and fold yards, all the types of building for livestock demanded by high farming. The Chaplin estate prepared a schedule of more than 7,000 acres in 1877 for which application was being made to the Lands Improvement Company. The money would be spent on new buildings and general improvements to the farms. The finance companies expected buildings to be 'erected in a substantial and durable manner'. This meant that new farmsteads of this period built by the large estates were usually of stone, brick, and tile. As well as meeting the terms of the loan, this suited the confidence of the times and demonstrated a degree of status on the part of the landowner. Scopwick House Farm was built with Lands Improvement Company finance, and met their criteria by being constructed mainly of locally quarried stone, with slate roofing.[36]

Land drainage

While improvements to the surface drainage in the Fens, Isle of Axholme, and Ancholme valley were benefiting the infrastructure of those parts of Lincolnshire, sub-surface drainage was also identified as one of the best general improvements that a farmer could undertake. There was nothing new in the basic principles of land drainage. For centuries trenches had been dug across fields to be filled with stones, brushwood or turves. The 18th century saw several new types of plough for drainage work being designed.[37] The extent of land that could be treated by these methods was limited, and when the Board of Agriculture conducted its surveys of British agriculture at the end of the 18th century, land drainage was highlighted as an improvement that was most needed. Agricultural improvers of the mid-19th century continued to stress the efficacy of better drainage. Now, however, there was greater chance of living up to the hopes of the experts. Drainage tiles and pipes made of clay were introduced to go along with the improved drainage ploughs. Machines to make the clay pipes at low price were introduced in the 1840s, and then came steam-powered mole ploughs. The possibilities being opened up seemed immense, and underdrainage became one of the features of the mid-century high-farming period.

The work of improving sub-surface drainage was getting under way in Lincolnshire by the 1820s. On estates in south and west Kesteven, and in the northern vales, including the Jarvis, Thorold, and Dixon estates, drainage was becoming a common feature.[38] Much of this work was by the traditional methods, for they were effective and cheap, costing 18s 6d an acre, much less than the hand-made clay tiles then available. Once the machine-made pipes were introduced there was a marked rise in the practice of underdrainage. A few estates went so far as to invest in their own tile works. This made sense, for in paying for drainage work, the standard practice was that the landlord provided the tiles while the tenant took on responsibility for laying them, and this arrangement became the basis for tenant right valuation.

The principal value of underdrainage was to clay lands, and there was a strong belief that this would make a real difference to productivity on heavier soils. Drainage would be to these soils what oilcake and bones were to the light-soiled districts. Farmers in these districts would be able to take advantage of all the other agricultural improvements, especially shorter rotations including root crops. Clarke noted with approval in 1851 the parts of the Marsh in which underdrainage had enabled farmers to grow roots where before there was fallow. Many more places needed similar treatment, he believed. As well as further benefit to the Marsh, the principal areas that stood to gain from underdrainage were the clay vales of the Ancholme and the west of the county. Clarke also identified the boulder clays of south-west Kesteven as another district in need of drainage 'on a large scale' in order to break up the subsoil and create conditions for good root crops. Subsoil drainage was also a major requirement in the Fens, he thought.[39] J. Bailey Denton shared this belief that there was a great need for drainage improvement. In 1855 he reckoned that in the counties of Lincolnshire, Cambridgeshire, and Huntingdonshire together 53.4 per cent of the land was wet land, and therefore in need of draining. His was a

Fig. 12 Laying drainage tiles by hand
Source: Museum of English Rural Life

somewhat crude estimate based on the gross extent of geological formations. There was a certain amount of special pleading, perhaps, since he was engineer to one of the leading drainage companies. It is easy to see, therefore, that with large areas of light soils, Lincolnshire's need was probably less than this. Other estimates suggest that up to 30 per cent of the clay and loam soils of the county would benefit from drainage.[40]

Vigorous promotion of land drainage by Bailey Denton and other experts encouraged the belief that here was the means of significant improvement. Loan finance became available to landowners, officially sanctioned by the Public Money Draining Act 1846 and the Private Money Draining Act 1849. Finance companies, established through these measures, the largest of which was the Lands Improvement Company, were the means by which the loans were advanced.[41] These loans were taken up in Lincolnshire from the 1850s onwards. By 1899 £147,765 had been borrowed through these major loan schemes, with larger landowners taking up a proportionately great amount of the total.[42] Parishes affected by this loan-financed drainage were concentrated in the clay vales, with a number of other schemes in the inner marsh, the peat fens and parishes on the edge of the uplands.[43] Drainage in these clay areas was common, and it is evident that rather more land was being drained without resort to the finance companies.

In a national pecking order of counties Lincolnshire was below average in the share of the grand total of loan finance, and also in expenditure per acre. Experts in the subject continued to regard the county as in great need of further drainage work.[44] Bailey Denton produced another estimate of the extent of wet land in 1885, and his reckoning for Lincolnshire, Cambridgeshire, and Huntingdonshire together was now 56.6 per cent, actually a slight increase from his figure of thirty years previously. Drainage continued to be valued as an improvement. A common response to the wet seasons of 1878 to 1882 was an increased demand for drainage of the clays to improve their condition for arable cropping.[45] Conversion of the land to grass generally came as a later change. The 1880s was thus one of the main periods for Lincolnshire landlords undertaking loan-financed land drainage. Thirty per cent of the total amount borrowed during the 19th century was raised during this decade, compared with 15 per cent in the 1870s and 4 per cent in the 1890s.[46]

If there were hopes that investment in drainage would make the clays the equal of the light-soiled districts they were probably disappointed. Some remained intractable whatever was done to their drainage. F. I. Cooke wrote of clays between Wold and Heath that 'have not a rich or inviting appearance …and not a few of them must be very poor and thin'.[47] Even so, shorter rotations were being introduced on the heavier soils during the middle decades of the 19th century, bare fallow all but disappeared, and root crops established and retained a place in the rotation, often around ten per cent of the cultivated acreage through to the end of the century. John Macvicar, land agent to Christopher Turnor, was sure that drainage was beneficial. Of Wispington Farm he said the rent had been 15s per acre before drainage was undertaken in 1855, and arable crops were poor. 'Since the drainage the meadow land has been broken up, and produces in green crops and straw much more keep, both for cattle and sheep, than formerly it did as meadow.' Rent for the farm was now 25s per acre.[48]

Mechanization

Nothing symbolizes the change of agriculture into an industry so much as mechanization. Cornelius Stovin was an enthusiast. He wrote in his diary in January 1872, 'The reaper, the steam engine and threshing apparatus, the double plough are Divine gifts to agriculture of the 19th century.'[49] He put this enthusiasm into practice, having a few months previously bought a double-furrow plough, a Hornsby, and he was the first in his district to buy a self-binding reaper.

Arthur Young had commended Lincolnshire farmers for adopting better implements, including improved iron ploughs, seed drills, and small threshing machines. The next half century built upon that. J. A. Clarke wrote of farmers 'having been liberal purchasers of recent inventions and improvements'. Hornsby's drills, Crosskill's clod crusher, Garrett's horse hoes, new types of iron plough and harrows were among the implements he noted. These were becoming common, although not universal. Ploughs with shares of wrought iron had not

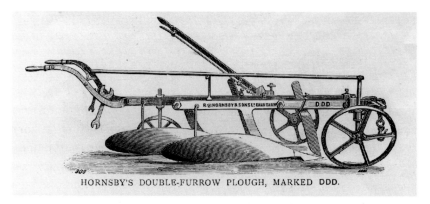

HORNSBY'S DOUBLE-FURROW PLOUGH, MARKED DDD.

**Fig. 13 A two-furrow plough made by Richard Hornsby & Sons,
similar to the type that Cornelius Stovin bought.
An illustration in the firm's catalogue for 1891**
Source: Museum of English Rural Life

been ousted entirely by those of cast iron, Clarke reported, although
most larger farmers had the newer type. On the Heath the subsoil
plough was becoming more popular. The small implements collectively
known as barn machinery appeared on almost every farm in increasing
number, and of improved design. Chaff cutters and turnip slicers
became essential tools. Those farming on a small scale would retain the
hand-operated versions, but on most farms a horse gear to drive the
barn machinery was another essential. Growth of demand was
sufficient to form the foundation for one of Lincolnshire's most
successful industries, in agricultural engineering. Richard Hornsby was
one of the earliest to set up business, in Grantham in 1815, making
ploughs, seed drills, and threshing machines. Other firms followed.
James Coultas was another manufacturer of seed drills at Grantham.
John Cooke, of Lincoln, was locally celebrated as a maker of ploughs
and wagons.[50]

    'Latterly portable steam engines for threshing have very much
increased in number,' Clarke observed, although he thought the lack of
fixed steam engines 'one of the larger deficiencies'.[51] He cited an
example of a large farm which had a fixed steam engine driving a
threshing machine and other equipment. However, it was the flexibility
of the portable engine that brought more farmers to turn to steam. The

engine could be used to drive machinery in the barn, in the stackyard, or out in the fields. The firm of Tuxford of Boston was one of those pioneering the development of the portable steam engine during the early 1840s. At the same time the threshing machine, which had been in existence for half a century, was undergoing renewed development. By the 1840s portable threshing machines were in fairly common use. In the Fens, Pusey noted, machines made by local Boston firms Tuxford and Howden were regularly hired out. These were small machines, powered by horses, two or four of them most usually. Separate winnowing and dressing equipment was needed along with the thresher. At the end of the 1840s the operations of threshing, winnowing, and dressing were combined into one machine, a much larger machine that really needed the steam engine to drive it. The portable steam engine and the large combined threshing machines became potent signs of agricultural progress. By the 1870s the proportion of the harvest threshed by hand was small. The steam engine could also be applied to power other machines, such as chaff cutters, cake breakers, corn grinding mills, and root choppers. The new firms of Marshall, Clayton & Shuttleworth, and Ruston were founded in the 1840s and 1850s to tap the potential demand from Lincolnshire farmers for these steam engines and machines. Initially their sales were heavily concentrated in Lincolnshire and other eastern counties, although by the late 1850s their growth was already outstripping local needs, and most of production went to export.[52]

The most striking application of steam power was in ploughing. In the early 19th century several people had tried to develop a means of using steam for ploughing. One of them was Lord Willoughby d'Eresby, who carried out a number of trials on his estate at Grimsthorpe between 1850 and 1855. The successful steam ploughing system was developed by John Fowler shortly after that. The high cost of two engines and the large ploughs and cultivators to go with them meant that steam ploughing was not something that all would take up, and it was almost always a job for contractors. However, its value for deep cultivations on heavy lands was recognized, and by the 1870s it was regularly employed. William Torr used steam to prepare turnip land instead of horse-drawn subsoil ploughs. With steam cultivation it was

**Fig. 14 Clayton & Shuttleworth's threshing machine of 1851,
depicted in their catalogue against a background
featuring Lincoln cathedral**
Source: Museum of English Rural Life

becoming possible, J. A. Clarke said, to grow more roots and green crops on the Marsh in place of bare fallow.[53]

Steam was the high-profile aspect of mechanization. Farm inventories and valuations show the more general adoption of the newer types of ploughs, harrows, rollers, horse hoes, and drills made by the leading manufacturers. A few farmers, among them William Torr, had reaping machines for the cereal harvest by the late 1860s. Cornelius Stovin was also quick to take up the reaper. He comments in August 1871 on that being the third season with Hornsby's reaper. Hornsby's, he said, was more easily managed than Burgess & Key's, which presumably he had had some time before. More general use of the reaper came later in the 1870s. The machines were used at first for the wheat crop. Anxiety about damaging the malting quality meant that barley was not turned over to the machine until much later.[54] Hay mowers were introduced in the 1850s. Haymakers, or tedders, were also being taken into wider use, with Blackstone of Stamford one of the leading manufacturers. Mechanical potato lifters were invented in the

1850s. By the late 19th century the old potato-raising plough was used by a minority. The humble wagons and carts were improved, for greater output needed stronger wagons, the greater quantities of manure to be carted needed good means of carrying them. Preferably they should require less horse power. The versatile William Torr designed a number of improved farm implements, among them a light, spring wagon, the manufacture of which was taken up by Crosskills of Beverley. John Cooke of Lincoln was another firm leading the trend towards factory-made wagons in place of the wheelwright's product.

Economy was a prime motivation in the introduction of new implements. Field implements were usually of lower draught, requiring fewer horses to pull them, often two where three had been usual. This could result in considerable saving, both of horses and labourers, especially at peak seasons, such as autumn ploughing. Cornelius Stovin revealed that his purchase of a two-furrow plough had enabled him to dispense with the third waggoner and a pair of horses. Even more labourers could be saved by barn machinery, threshing machines, steam

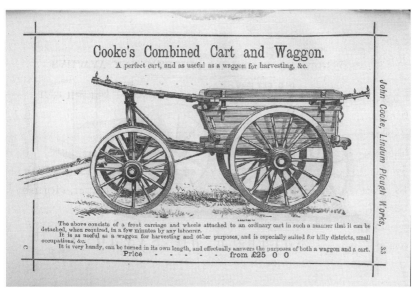

**Fig. 15 The Lincolnshire hermaphrodite wagon
as manufactured by J. Cooke of Lincoln**
Source: Museum of English Rural Life

engines, and harvesting implements. Farmers needed these savings, for labourers leaving the land were at times leaving shortages of labour. Of the decline in the number of agricultural labourers of 14 per cent between 1851 and 1881 shown in Table 2, at least part led mechanization rather than followed it.

Farm capital and tenant right

It was becoming a major concern of landowners during the mid-19th century to find tenants with enough capital to maintain the investment in high farming. Agricultural writers at least since the 1840s regarded £10 per acre as a desirable minimum for tenants' capital, and were concerned at apparent shortfalls.[55] E. P. Squarey, a leading land agent and surveyor, writing in the *Journal of the Royal Agricultural Society of England* in 1878, complained that 'as a rule it may be accepted that tenant's capital has not flowed liberally into farming investments in England, and is more or less deficient in the amount which might be profitably employed'.[56]

Establishing just what capital tenants had has always been difficult because of the ways the farmers kept accounts. There were certainly several farmers in the 1870s who did have as much as £10 an acre in capital, ranging from William Frankish with his vast holding on the Wolds to the tenant of 280 acres at Claythorpe. Just as many accounts, however, from the time when Squarey wrote show tenants' capital at best of about £6–£8 per acre. A farmer from the Marsh reckoned in 1880 that farmers' capital was often only about £6 an acre, and the Royal Commission on agriculture sitting from 1879 was presented with similar evidence.[57] Estimates by B. A. Holderness for the nation as a whole suggest that average tenant's or working capital was about £8 6s per acre in 1860, falling to about £7 12s by 1910.[58]

Landowners lived in hope, possibly expectation, that their tenants would have capital of £7–£10 per acre.[59] They might sometimes have been disappointed, but the tenant's capital invested in farming was certainly increasing as many of the changes in farming involved his capital to a greater extent than hitherto.[60] It was his money that bought the bones, the oilcake, the new types of farm implement. He invested in the improvement of livestock. The tenant was becoming more involved in areas traditionally the landlord's sphere of responsibility. He was quite likely to take the initiative in such improvements as underdrainage. It was common for the tenant to buy the drainage tiles, but occasionally he might even finance and undertake the whole of the work. There were a number of instances of tenants' money going into the improvement of farm buildings. The estates of the Marquis of Ripon and the Marquis of Bristol were two where this was reported to be not unusual. On a much more modest estate at Claythorpe a tenant in the 1870s was reminding his landlord that he had undertaken some extensive repairs to buildings.[61] General repair and maintenance, often of substantial scale, was commonly done by the tenant, causing Rider Haggard to remark that landlords in his county of Norfolk could not pass on this responsibility to their tenants.[62] It was the tenant as much as his landlord who instigated and carried forward most of the agricultural developments of high farming. By the 1880s about £3 per acre was needed by most tenants to finance their needs for oilcake, bones, and other fertilizer.[63]

Bones applied to the soil had a life of up to five years before their fertilizing value was gone. Facts such as this lay behind the development of tenant right, whereby the farmer on leaving his tenancy could claim for the value of any 'unexhausted' improvements he had made. As the practice of using bones grew after the Napoleonic Wars this system of tenant right was developing in parallel, and it was extended to include oilcake and other improvements. It was this that in large part accounted for the farmer's willingness to invest his own capital while holding land on annual tenancy, although writers also liked to stress their confidence in the great landowners, such as Lord Yarborough.[64]

The Lincolnshire Custom, as it came to be called, was becoming well developed by the 1840s. On the Yarborough estate the customary terms were 'so well established … that it is quite unnecessary to insert them in the ordinary agreements for farms'.[65] Tariffs for the different improvements were established by which compensation to outgoing tenants could be assessed. For example, bones applied to a turnip crop were valued on a three-year cycle. Allowances for oilcake were only just being introduced in the 1840s, an indication of the way the feeding of oilcake and tenant right were both developing contemporaneously.

Thirty years later, 'cake of one kind or another is now so commonly used that in almost every case the claim of the tenant is governed by the allowance which was made when he entered the farm, and this varies even on different farms forming part of the same estate'.[66] There were payments for the application of lime, for acts of husbandry on the fallow, and for work done on the autumn-sown wheat, this last resulting from the fact that tenancies started at old Lady Day.

Tenant right continued to develop during the middle decades of the century alongside high farming. By the 1870s it was such an established part of the county's agriculture that the principal rates of compensation were often written into tenancy agreements. The system was developed over the years, with adaptations, some of universal application, others peculiar to particular estates. The Ancaster and Chaplin estates were among those where expenditure on buildings was specifically drawn into the system.[67] The Great Depression brought further concerns. One of the major ones was compensation for underdrainage. Allowances under tenant right were increased by extending the depreciation from five years to between seven and ten years if the landlord provided the tiles and the tenant the labour, fifteen years if the tenant provided both tiles and labour.[68] Other matters which attracted attention during these years were marling and the use of home-grown corn as feed. Provision for laying arable land down to pasture was rarely made, mainly because conversion to permanent grass was not a major issue with Lincolnshire farmers.

Valuations under the Lincolnshire Custom were made by independent valuers acting on behalf of the two tenants, with provision for a third valuer to arbitrate if there was disagreement. The whole transaction was conducted between the incoming and outgoing tenants with the landlord rarely involved until the Agricultural Holdings Acts prescribed a role for him. The role of the valuer, acting on behalf of the tenants, was important. The Lincolnshire Land Agents' and Tenant Right Valuers' Association had strong influence on the evolution of the rates of compensation. By 1879 the Association's standard schedule was commonly used.[69] Lincolnshire custom had become so well established that the introduction of a statutory system was resisted, even though it was inspired by the practice of the county. The first

Agricultural Holdings Act of 1875, being permissive in its application, was ignored throughout Lincolnshire. The subsequent Act, of 1883, was supposed to be compulsory; even so it was avoided as far as possible by Lincolnshire valuers and farmers. Lincolnshire farmers adopted a superior attitude to the Acts. They were 'a bad imitation of the Lincolnshire custom', Wilson Fox was told, and this view continued to be common for at least another decade. A fundamental objection to the law was that compensation was to be assessed on the value of improvements to the incoming tenant rather than the amount spent by the outgoing tenant. Lincolnshire men took advantage of the clause in the 1883 Act that allowed local schemes to be substituted for those prescribed. The new law could not be ignored entirely, however, for many of its allowances were more generous than those of the custom. By the 1890s tenancy agreements on some estates were specifically including provision for compensation according to the Act.[70]

The Agricultural Holdings Acts presumed a valuation being agreed between the outgoing tenant and the landlord. This was regarded as an unnecessary and expensive complication, and another provision that was ignored as much as possible. The involvement of the landlord was bound to increase, however, not only because of the new laws but because the depressed conditions of the time often meant the landlord was himself the incoming tenant. Tenant right payments could be a burden on a new farmer's capital and, to attract tenants, there were occasions when landlords might take on the customary charges. Lord Yarborough spent nearly £4,000 on redeeming following crops between 1881–82 and 1884–85.[71] Some advertisements for farms to let mentioned absence of tenant right payments as an attraction.

A Golden Age

The extent to which all the investment in new means of farming paid off has become a more open question. The 'golden age of English agriculture', a phrase of Lord Ernle's, has firmly stuck to this third quarter of the 19th century. Peace and free trade, bountiful harvests and good prices all contributed to a feeling of well being among farmers. Ernle, however, confined his golden age to the decade 1853–62. Much recent research has supported his assessment, and suggests that the extent of the gilding was quite variable.[72]

Certainly there was growing confidence in Lincolnshire at this time, with farmers and landowners enthusiastically adopting the new practices of high farming, and it was not restricted to the one decade. Corn-growers, as most farmers in Lincolnshire were, gained encouragement from the recovery of prices for cereals from the depths to which they had fallen in the mid 1830s. In actual fact, price fluctuations meant that for much of the time, including the golden decade of 1853–63, prices of wheat were no higher than they had been during the 1820s, universally regarded as a depression. While wheat prices were lower in the early 1870s than they had been in the early 1840s, barley and oats both showed healthy increases, and this was of great value to Lincolnshire's farmers, for many of whom barley was at least as important as wheat.

Fig. 16 The Lincolnshire Longwool sheep was one of the foundations of the county's farming in the Golden Age. These shearling rams were prize-winners at the Lincolnshire show, 1933
Source: Museum of English Rural Life

Prices for Lincoln wool were very high from the 1850s to the 1870s, rising from 10d to 13d per pound in the 1840s to 18d to 22d throughout much of the 1850s and 1860s. Meanwhile, prices for fatstock were rising, slowly and fitfully much of the time, but significantly over the long term. Prices quoted at Lincoln market were about 7s 6d per stone in the late 1850s. They fluctuated during the next ten years, but around a gradually rising trend, with returns of 7s 9d to 8s 6d per stone appearing more regularly. By the early 1870s about 10s a stone was a more frequent quotation. Prices for fat mutton followed a similar upward trend.[73] Lincolnshire might be concerned primarily with arable and cereal growing, with farmers likely to dismiss livestock on the grounds of cost, inconvenience, and disease, but movements in prices on this scale were having their effect on farmers' practices and returns.

Rents rose under the stimulus of this confidence in farming. Getting anything like a precise measure of the increase is extremely difficult. The recently constructed national rent index shows an increase of 34 per cent on rents received between 1850 and 1875.[74] An average increase in Lincolnshire may be put somewhat lower than the national figure, at around 15 to 20 per cent. There were, of course, wide variations. Some of the extreme changes were due to the relatively late development of some areas of Lincolnshire agriculture. In the 1850s it was still possible to find farms at very low rents where improvements were still being undertaken, or were sufficiently recent for rents to be held down in compensation. J. A. Clarke noted unimproved lands near Corringham and Scotton rented at no more than 15s an acre while better farms were let at 21s to 35s.[75] In parts of the Fens recently drained, and recently reclaimed parts of the Wolds and Heath, there were farms still at low rents. By the 1860s their rents were up to the local average.

On the Wolds average rents of 25s to 28s an acre in the 1850s were up to 30s to 35s by the mid 1870s. Even then, while some rents were being pushed towards 40s an acre, Mr Chaplin's estate in 1879 was almost all let at about 25s. Rents in most districts of Lincolnshire were of similar order in the late 1870s, except on the good soils in the Fens where 50s an acre was about the average and £3 or more not uncommon.[76]

Increases in rent, however, generally lagged behind that of farmers' gross incomes, and this contributed to profitability, which certainly appears to have been quite good. Measuring farmers' profits is a difficult task because farmers themselves were inexact, often making no allowance for such items as family labour and interest on capital. Few detailed farm accounts survive from this period. One of these few was kept by William Scorer, farmer of 600 acres on the northern Wolds, and this demonstrates some of these effects. In summarizing his annual accounts for the 1850s, he first extracted the household and personal expenses before arriving at a figure for profit. He made a loss of £68 in 1853–54, but this was after the extraordinary expenditure of £250 on the farmhouse, a sum which not all would charge to profit and loss account. Without that expense the operating profit for that year was £182. Otherwise, the six years starting in 1848–49 yielded an average profit of £339 per year, approximately 11s per acre. Profits in individual years ranged from £693 to £135.[77] For a wider picture, E. J. T. Collins has turned to the reports of the Inland Revenue and the agricultural returns. He has calculated that farming profits in Lincolnshire increased by 30.8 per cent between 1851–52 and 1876–77. In this Lincolnshire was well above the average increase of 25.3 per cent for England and Wales. These calculations suggest that profitability in the arable mixed-farming counties, of which Lincolnshire was one, rose by more than the pastoral counties.[78]

Mixed farming clearly had its benefits in these conditions. Good returns from livestock could compensate for poor years for cereals. In 1863–64 barley prices were low, but income from wool and stock helped many farmers, and left them unconcerned about the current campaign against the malt tax. Although much of the investment in Lincolnshire high farming had gone into the arable, it was often the livestock, through the high-feeding regimes and the better housing, that produced the returns. Surviving accounts from some of the large farms show the trend of things. In the mid 1840s at Nocton Rise, a farm of 450 acres, wheat was the main source of income, while cattle and sheep between them accounted for about 37 per cent of the total. In the 1860s John West, of Dunholme and Washingborough, was deriving in most years about half, often more, of his gross income from livestock, and this continued into the 1870s. Likewise, 63.1 per cent of Scorer's income came from livestock, including wool, by 1875–76.[79]

The contribution of the spending on the inputs into farming was not a simple one. High spending did not automatically result in high returns. The extent to which yields of arable crops improved has been a subject of debate, for clear figures are rare. On one measure, yields of wheat in Lincolnshire increased by 20 per cent between about 1850 and the 1870s, on another measure hardly at all.[80] Where the expenditure on inputs was paying off was in reducing costs. Prices for linseed cake and imported fertilizers were stable, and in some years falling, during the fifteen or so years after the Crimean War. Machinery prices, too, were stable. Better buildings were providing better storage, better manure capture, and in many cases more efficient handling of stock. The improved implements meant savings in horse power: where three horses had been needed for the plough, only two were now, and this effected significant savings at the autumn peak times. They also brought even bigger savings in manpower. The productivity of labour increased considerably during this period, and the large arable farmer benefited more than most. Their labour bills remained relatively stable throughout these decades, demonstrated in some of those farm accounts that survive such as John West's and Frederick Scorer.[81]

High farming was a delicate balance, with costs and returns, and natural conditions all playing their part. Cornelius Stovin on the Wolds came to appreciate this. In 1872 he noted in his diary a remark by his neighbour, Mr Fieldsend, that there had not been a good crop of wheat since 1862, 'a very strong complaint to make against our cold hills. The winters destroy our plant and nothing has yet been discovered to preserve the root against the severe frosts'. Against this, he complained, landlords were trying to raise rents above what the conditions would really bear.[82] By the 1870s farmers were coming to realize more fully that high-input farming also needed strong control over costs. The strength of resistance to the labourers' campaigns for higher wages was a reflection of this. There was good reason for this, for if labour bills had remained fairly stable for several years, the problem was that they showed little sign of changing as prices fell in the 1880s and 1890s. In the next two decades the importance of these connections was really driven home, as the extent to which it was possible to farm high while prices were generally falling became one of the major questions of the Great Depression.

Notes to Chapter 6

1   J. A. Clarke, 'On the Farming of Lincolnshire', *JRASE,* v. 12 (1851) p. 338.

2   Philip Pusey 'On the Progress of Agricultural Knowledge during the last Four Years', *JRASE,* v. 3 (1843), p. 205. B. A. Holderness, 'The Origin of High Farming', in *Land Labour and Agriculture 1700–1920,* ed. B. A. Holderness and M. Turner (1991) pp. 149–50.

3   Clarke, 'On the Farming of Lincolnshire', p. 328.

4   J. Stovin, *Journals of a Methodist Farmer, 1871–1875* (1982) pp. 46–7.

5   *Stamford Mercury,* 19 April 1872.

6   Holderness, 'The Origin of High Farming', pp. 149–64.

7   David Grigg, The *Agricultural Revolution in South Lincolnshire* (1966) pp. 126ff.

8   National Archives, MAF68, Agricultural returns, parish summaries.

9   J. A. Clarke, 'On the Great Level of the Fens, including the Fens of South Lincolnshire', *JRASE,* v. 8 (1847) p. 132. J. A. Clarke, 'Practical Agriculture', *JRASE,* v. 39 (1878) p. 611. G. M. Robinson, *Agricultural Change* (1988) p. 127.

10   Grigg, *The Agricultural Revolution in South Lincolnshire,* pp. 155ff.

11   Clarke, 'On the Farming of Lincolnshire', p. 330. Philip Pusey, 'On the Agricultural Improvements of Lincolnshire', *JRASE,* v. 4 (1843) p. 307. T. W. Beastall, *Agricultural Revolution in Lincolnshire* (History of Lincolnshire VIII, 1978) pp. 212–14.

12   G. E. Collins, 'Agriculture', *Victoria County History, Lincolnshire,* v. 2 (1906) pp. 399–401.

13   Pusey, 'On the Agricultural Improvements of Lincolnshire', pp. 301–2.

14   Clarke, 'On the Farming of Lincolnshire', pp. 344, 355–7. S. A. Johnson, Enclosure and the Changing Agricultural Landscape of Lindsey from the Sixteenth to the Nineteenth Century, University of Liverpool MA (1957) pp. 59–60.

15   F. M. L. Thompson, 'The Second Agricultural Revolution', *EcHR,* 2 ser. v. 21 (1968) pp. 67–8. Agricultural Returns, 1885. H. W. Bracey, *History of Seed Crushing in Great Britain* (1960).

16   Grigg, *The Agricultural Revolution in South Lincolnshire*, pp. 49, 56, 146.
     Pusey, 'On the Progress of Agricultural Knowledge during the last Four
     Years', p. 205.

17   Clarke, 'On the Farming of Lincolnshire', pp. 398–9.

18   Pusey, 'On the Agricultural Improvements of Lincolnshire', p. 301.
     Thompson, 'Second Agricultural Revolution', p. 68. G. M. Williams,
     'On the Tenant's Rights to unexhausted improvements according to
     the custom of North Lincolnshire', *JRASE*, v. 6 (1845) p. 46.

19   Philip Pusey, 'The Improvement of Peaty Ground', *JRASE*, v. 2 (1841)
     p. 408. James Caird, *English Agriculture in 1850–51* (1852) pp. 190, 320. M.
     E. Turner, J. V. Beckett, and B. Afton, *Farm Production in England
     1700–1914* (2001) p. 103.

20   Holderness, 'The Origins of High Farming', pp. 154ff.

21   Clarke, 'On the Farming of Lincolnshire', pp. 331–4.

22   G. G. S. Bowie, 'Northern Wolds and Wessex Downlands: contrasts in
     sheep husbandry and farming practice, 1770–1850', *AgHR*, v. 38 (1990)
     pp. 117–26.

23   Thompson, 'The Second Agricultural Revolution', p. 68. G. M.
     Williams, 'On the Tenant's Rights to unexhausted improvements
     according to the custom of North Lincolnshire', *JRASE*, v. 6 (1845)
     p. 46. Pusey, 'On the Agricultural Improvements of Lincolnshire',
     pp. 300–4.

24   H. M. Jenkins, 'Farm Reports 3. Aylesby, Riby and Rothwell Farms, near
     Grimsby, Lincolnshire, in the occupation of Mr William Torr', *JRASE*,
     v. 30 (1869), p. 424.

25   Clarke, 'Practical Agriculture', p. 622. Caird, *English Agriculture in
     1850–51,* pp. 190, 320.

26   Thompson, 'Second Agricultural Revolution', pp. 68–9. Susanna
     Wade-Martins and Tom Williamson, *Roots of Change (Agricultural History
     Review*, supplement ser. 2, 1999), pp. 134–5.

27   Pusey, 'The Improvement of Peaty Ground', pp. 405ff. Gordon
     Saunders, 'The Claying of the Fen Lands', *Journal of the Ministry of
     Agriculture*, v. 48 (1942) pp. 42–3.

28   Clarke, 'On the Farming of Lincolnshire', p. 400. G. E. Collins
     'Agriculture', *VCH Lincolnshire*, v. 2 (1906) pp. 409–12. G. E. Collins,
     'Lincolnshire Red Shorthorns', *JRASE*, v. 75 (1914), pp. 33–40. G. E.
     Collins, 'From Fen to Farm, Heath to Husbandry', *Lincolnshire Magazine*,
     v. 1 (1934) pp. 232–3, 280–1. R. Trow-Smith, *A History of British Livestock
     Husbandry 1700–1900* (1959) p. 242.

29   M. Skehel, *A Taste of Lincoln Red* (1995) pp. 5–10. *Stamford Mercury*, 14 April 1882.

30   J. A. Perkins, *Sheep Farming in Eighteenth and Nineteenth Century Lincolnshire* (1977) pp. 35–51. Bowie, 'Northern Wolds and Wessex Downlands: contrasts in sheep husbandry and farming practice, 1770–1850', pp. 117–26. *Bell's Weekly Messenger*, 2 March 1857.

31   Clarke, 'On the Farming of Lincolnshire', p. 352.

32   Pusey, 'On the Agricultural Improvements of Lincolnshire', p. 305.

33   P. S. Barnwell and C. Giles, *English Farmsteads 1750–1914* (1997), pp. 42ff.

34   *Ibid.*, pp. 47–9. J. Bailey Denton, *The Farm Homesteads of England* (1864 edn) pp. 19–23, 47–9. A. S. Brook, 'Farm Buildings of North Kesteven: two examples', *Journal of the Historic Farm Buildings Group*, v. 9 (1995), 15–18. 'The survey of Christopher Turnor's farm buildings', paper presented by Catherine Wilson at Society for Lincolnshire History and Archaeology conference, Lincoln, July 2003.

35   LAO, JARVIS III/A/5/6.

36   Brook, 'Farm Buildings', p. 18. A. D. M. Phillips, 'Landlord Investment in Farm Buildings in the English Midlands in the Mid 19th Century', in *Land Labour and Agriculture 1700–1920,* ed. B. A. Holderness and M. E. Turner (1991) pp. 199, 201, 208.

37   See G. E. Fussell, *The Farmer's Tools* (1952), chapter 1 for some of these new implements.

38   Grigg, *The Agricultural Revolution in South Lincolnshire*, pp. 141–4. Turner, Beckett and Afton, *Farm Production in England 1700–1914*, p. 90.

39   Clarke, 'On the Farming of Lincolnshire', pp. 345–6, 380, 387.

40   A. D. M. Phillips, *The Underdraining of Farmland in England during the Nineteeth Century* (1989), pp. 28–30, 119.

41   Grigg, *The Agricultural Revolution in South Lincolnshire* , pp. 141–4. Phillips, *The Underdraining of Farmland,* pp. 50ff. Pusey, 'On the Progress of Agricultural Knowledge during the last Four Years', p. 177.

42   LAO, BS13/1/13/12c.

43   Phillips, *The Underdraining of Farmland ,* pp. 62–88.

44   Select Committee of the House of Lords on the Improvement of Land. (1873), QQ. 3659–60, evidence of James Sanderson.

45   LAO, MON 25/13/18, 18 November, 17 December 1883.

46   Phillips, *The Underdraining of Farmland,* p. 125.

47   F. I. Cooke, 'Report on the Farm Prize Competition in Nottinghamshire and Lincolnshire in 1888, class I', *JRASE,* v. 49 (1888) p. 525.

48   Denton, *The Farm Homesteads of England,* p. 49.

49 Stovin, *Journals of a Methodist Farmer, 1871–1875,* p. 47.

50 Clarke, 'On the Farming of Lincolnshire', p. 337, 412. Grigg, *The Agricultural Revolution in South Lincolnshire,* pp. 150–1. Stovin, *Journals of a Methodist Farmer, 1871–1875,* p. 23. Neil R. Wright, *Lincolnshire Towns and Industry* (1982) pp. 142–5.

51 Clarke, 'On the Farming of Lincolnshire', p. 412.

52 Museum of English Rural Life, Marshall and Clayton engine registers.

53 Jenkins, 'Farm Reports 3', p. 440. Clarke, 'Practical Agriculture', pp. 613–14

54 Jenkins, 'Farm Reports 3', pp. 423, 426–7. Stovin, *Journals of a Methodist Farmer, 1871–1875,* p. 26.

55 C. S. Orwin and E. H. Whetham, *History of British Agriculture 1846–1914* (1964), p. 35.

56 E. P. Squarey, 'Farm Capital', *JRASE,* v. 39 (1878), p. 437.

57 LAO, Higgins 4/4. RC1879, QQ. 33226–7, 49250–2.

58 *The Agrarian History of England and Wales, vol. VII, 1850–1914,* ed. E. J. T. Collins (2000) p. 914.

59 RC1879, Q. 7180.

60 B. A. Holderness, 'Landlord's Capital Formation in East Anglia, 1750–1870', *EcHR,* 2 ser, v. 25 (1972) pp. 445ff.

61 *Mark Lane Express,* 24 April 1882. LAO, HIGGINS 4/4.

62 H. Rider Haggard, *Rural England* (1902) v. 2, pp. 215–16.

63 Thompson, 'The Second Agricultural Revolution', p. 71.

64 Pusey, 'On the Agricultural Improvements of Lincolnshire'. J. A. Perkins, 'Tenure, Tenant Right and Agricultural Progress in Lindsey 1780–1850', *AgHR,* v. 23 (1975) pp. 1–23. David Grigg, 'The Development of Tenant Right in South Lincolnshire', *Lincolnshire Historian,* v. 2, no. 9 (1962) pp.41–3.

65 G. M. Williams, 'On the tenant's rights to unexhausted improvements acccording to the custom of north Lincolnshire', *JRASE,* v. 6 (1845), p. 45.

66 LAO MON25/13/18.

67 Williams, 'On the tenant's rights to unexhausted improvements', p. 44–51. LAO, 9ANC 5/1/7, 5/1/8; BS13/1/7/4.

68 C. Cadle, 'The Farming Customs and Covenants of England', *JRASE,* v. 29 (1868) pp. 156–7. Grigg, *The Agricultural Revolution in South Lincolnshire,* pp. 199–200. LAO, DIXON 22/7/3/1, 6/5/1.

69 RC1879, Appendix to Minutes of Evidence, p. 113. RC1893, Q. 36019.

70   RC1879, Q. 4639. RC1893, Wilson Fox, pp. 17ff; Minutes of
      Evidence, QQ. 14405–7. *SM,* 22 December 1882, 9 February, 5, 12, 19
      October 1883. LAO, 9ANC 2/C/1/4; BS13/1/6/8, 9; 2HEN
      2/26/14–16; DIXON 22/7/3/7. Frederick Clifford, 'The Agricultural
      Holdings (England) Act, 1883', *JRASE,* v. 45 (1884) pp. 1–77.
      Thomas Stirton, 'Report on the Farm Prize Competition in
      Nottinghamshire and Lincolnshire, classes 2 and 3', *JRASE,* v. 50
      (1889) p. 69.
71   LAO, YARB5, summaries of accounts.
72   Lord Ernle, *English Farming Past and Present* (6th edn, 1961) pp. 373–5.
      For a survey of the state of study on the golden age, see E. J. T.
      Collins, 'The High Farming Period', in *The Agrarian History of England
      and Wales, vol. VII, 1850–1914* (2000) pp. 72–137.
73   Prices quoted in newspaper market reports; those for the first quarter
      of the year are the ones mentioned here. *The Agrarian History of England
      and Wales, vol. VII, 1850–1914,* pp. 2050–83 reproduces various series
      of prices for store stock and meat.
74   M. E. Turner, J. V. Beckett and B. Afton, *Agricultural Rent in England
      1690–1914* (1997) pp. 312ff, and *The Agrarian History of England and
      Wales, vol. VII, 1850–1914,* pp. 1914–38.
75   Clarke, 'On the Farming of Lincolnshire', p. 364
76   Charles K. Rawding, *The Lincolnshire Wolds in the Nineteenth Century*
      (2001) pp. 96–7. Clarke, 'On the Farming of Lincolnshire', pp. 336–7.
      RC1879, Second Report of S. B. L. Druce, p. 53; Minutes of Evidence,
      QQ. 43192–3. LAO, BS13/1/7/6.
77   LAO, Scorer Farm, and summary in *The Agrarian History of England and
      Wales, vol. VII, 1850–1914,* pp. 795–6, article by G. E. Mingay.
78   Collins, 'The High Farming Period', in *The Agrarian History of England
      and Wales, vol. VII, 1850–1914,* pp. 136–7.
79   Museum of English Rural Life FR LIN P323. R. J. Olney, *Lincolnshire
      Politics 1832–1885* (1973) p. 172. Turner, Beckett, and Afton, *Farm
      Production in England 1700–1914,* pp. 111–12. Collins, 'The High
      Farming Period', p. 119. LAO, West of Dunholme.
80   See the table in Collins, 'The High Farming Period', pp. 132–3.
81   *The Agrarian History of England and Wales, vol. VII, 1850–1914,*
      pp. 128–30, 2098, 2102.
82   Stovin, *Journals of a Methodist Farmer, 1871–1875,* pp. 46–8.

7
THE GREAT DEPRESSION 1875–1896

In 1881 S. B. L. Druce began a report on Lincolnshire: 'I found that agricultural depression existed in all parts of this county, but that some parts of it were affected more than others.'[1] Here was a sharp contrast to the optimism to be found in the reports by Pusey and Clarke some years before. Druce was an assistant commissioner for the Royal Commission on the Depressed State of the Agricultural Interest (commonly known as the Richmond Commission after its chairman, the Duke of Richmond). This Royal Commission had been appointed in 1879 after agriculturalists throughout the nation had complained loudly enough and often enough for the government to take some action. The problems did not all go away and another Royal Commission on Agricultural Depression was appointed in 1893. The assistant commissioner reporting on Lincolnshire, Arthur Wilson Fox, came to this conclusion: 'The farming industry has suffered blow after blow until the present time when the situation is extremely critical and the future outlook of the gloomiest character.'[2]

After the confidence of the previous few decades this period came as a shock. The last quarter of the 19th century became known as the Great Depression in agriculture, a name which has stuck. In historical perspective it is generally accepted as one of the major cyclical changes in the fortunes and development of farming. The period was characterized by low prices, rents, and land values, and by some major changes in farming management and land use. These conditions did not necessarily result in a decline in production: nationally, real output, adjusted for changes in prices, was little changed in the 1900s from what it had been in the 1870s.[3] Regional experience was varied. Output for

England changed little, but there was a marked contrast between the increase in output of 22 per cent in Cheshire from 1873 to 1911 and the decline by 31 per cent in Bedfordshire. Broadly, these contrasts reflected a shift in balance from arable towards livestock husbandry. Lincolnshire came out approximately in the middle: output decreased by 2 per cent between 1873 and 1911, with a deeper decline of 9 per cent between 1873 and 1894, followed by a good recovery.[4]

Seasons, imports and prices

What prompted the appointment of the Royal Commission in 1879 was a run of exceptionally bad seasons, in which poor weather led to poor harvests and some disastrous financial results for farmers. These were notoriously wet years. The year 1879 was especially bad, and a disaster for almost all farmers. The rainfall records for Boston were typical: 38 per cent above average during the twelve months from November 1878. In particular it rained in early summer when the crops should have been ripening. In consequence, the harvest was at least a month late, starting in early September and not finishing until late October.[5] Yields were down as well. S. B. L. Druce collected several sets of figures for yields, and they were generally about half the average: 2 quarters of wheat to the acre instead of 4 quarters for an average of years before 1878, 2½ instead of 4¾ quarters of barley, reported the Louth branch of the Lincolnshire Chamber of Agriculture.[6] In the Fens potatoes did no better than wheat, and much of the crop was reckoned to be barely worth lifting in 1879.[7] The one exception seems to have been oats. In nearly all the examples of yields collected by S. B. L. Druce oats was the crop which in 1878 and 1879 yielded no more than one fifth less than the average of previous years.[8]

If 1879 had been bad, 1880 was as bad or even worse. Again it was wet. The rainfall in the Fens was 33½ inches compared with the average of 22 inches. Until June prospects for harvest seemed good, but then the rain came, with storms in late June and July, and especially heavy downpours in September and October. There were floods in parts of the Fens. Harvest was delayed again: there were even some reports of fields remaining unharvested until December.[9] Yields again were generally low, although some farmers achieved almost normal returns, and oats were again counted as the best corn crop.[10] Whether yields were high or low, the quality of the produce was generally low. Wheat was often condemned as of feeding quality only, while barley growers found it difficult to supply good malting samples. Livestock farming fared little better in the wet years. The land was too wet for animals to benefit from growth of grass. Graziers as a result found that they were getting less weight on their animals and were unable to gain full advantage of fairly favourable prices.[11] In addition, livestock farmers had to contend with serious outbreaks of disease, principally foot and mouth in cattle and liver rot in sheep. Nationally, the second of these was especially serious and resulted in the loss of nearly one tenth of the sheep in the country between 1879 and 1882.[12] Low-lying districts, such as the Lincolnshire marshes, were affected especially badly, and as a result the number of sheep in the county fell by 17 per cent between 1879 and 1882.

These two years were regarded as the culmination of a run of bad years. It was common to start counting seven lean years from 1875, although the first three of these produced crops that were disappointing, but not so very much below average. They were made to look worse by comparison with the harvest of 1874 which was 'one of the most abundant and profitable that has been known for some years'.[13] Such were the workings of memory that 1874 was made to seem far more typical of early 1870s 'prosperity' than the years immediately preceding, which had produced generally poor yields.

With the rain falling heavily in 1879 and 1880 it is hardly surprising to find that many regarded the poor weather as prime cause of their problems. Prominent landlords such as Heneage and Chaplin said so, and many farmers agreed. Henry Chaplin told the Lincolnshire Chamber of Agriculture: 'The immediate cause of agricultural depression was owing to the succession of bad seasons, which had seldom been equalled in England before.'[14] A Sleaford correspondent of the *Stamford Mercury* wrote that 'after all that has been written and said, the present depression arises more from a cycle of bad seasons than from any foreign competition'. S. B. L. Druce accepted this evidence and put wet seasons first when he listed causes of the depression in his report. Next came the effect of imported produce on prices, and in third place he had the high cost and low efficiency of labour.[15] If poor seasons were the problem then it followed that good seasons would be the solution. Depression should be a passing phase. Lord Monson's agent wrote to his employer that 'notwithstanding all that is said of the competition with America I cannot doubt that two or three good harvests would restore the previous state of things'.[16]

In 1884, a year that had been good for weather, and reasonable for yields, Henry Chaplin told the Alford Agricultural Society that he had been forced to the conclusion that low prices rather than bad seasons were the root of agriculture's difficulties.[17] Almost everyone in the agricultural world had by now reached the same conclusion. The search for signs of recovery became concentrated on changes in the markets. Lord Monson's agent thought things had 'touched bottom' in December 1888.[18] Before the harvest of 1889 the *Retford News* was sure that 'Agricultural prospects are improving ... the agricultural classes and political economists may venture to hope that the farming troubles of the past years are over, and long looked-for "better times" are reached at last'.[19] However, though there might be periodic rallies, the downward cycle continued for a few years more. The price of wheat fell

Fig. 17 Stacking hay, Cowbit Wash, 1890s
Source: North East Lincolnshire Libraries

by 51 per cent between 1871–75 and 1894–98.[20] There was already marked change even in the late 1870s when seasons were at their worst. From an average of more than 55s per quarter in the early 1870s, wheat was down to 43s 10d in 1879, and 41s 7d by 1883. In 1884 the average price of wheat was 35s 8d, and by 1889 it was 29s 9d. Another sharp fall came in the early 1890s. The price reached 26s 4d in 1893 and 22s 10d a quarter in 1894, the low point in this cycle. That coincided with some more poor seasons, this time dry ones, but when the second Royal Commission reported on Lincolnshire these were passed by: 'There can be no question as to what the cause of the present agricultural distress is, namely the low prices now obtained for practically all that the land produces.'[21]

Wheat traditionally had been the barometer of agricultural prosperity, so, not surprisingly, the falling price created a sense of despair about agriculture's fortunes. 'The continued fall in the price of wheat is having a very depressing effect upon the farmers and indeed upon the district generally,' a commentator from Spalding wrote in 1884.[22] The prices of barley and oats also fell, but not by quite so much. The average price of barley declined by 39 per cent over the period 1871–75 to 1894–98, and that of oats by 38 per cent.[23] The result was that differences in price between the three major grains were reduced. At times, indeed, the price of barley in Lincolnshire markets was higher than that of wheat.[24]

What was new about this period was that prices did not respond to seasons in the way that they had, and the old rule of 'small crop, high price' was broken.[25] Globalization in the grain trade was now making itself felt in the farms of Lincolnshire, and farmers were deprived of their former compensation in the market place for disappointment in the harvest field. A shortfall in home production could now be made up from increased imports. In one sense there was nothing new in this. About a quarter of Britain's wheat supply was imported in the early 1850s, and this proportion reached 50 per cent by 1873–75, 60 per cent by 1878–80. In 1879 *The Economist* reviewed the state of the grain trade thus: 'The home production of corn is not the over-ruling power in the land which it once was … corn factors are accustomed to look as much to the "visible supply" in the United States as to the harvest returns here.[26] Continuation of this trend brought imports to 71 per cent of total consumption of wheat by 1891–93. Set against this long-term trend, sharp rises in imports in the late 1870s became a little less dramatic. However, it was only then that imports began seriously to undercut the price of British wheat, as the expansion of agriculture in the prairies and the low costs of bulk transport by rail and steamship combined to bring imports of wheat to Britain at prices below those prevailing at home. This was something that seemed to take people by surprise. The *Stamford Mercury*, commenting on the final report of the Richmond Commission, thought fears of large-scale imports of cattle, meat, and corn from America were proving to be unfounded.[27] By no means everybody took that view. There were those, such as William Frankish, a leading farmer in the Wolds, who told the Richmond Commission that the increased foreign competition had caused a crisis that was 'bound to come at some time'.[28] The agent for a small marshland estate is to be found advising the owner in 1879 not to expect higher rents for some years as 'I fear that newly developing

Table 4 Prices obtained for wool on C. S. Fieldsend's Farm, South Willingham

Year	Price per tod	Year	Price per tod	Year	Price per tod
1873	42s 0d	1881	25s 6d	1889	23s 0d
1874	38s 0d	1882	23s 6d	1890	23s 0d
1875	43s 0d	1883	22s 0d	1891	21s 0d
1876	33s 6d	1884	21s 6d	1892	19s 0d
1877	34s 6d	1885	21s 6d	1893	21s 9d
1878	33s 6d	1886	20s 0d	1894	21s 0d
1879	26s 6d	1887	21s 6d		
1880	34s 0d	1888	23s 0d		

Source: RC1893, Wilson Fox, p. 133

Fig. 18 Washing sheep at Fulstow
Source: North East Lincolnshire Libraries

wheat-growing areas, and newly established meat-growing districts will make the Landed Interest of this Country suffer, and lower the fee simple and the Rental Value of Land'.[29]

Only wool prices fell by as much as wheat. Between 1871–75 and 1891–95 the price of Lincoln wool fell by almost 50 per cent. The downward trend covered a much longer time, however, beginning in the 1860s, with the price at 28½d a pound in 1866, and not ending until 1902, when the price reached 6¼d a pound.[30] A combination of foreign competition and changes in fashion lay behind this trend. Imports, mainly from Australia and New Zealand, rose from 200m lbs in 1874 to 370m lbs in 1895, by which time they represented nearly three-quarters of British consumption. Trends in fashion especially affected long wools, which went out of favour. Lincolnshire farmers were directly affected, as the Lincolnshire Longwool breed reigned supreme in the county. Table 4 shows the prices (in shillings and pence) received by C. S. Fieldsend, of South Willingham. His prices in 1894 were half those of 1873, with the sharpest falls in the first part of the period, down to 1881.

After wool and wheat it was the turn of meat, which confounded all who had considered meat to be safe from large-scale overseas supply.[31] Imports of meat had, however, been steadily increasing since the 1860s, and they continued to do so, almost doubling between the 1870s and 1890s. The introduction of refrigerated transport allowed supplies of dead meat to come from more distant places, principally Australia and New Zealand. The bulk of imports continued to be live animals until the government banned them under measures to control contagious diseases. Imports did not achieve the same dominance of the British market as they did with cereals, and in consequence prices did not fall by as much. Between 1876–80 and 1891–95 the price of best quality British beef at the Metropolitan cattle market fell by 20 per cent, and that of third-quality beef by 38 per cent. The corresponding figures for mutton were 17 and 31 per cent.[32] The effect of this trend on Lincolnshire's markets is shown in Fig. 19 based on samples of fatstock prices at Lincoln from market reports in the *Stamford Mercury*. These reports did not distinguish between different grades of meat, so the graph charts the broad trend of a fall in prices by roughly one-third for both beef and mutton between the mid 1870s and the mid 1890s.

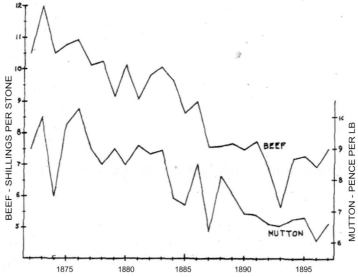

Fig. 19 June prices at Lincoln Fatstock Market, 1882–1897
Source: *Stamford Mercury*

Table 5   Accounts of a turnip and barley farm in Caistor Union, 1800 acres

Year	Profit	Loss	Capital	Capital/acre
1879–80		£3,736 19s 0d	£17,983 14s 11½d	£9 18s 0d
1880–81		£1,499 0s 10½	£18,100 10s 0d	£10 1s 6d
1881–82	£512 9s 9½d		£18,327 15s 0d	£10 3s 6d
1882–83	£1,069 13s 8d		£18,443 19s 6d	£10 5s 0d
1883–84		£80 10s 9d	£17,312 13s 0d	£9 12s 0d
1884–85	£479 7s 9½d		£17,210 9s 0d	£9 11s 0d
1885–86		£1,392 4s 3d	£15,506 2s 0d	£8 12s 0d
1886–87		£845 19s 4d	£14,378 7s 0d	£7 19s 6d
1887–88	£1,531 19s 2½d		£13,503 3s 0d	£7 10s 0d
1888–89		£365 10s 6½d	£13,748 9s 0d	£7 12s 6d
1889–90	£564 13s 7d		£12,801 0s 0d	£7 2s 0d
1890–91	£659 6s 7d		£13,454 7s 0d	£7 9s 6d
1891–92		£1,263 14s 8d	£12,285 7s 0d	£6 16s 0d
1892–93		£1,432 14s 6½d	£12,109 2s 0d	£6 14s 0d
1893–94		£1,532 7s 10d	£11,632 15s 6d	£6 9s 0d

Notes: no charge for management; no interest charged on capital
Source: RC1893, Wilson Fox, p. 125

Livestock prices followed the downward trend. The average price of sheep at the Lincoln sheep fair, at 53s 3d in 1894, was 22 per cent below the 68s 3¾d obtained in 1877.[33] There were several short-term fluctuations in livestock prices, the result of such influences as the supply of feed, or the relative profitability of fattening and breeding. Abundant crops of turnips kept prices quite high in the spring of 1872: farmers held off selling sheep while the turnips were eaten. During the drought of 1893 shortage of feed had the opposite effect.[34]

A crisis and beyond

The wet years at the end of the 1870s might have disguised longer-term trends, but their combination of poor yields and falling prices created a serious crisis for farming. The farm accounts in Table 5, one of a number collected by the Royal Commission on Agriculture in the 1890s, show substantial financial losses for the years from 1879 to 1881.[35] This farm in Caistor Union lost 20 per cent on capital in 1879–80, followed by 8 per cent the next year. Other accounts collected by the Commission showed similar results for these years. It is reasonably certain that most farmers lost money in those years, many by large amounts, especially if their business was largely dependent upon corn. Farmers on the Wolds found most of the 1870s difficult. Mr Coates Sharpley told a survey for a newspaper in 1881 that he had lost money for seven years running, and there were other reports in the local press from farmers reminding readers of difficulties starting from 1875–76. William Frankish told the Richmond Commission that he had only made £6 an acre on cereals against his break-even figure of £10 during the years 1878–80. The accounts from the farm of Thomas Dudding at Garthorpe, in the Isle of Axholme (Table 6), not from the Commission's set, show that a few farmers did make a surplus even during the worst years. Not all of Mr Dudding's neighbours were as fortunate, however, for poor potato and wheat harvests upset accounts for many. For most farmers cash-flow became a serious problem, especially in the immediate aftermath of the wet seasons. Farmers were often forced to market for ready money when seasonal prices were low, unable to hang on until the markets rose in spring. Heavy seasonal losses prevented graziers on the Wolds from making the best of good crops of roots in 1880.[36]

The poor seasons of 1879–81 rather set the tone for many years to come. The immediate crisis passed: summers dried out and harvests were within a more normal range of yields. But prices continued to fall, and the losses of 1879–81 tended to cast a gloomy shadow over succeeding years. Farmers' confidence had taken a severe beating. Throughout the 1880s farm and estate correspondence and the local press refer to each succeeding year as 'the worst yet'. Financial results of farming were mixed, as the Caistor account shows. Fourteen of the eighteen accounts collected by the Royal Commission showed a net loss over the period for which they ran. One of the smallest farms in their sample, 73 acres in the Isle of Axholme, had only one year in surplus between 1881–82 and 1892–93. The Boston Chamber of agriculture

Table 6 Accounts of a farm at Garthorpe, Isle of Axholme

Year	Income	Expenditure	Surplus	Deficit
1876	£5,016 6s 10½d	£3,541 5s 8d	£1,475 1s 2½d	
1877	£6,630 3s 0½d	£4,408 17s 7½d	£2,221 5s 5d	
1878	£4,445 4s 3d	£4,049 3s 9½d	£396 0s 5½d	
1879	£4,930 18s 0d	£3,892 19s 7d	£1,037 18s 5d	
1880	£5,137 13s 9½d	£4,124 15s 2½d	£1,012 18s 7d	
1881	n/a			
1882	£5,047 3s 4d	£4,405 9s 4d	£641 14s 0d	
1883	£4,723 11s 9½d	£3,843 9s 3¼d	£880 2s 6¼	
1884	£3,989 11s 6d	£3,756 8s 9d	£233 2s 9d	
1885	£3278 14s 11d	£2,548 2s 7d	£730 12s 4d	
1886	£1,720 2s 0d	£1,860 11s 7d		£140 9s 7d
1887	£1,783 15s 4d	£1,200 10s 4d	£583 5s 0d	
1888	£1,426 9s 11d	£1,266 15s 3d	£159 14s 8d	
1889	£1,092 17s 8d	£1,410 15s 4d		£317 17s 8d
1890	£1,279 11s 3d	£1.223 1s 8d	£56 9s 7d	
1891	£1,956 7s 3d	£1,552 13s 5½d	£403 13s 9½d	
1892	£1,173 4s 9½d	£1,311 6s 11d		£148 2s 1½d
1893	£1,509 10s 9d	£1,583 3s 10½d		£73 13s 1½d

Note: Taken from a simple income and expenditure account. The acreage of the farm is unknown, but there was evidently a change in 1885–6.
Source: LAO, 3 Dudding

reckoned that in the 1880s tenant farmers had been making about a pound an acre, but by 1895 no profits were to be had. Yet the Royal Commission was also told by one of Mr Chaplin's tenants that 'farmers in normal seasons and with industry and economy can still make a livelihood from farming'.[37] Further study of the accounts collected by the Royal Commission lends support to this, for in most years of the 1880s and 1890s it was possible to make a reasonable return, as much as 12 per cent. Other surviving accounts, such as Thomas Dudding's present an even more favourable picture. Herbert Carter of Holbeach demonstrates the advantages that could be gained from entering farming at a time of low costs, for his income and expenditure accounts show increasing surpluses throughout the 1890s: £800 in 1893, £2,000 in 1899, £5,000 in 1900. He almost certainly had much more land by the later date to reinforce the growth in income.

The accounts of the farm in Caistor Union reveal one of the means by which farmers survived. Capital was run down, in this instance by 35.3 per cent from just under £10 an acre in 1879–80 to £6 10s in 1893–94. Lord Monson's agent wrote in 1885, 'the truth is that many of the tenants … are almost at the end of their capital', and here one of the deleterious effects of the poor seasons was making itself felt. Equally, with lower prices and costs, substantial capital was less necessary. The landlords' favoured figure of £10 an acre for tenants' capital (see above p. 106) was abandoned. Edmund Turnor told the Royal Commission in the 1890s that he would be satisfied with tenants having no more than £6–£7 per acre capital.[38] A result of the decline in farm incomes and capital was that tenants were not as keen to invest their own money as they had been in the mid-19th century period of high farming. There was a tendency to push responsibility for such works as drainage back on to the landlord, while requests for new buildings and repairs to existing ones became a regular feature of dealings between landlord and tenant.[39]

If capital was not to be completely exhausted farmers had to reduce their costs, and the fall in rents played a major part in their attempts to achieve that. Lower rents represented the biggest saving in expenses for the farmer, and kept many a farmer afloat. Rents everywhere fell during this period. The index for rents for England and

Wales shows a decline of 29 per cent from the mid 1870s to the first few years of the 20th century. From a peak of 28.4s per acre in 1878 rents had fallen to 20.1s per acre by 1895, and reached a low point in 1904, when the average was 19.7s per acre.[40] The east of England, being more arable, suffered to a greater extent than the average. A broad regional analysis of rent movements shows rents for pastoral regions overtaking arable rents in the 1870s, and then falling less rapidly during the depression years.[41] F. M. L. Thompson, using Schedule A income tax assessments as a proxy for rents, calculates the decline of rent in Lincolnshire as being 2.6 percentage points greater than the average for England between 1872–73 and 1910–11.[42] Variations within Lincolnshire itself were broad. The Royal Commission on Agriculture in the 1890s presented figures collected from fifteen of the largest estates. Between 1879 and 1894 rents on these estates were reduced by amounts ranging from 20 per cent on Mr Sutton Nelthorpe's estate to 50 per cent on the Marquis of Bristol's. The average was 33 per cent. The large estates were the ones that attracted attention, but smaller estates follow the same trend. The Dixon family's estates at Searby (1,400 acres) and Holton le Moor showed reductions in the rental of 44 per cent and 39 per cent between 1879 and 1890. Rents fell by 30 per cent between 1871 and 1895 on a small marshland estate of 500 acres.[43]

There were some very large rent reductions on individual farms and estates, as landlords were sometimes driven to extreme measures to obtain or retain tenants. The newspapers carried reports of farms let at nominal rents only, or of farms let at auction not fetching half their previous rents. In 1880 Lord Monson received a report of a farm belonging to one of his neighbours being on offer for five shillings an acre for the first two years of a tenancy, after which a fair rent was to be fixed. At Norton Disney, in the clays, a farm was advertised rent free for the first year, and in the Fens in 1881 it was reported that farms were on offer to anyone prepared to pay rates and taxes. Mr Heneage wrote to his agent that 'landlords are in such a panic that they are letting at any price'.[44]

For the farmer, rent reductions were a major contribution to solvency. Rent was one of the bigger items in the farmer's budget, and was for him more of an overhead than a variable cost. About 15 per cent of expenditure was a common proportion in the 1870s, and for some farmers quite a bit more. William Frankish told the Richmond Commission that his rent on the Wolds was a quarter of his outgoings and for Frederick Scorer at Binbrook it was about 22 per cent.[45] Reductions in rent, therefore, stood to make a major difference to the farmer's ability to survive. On Mrs Dixon's Searby estate the tenant of the largest farm, of 1,000 acres, was paying £2,000 per year in 1874. His rent was reduced in stages to £1,602 in 1882, £1,400 in 1886 and £1,000 in 1888. The same process brought the rent paid on a more modest holding of 205 acres down from £335 per year in 1874 to £220 in 1888, a drop of 35 per cent compared with the larger farmer's 50 per cent.[46] Similar examples can be multiplied across the range of the county's estates. Some of the accounts collected by the Royal Commission show rent falling as a percentage of the farm's total outgoings. On a middle marsh farm of 1,200 acres, for example, rent was 17.4 per cent of expenses in 1884–85, and 13.5 per cent in 1893–94. Frederick Scorer of Bracebridge paid out 22.5 per cent of his costs in rent in 1875–76, and this fell to 18.7 per cent by 1892–93. This was not the universal experience, however, for some farms showed no change in the proportion of their expenses going to rent, while the successful Herbert Carter at Holbeach was paying out more of his expenses in rent in the 1890s than he had done ten years previously.[47]

The ways in which reductions in rent came about varied from estate to estate. Some landlords made general revaluations of their rent roll. The Earl of Yarborough made reductions of 15 per cent in 1884, 10 per cent in 1886 and 8 per cent in 1894. On the Hainton estate there was a general reduction of 12 to 15 per cent in 1881, and similar reductions were made by Sir F. Astley Corbet in 1884 and Mr Cracroft of Hackthorn in 1886.[48] Other landlords, hoping to get better terms for themselves, preferred to negotiate changes in rent with tenants individually, usually when they complained or threatened to leave. Lord Monson and Henry Chaplin were two who did this.

Farmers could receive further assistance in the form of rent remissions. The official rental value was retained, but the landlord made a 'return' on the rent when it was paid. It was a customary means by which landlords would help farmers through temporary difficulties.

This was how Lord Monson compensated two tenants in 1872 when new buildings on their farms were not completed on time.[49] Rent remissions were the almost universal response to the crisis of the wet seasons. Ten per cent on each half year's rent was common at first, but by 1879–80 remissions of 15 to 20, even 30 per cent were being offered. The landlords believed they were doing the right thing. As Robert Toynbee wrote to Lord Monson, 'believing as I do most firmly that the existing depression is due to temporary causes and that it will pass away when such causes no longer exist, I think it is much better to meet it by temporary rather than by permanent measures. To reduce and hereafter to raise rents again, produces an unsatisfactory and unsettled feeling between landlord and tenant.' There were farmers who thought the same: 'What farmers most want at the present time is temporary relief,' wrote one to the *Stamford Mercury*. Many others, however, would much sooner have seen permanent reductions of rent, which offered a greater sense of security, and could be used to claim reductions in income tax. By 1881, however, landlords were recognizing what Col. Amcotts expressed later in a circular to his tenants: 'The time is now past for making returns of rent. I will from Lady Day 1883, reduce your rents permanently.'[50]

Rent remissions that were supposed to be temporary often took on a more permanent character. There were estates where remissions granted in the late 1870s were still being paid in the 1890s. These were in addition to permanent changes to the rental. Farmers, for their part, came to expect a remission as of right. In the late 1880s when numbers of estates tried to do without remissions on the grounds that the permanent reductions in rent should by now be enough, agents could be faced with uncomfortable rent audits. Lord Monson's agent reported in January 1887, 'Every tenant, no matter how recently his rent had been adjusted, assumed that he was going to receive a liberal return and urged his claims to it on the grounds that the tenants could not pay and that landlords were generally recognising the fact.'[51]

In evidence to the Royal Commission of the 1890s, the representative of one of Lincolnshire's large institutional landowners said that reductions were generally lower on large farms. The secretary of the Ecclesiastical Commissioners contradicted him. He thought rents fell by more on large farms, and as a generalization he was the more nearly correct.[52] However, experience on individual farms varied greatly. On the Heneage estate, for example, the average reduction of rent on large farms was greater than for small farms, but the reductions on individual farms ranged from 22 to 40 per cent for small farms of up to 100 acres, and 21 to 44 per cent for farms greater than 300 acres.[53]

Such wide differences may in part be explained by the negotiating power of individual farmers, and here large farmers tended to have an advantage in that landlords might make concessions in order to avoid having very large farms in hand. As important an influence on rents was the quality of the land. Good quality land was always at a premium. The rich warp land of the Isle of Axholme could command £5 an acre in the 1870s, falling to £3 in the 1890s. Wold farms were 35s in the 1870s, 20s to 25s an acre in the 1890s.[54] Differences could be far more detailed. Land at all difficult to work was unwanted, and in particular this meant hilly land and, especially, strong clay land. A portion of strong land on a farm would push its rent down, while farms consisting completely or predominantly of strong land had the biggest reductions. In the Fens rents fell by about one-third on good soil, by half or more on heavy land. In south-west Kesteven there were instances of rents reduced by as much as 75 to 90 per cent. Further north, good turnip and barley land lost a quarter of its letting value, while strong land fell by up to two-thirds. Toynbee commented in 1883 that strong clay farms 'have scarcely any letting value at all', and Wilson Fox found some extreme examples of heavy clays being let for as little as 5 shillings per acre. One of Miss Dixon's tenants at Searby was to be allowed greater concessions because, whereas other tenants had 'Wold land to back their lowland ... Lingard's is all lowland'.[55]

The tenant could receive what was effectively credit from the landlord in the form of rent arrears, for, while tradesmen and bankers sooner or later demanded payment of their bills, the landlord could be put off almost indefinitely.[56] Rent arrears increased greatly. On Edmund Turnor's estate they were 4 per cent of the total roll in 1878 and 11 per cent in 1893. Again it was the early years that did the most damage. The Ancaster estates had one per cent of the rental in arrear in 1878, but ten per cent by 1883; and likewise on the Brocklesby estate there were £4 in arrear in 1877, £8,500 in 1881 out of a rental of £63,000. By the later date several farmers were owing more than one year's rent. Once in arrear it was difficult to pay off the debt. The Ancaster estates continued to have between 10 and 13 per cent of the rental in arrear throughout the 1880s, and on the Yarborough estates accumulated arrears amounted to about £25,000 by 1891 which the agent could only conclude 'must be taken as permanent'.[57]

Landlords gave additional support to their tenants by their expenditure on improvement and maintenance, including repair work which tenants had done previously. Lord Ancaster was in the 1890s even assisting some tenants with the cost of house painting.[58] The problem for landlords was that they were presented with increased demands from their tenants when they felt they could least afford to meet them. At first, although the Dixon estate agent informed one disputative tenant that it was not 'a landlord's duty to remunerate for bad seasons', landlords were willing to spend capital to meet what were regarded as temporary difficulties, especially if rents could thereby be maintained.[59] On several estates expenditure on improvements increased in the early 1880s. Lord Yarborough's expenditure at Brocklesby of £2,075 in 1879 rapidly increased to a maximum of £6,270 in 1883. In particular there was a strong demand for draining after the wet seasons and the flooding up to 1883, and landlords had to spend greater sums on both draining tiles and labour. On Lord Yarborough's estate, again, £436 was spent on draining tiles in the two years 1878–79, which rose to £1,469 in the two years 1883–84. The amount spent on labour for draining on the Heneage estate, £20 in 1879, was £285 in 1881, and remained between £160 and £180 for much of the 1880s.[60] The 1880s were also a decade of high borrowing from the land improvement companies for drainage work. The total sums spent on estates could be very large. Between 1872 and 1893 the Earl of Ancaster had spent £689,197 on all his estates.[61]

As it began to appear that depression was more permanent landowners grew more concerned about their expenditure. Robert Toynbee wrote to Lord Monson in 1884 that 'the demand for expenditure on the estate … grows daily while the means of meeting it diminishes'. There was no avoiding at least some of the demands, especially if new tenants were to be attracted to take up vacant farms, and existing tenants dissuaded from giving notice. Advertisements of farms to let would often stress the amount which the landlord had laid out on the farm, usually on drainage, and tenancy agreements had endorsements detailing improvements that the landlord agreed to make.[62]

The need for this type of expenditure probably kept landowners' outlay on their estates higher than might have been otherwise, especially in the early 1880s. From about 1884 most landlords were attempting to restrict their estate expenditure, for, as one agent put it in a reply to a tenant's request, 'in these times I do not feel justified in spending so much money at one time'.[63] He therefore proposed to carry out the improvements the tenant asked for in instalments. By means such as this most landlords reduced the total amounts they spent on improvements and repairs. On Lord Brownlow's estate expenditure on improvements and repairs rose from £3,837 in 1877 to reach £5,905 in 1883, but by 1893 the sum had been reduced to £2,740. Although the amount spent on improvements and repairs was reduced, the reduction in rental income could mean that as a proportion of gross rent more was being spent in this way. Lord Yarborough was spending 10.6 per cent of gross rent on improvement and repairs in 1880, but by 1890 this proportion had increased to 14.7 per cent. On the Ancaster estates, although the proportion of rental income spent on the estate was reduced from its peak of 1883, it was in the 1890s still higher than it had been in the early 1870s.[64]

Tenant farmers were relying heavily on their landlords for support, mainly through lower rents, but the other contributions were not insignificant. After rent, the labour bill was the next thing on which farmers had to concentrate. This was one of the largest items of farm expenditure, and farmers had already grown anxious about it long before 1879. Complaints that labour was too expensive were common in the late 1860s and early 1870s as wage rates rose.[65] About 25s per acre was a common amount paid for labour in the 1870s, though on heavily worked arable land, especially in the Fens, this figure could be as much as 35s or 40s.[66] Although there could be great variation from farm to farm, labour tended to take a smaller proportion of total costs on larger farms. On Frederick Scorer's farm of about 400 acres at Bracebridge labour was 16 per cent of expenditure in 1875–76, whereas on a 260-acre middle marsh farm it was 32 per cent in 1879. On the farm of 73 acres in the Isle of Axholme as much as 45 per cent of expenditure went on labour in 1881–82.[67]

When the second half of the 1870s brought falling prices and poor seasons farmers quickly sought to reduce wages. By 1880 the rate for day labourers had lost the 3d to 6d a day which had been gained between 1872 and 1874. At the statute fairs yearly men were being hired for about £3 a year less than in previous years. The Spalding farmer who was paying 18s 6d a week to his labourers in 1874 had reduced this to 15s 6d by 1879.[68] Farmers justified the reductions in wages by arguing that the burden of hard times should be shared by all; therefore, it was proper for wages to revert to their earlier rates. The unions, which had run out of steam after the hard-fought strikes and lock-outs of 1874, were much depleted in strength and could only acquiesce in the downward movement of wages.[69] Most farmers pursued the cause of lowered wages with vigour throughout the 1880s. Some were unhappy at this and argued that to reduce wages was a false economy, which saved the farmer only a small amount, at the cost of 'further impoverishing his already too poor work men'.[70] The trend was inexorable, however. Farmers would insist on reducing wages each winter. Thus from Sleaford the *Stamford Mercury* reported in 1891 that 'farmers in some of the villages in this district feel it their duty to lower the labourers' wage to 2s a day'. Average weekly wages remained 13s 6d to 15s into the 1890s. From about 1895 they began to rise again and by 1900 were 16s 6d to 18s a week.[71]

As well as cutting wages farmers economized in their use of labour. Again, the period of labour shortages and union agitation in the early 1870s had already acted as a stimulus to economy, for many farmers decided that they should meet higher wages by employing fewer men. One correspondent of the *Stamford Mercury* claimed that farmers were growing less of the labour-intensive crops, such as potatoes, in reaction to the pressures put upon them for higher wages; and it seems that not all of this assertion can be discounted as a war of words against the unions.[72] However, the changes in the second half of the 1870s had greater effect on the demand for labour. Gone were the complaints that labourers were hard to come by. In their place came reports of labourers being out of work. At first such unemployment was confined to the winter months, but by May 1879 there were still fifty unemployed labourers in Crowland, for whom, it was said, the 'prospect is dark indeed', and thenceforward it seems there was no guarantee of full employment even in summer.[73] In the mid 1880s there was such a good supply of labour for harvest in the Fens that the seasonal piece-work wages were reduced, while further north at Kirton Lindsey there were even said to be men out of work during the harvests of 1885 and 1886.[74]

One way to save on labour was to make employment more casual by being quicker to pay off men at seasons and on days when work was slack. In November 1884 farmers at Horncastle were reported to have got the autumn's work done quickly because of favourable weather, which enabled them to effect savings by dismissing their labourers. The following year heavy rains prolonged the autumn sowing, but this time many labourers were being laid off on bad days, thus only having two or three days' work a week.[75] Harsh winter weather also caused farmers to

Fig. 20 The Laceby sheep-shearing gang at the Mount, Keelby, c. 1900
Source: North East Lincolnshire Libraries

dispense with their labourers' services for a while, as for instance in January 1894, when at Crowland 'the recent severe frost threw a great many agricultural labourers out of employment'.[76] The Royal Commission on Labour in 1893 concluded of the Louth area that distress among agricultural labourers was mainly the result of there being too many men with intermittent work. But irregularity of employment was a somewhat patchy feature, varying widely from area to area. The same Royal Commission also found that there was more winter unemployment in the Marsh, where there were many small arable farms, than on the Wolds, where there was a more constant demand for work with livestock. In the Fens at the same time demand for labour was such that farmers would not risk paying men off for a day for fear of losing them permanently.[77]

Labour could also be saved by cutting back on such tasks as weeding, hedging, and ditching. Farmers quite commonly sought economies in this way, especially when such work was done at piece rates, but the effect was limited and landlords were also on guard lest the land should be impoverished.[78] The introduction of barbed wire for fencing, which became quite common in the late 1880s, much to the annoyance of huntsmen, had some labour-saving benefits.[79] The cultivation of grass, whether as permanent pasture or seeds in rotation, required less labour than arable, so an increased acreage of grass helped keep the wages bill down.[80]

Then there were machines. Joseph Arch told the Richmond Commission that farmers could not expect greatly to reduce their labour bills by using more machines.[81] But this was precisely what farmers aimed to do. As the Caistor correspondent of the *Stamford Mercury* observed in 1872, 'Farmers are awake to the necessity of procuring every mechanical means and appliance that can economize labour.'[82] The labour troubles of the early 1870s encouraged such wakefulness. 'An Old Farmer' writing to the *Stamford Mercury* commented that because manual labour had become unreliable farmers 'have supplied themselves with reaping-machines in abundance. I scarcely know an intelligent farmer who farms to any extent who does not possess one, and large farmers provide themselves with several. We have also capital sheaf elevators to aid in stacking.'[83]

The use of machinery was a most effective means of economy. Thomas Aitken, of Spalding, calculated that reaping corn by machine cost 7s per acre compared with 16s per acre when it was cut by hand.[84] Many savings could come from a reduction in demand for seasonal labour, especially at harvest. In Kesteven it was reckoned that the use of the self-binder meant 50 per cent fewer men were required at harvest. G. E. Collins went further, claiming that there was only enough work for one Irish harvestman where six had been employed before the binder. However, the decline in casual labour was not as great in Lincolnshire as in many other areas, for there were various contrary forces. In the Fens, especially, the number of small farms, and the adoption of labour-intensive crops, such as potatoes, meant that the migrant Irish harvestmen were still common in the 1930s.[85]

After all the effort to cut down on labour, the effect on the farmers' accounts could be limited. In some ways it appears as though they had been merely treading water, for as a proportion of total costs that for labour remained the same or even a little larger. William Scorer on his farm at Burwell was paying about the same amount for labour in

Fig. 21 Harvesting with a self-binder, not needing so many workers as the reaper. Near Alford, early 20th century
Source: North East Lincolnshire Libraries

the 1890s as he had been doing in the 1870s. On another farm near Lincoln 20 per cent of gross expenses went on labour in 1883–84 and 25 per cent in 1893–94, while, over a longer span of time, Frederick Scorer at Bracebridge had 16 per cent of his expenditure accounted for by labour in 1875–76 and 20 per cent in 1892–93. In most other accounts labour remained roughly constant as a proportion of total expenditure.[86] Expenditure on labour was, therefore, reduced by no more than the reduction in total expenditure, and quite often by less. The Royal Commission on Agriculture in 1897 concluded that 'the farmer has not been able in the matter of labour to adjust his expenditure to his diminished receipts'.[87]

This meant that the labour bill commonly fell by very little, no more than 10 per cent, while on some farms it increased by a similar amount. Wilson Fox found one where expenditure on labour was 13 per cent higher in 1890–94 than it had been in 1886–89, and a farmer on the Heath told the Commission that his wages bill was rising despite the fall in the rate of pay.[88] In the later 1890s labour costs again began to rise as pay was increased and demand for labour increased. In the Fens at the turn of the century farmers complained that labour costs had gone up to 40s per acre. Before then, however, many farmers had managed to curb their expenditure. Fenland labour costs were commonly 35s to 40s an acre in the 1870s, but they were down to 30s in 1894 according to the Boston Chamber of Agriculture.[89] A farmer of 73 acres in the Isle of Axholme succeeded in cutting his labour bill by 18 per cent between the years 1881–82 to 1885–86 and the period 1888–89 to 1892–93, while on a 619-acre Wolds farm the cost per acre for the five years 1874–78 was £1 3s 9d, which was reduced to £1 0s 8d for the years 1889-93. Most of this reduction came at the end of the 1870s, a change perhaps concealed by the other evidence, which is concentrated on years after 1880. The Richmond Commission was given the amount paid for labour on two Wolds farms in the 1870s, which show increases over ten years of 20 and 31 per cent. To have halted such increases is probably the true measure of the farmers' attempts to economize.[90]

Farmers were clearly having a difficult time at the end of the 19th century and the agricultural order as a whole had received a severe shock. The falling prices and the effects on profitability were enough to justify this being called a depression. Farmers needed support from their landlords; they economized on labour. They turned to political campaigning to have what they called the 'burden on the land' lifted, by which they meant local rates and taxes. They met with considerable success, for several poor law unions reduced their rating assessments and their valuations for rates as measures to help farmers. More substantial help came with the passing of the Agricultural Rating Act, 1896, which gave 50 per cent rating relief to agricultural land. All of these were vital elements for the survival of many farmers, but with cereal prices having fallen so much those in arable Lincolnshire could not avoid considering what they produced, and how. Did this mean they were going to have to abandon high farming? This is the issue for the next chapter.

Notes to Chapter 7

1   RC1879, First Report of S. B. L. Druce, p. 371.
2   RC1893, Wilson Fox, p. 35.
3   M. E. Turner, 'Output and Prices in UK Agriculture 1867–1914', *AgHR*, v. 40, (1992) pp. 38–51. F. M. L. Thompson, 'An Anatomy of English Agriculture 1870–1914', in *Land Labour and Agriculture 1700–1920*, ed. B. A. Holderness and M. E. Turner (1991) pp. 227–37.
4   Thompson, 'An Anatomy of English Agriculture 1870–1914', pp. 232–3.
5   J. C. Morton, 'The Past Agricultural Year', *JRASE*, v. 41 (1880) p. 215. *SM*, 13 June, 22 August 1879. LAO, Scorer Farm 2/1.
6   RC1879, First Report of S. B. L. Druce, pp. 373–4.
7   *SM*, 17 October 1879.
8   RC1879, First Report of S. B. L. Druce, pp. 373–5.
9   G. J. Symons, 'Recent British Weather', *JRASE*, v. 44 (1883) p. 420. *SM* 18 June–6 August, 3 December 1880.
10   *Agricultural Gazette*, 16, 23, 30 August 1880.
11   RC1879, QQ. 6873, 7060.
12   C. S. Orwin and E. H. Whetham, *History of British Agriculture 1846–1914* (1964), p. 244.
13   *SM*, 11 September 1874.
14   Address given 22 January 1880, reported in *SM*, 30 January 1880.
15   *SM*, 9 May 1879. RC1879, First Report of S. B. L. Druce, p. 372.
16   LAO, MON 25/13/18, 6 July 1879.

17   *SM*, 21 November 1884.
18   LAO, MON 25/13/18, 26 December 1887, 20 May 1888, for example.
19   *Retford News*, 26 June 1880.
20   W. T. Layton and G. Crowther, *An Introduction to the Study of Prices* (3rd edn, 1938) p. 88. B. R. Mitchell and P. Deane, *Abstract of British Historical Statistics* (1962) p. 489.
21   RC1893, Wilson Fox, p. 114.
22   *SM*, 4 April 1884.
23   Layton and Crowther, *An Introduction to the Study of Prices*, p. 88. Mitchell and Deane, *Abstract of British Historical Statistics*, p. 489. Orwin and Whetham, *History of British Agriculture 1846–1914*, p. 242.
24   See *London Gazette*, October–December 1884, for example.
25   *SM*, 4 February 1881.
26   *The Economist*, 5 July 1879.
27   *SM*, 28 July 1882.
28   RC1879, QQ 49180–1a; his sentiments were those of the convinced protectionist.
29   LAO, Misc Don157.
30   Mitchell and Deane, *Abstract of British Historical Statistics*, p. 496.
31   Thomas Brassey, 'Agriculture in England and the United States', *JRSS*, vol. 42 (1879) p. 763. RC1879, QQ. 56394–8. *Agricultural Gazette*, 22 March 1880.
32   Agricultural Returns, 1888–1896.
33   RC1893, Wilson Fox, p. 138.
34   *SM*, 22 March 1872. *Agricultural Gazette*, 9 March 1885, 23 January 1893.
35   RC1893, Wilson Fox, p. 125; Hunter Pringle, pp. 25–8.
36   RC1879, QQ. 49265, 49281–3. *Agricultural Gazette*, 4 October 1880. *SM*, 28 October 1881, 10 November 1883, 19 January 1883.
37   W. H. Wheeler, *History of the Fens of South Lincolnshire* (1896). RC1893, Wilson Fox, pp. 59–61.
38   LAO, MON 25/13/18, 20, 27 December 1885. RC1893, Wilson Fox, p. 125; Q. 14580.
39   Most estate archives contain record of this. For example, the Heneage estate memoranda books, LAO, 2HEN 2/1, 2, 4, 5.
40   M. E. Turner, J. Beckett and B. Afton, *Agricultural Rent in England 1690–1914* (1997) pp. 250–1, 312–13.
41   *Ibid*, pp. 191–8.
42   Thompson, 'An Anatomy of English Agriculture 1870–1914', pp. 223–8.
43   LAO, DIXON 22/7/1, 22/7/7; Misc Don 157.

44   LAO, MON 25/13/18, Toynbee to Monson 15 February 1880; 2HEN
      5/13/96 Heneage to Wintringham, 3 December 1886. *SM,* 3 October
      1879, 1 April, 13 May 1881, 10 March 1882.
45   RC1893, Wilson Fox, pp. 117ff. RC1879, QQ. 49404–5. LAO, Scorer
      Farm 2.
46   LAO, DIXON 6/1/12/1, 3, 22/7/1/5.
47   RC1893, Wilson Fox, pp. 117, 118, 120, 121. LAO, Scorer Farm 2;
      HD65/64.
48   RC1893, Wilson Fox, pp. 128–9. LAO, YARB5, 2 HEN 5/8/63, 71. *SM,*
      24 December 1886.
49   LAO, MON 25/13/18, 19 December 1872.
50   LAO, MON 25/13/18, 29 September 1879. *SM,* 22 November 1878, 23
      March 1883.
51   LAO, MON 25/13/18, 2 January 1887.
52   RC1893, QQ 478, 1695–8 (Guy's Hospital Estate).
53   LAO, 2 HEN 2/1/4.
54   H. Rider Haggard, *Rural England* (1902) vol. 2, pp. 167, 186.
55   LAO, MON25/13/18, 18 November 1883. RC1893, Wilson Fox, pp. 20,
      47–8. G. E. Collins, 'Agriculture', *VCH Lincolnshire,* v. 2 (1906) p. 405. W.
      H. Wheeler, *History of the Fens of South Lincolnshire* (1896) pp. 418–19. LAO,
      DIXON 6/5/1, 11 September 1879.
56   LAO, BS 13/1/13/75, 20 December 1884, where one of Henry Chaplin's
      tenants is explicit on this.
57   LAO, YARB5, summaries of accounts. RC1893, Wilson Fox, p. 130;
      Minutes of Evidence, QQ. 14532–6.
58   RC1893, Wilson Fox, pp. 13ff. LAO, Misc. Don. 157; 9ANC 2/C/1/11.
59   LAO, DIXON 6/5/1, 28 April, 4 December 1879; MON 25/13/18, 26
      December 1879.
60   RC1893, Wilson Fox, p.128. LAO, YARB5, Summary of Accounts;
      2HEN 2/1/67; MON 25/13/18, 18 November 1883.
61   RC1893, Final Report, p. 27.
62   *SM,* 21, 28 January, 11 February, 4 March 1881. LAO, 9 ANC 2/1/1.
63   LAO, 2 NEL 5/1, 12 February 1885.
64   RC1893, Wilson Fox, pp. 53–5, 128–30. LAO, YARB 5, Summary of
      Accounts. F. M. L. Thompson, *English Landed Society in the Nineteenth
      Century* (1963).
65   *SM,* 1 March 1872, 30 May, 6 June 1873.
66   RC1893, Wilson Fox, Appendices A1 and A6. *Agricultural Gazette,* 19
      October 1885. Wheeler, *History of the Fens of South Lincolnshire,* pp. 416–17.
67   LAO, Scorer Farm 2. RC1893, Wilson Fox, p. 120; Hunter Pringle, p. 25.

68   RC1879, QQ. 33211–2, 49246–9. *SM*, 7, 21 May 1880. *Agricultural Gazette*, 19 October 1885.

69   Rex Russell, *The 'Revolt of the Field' in Lincolnshire* (1956) pp. 112–19. J. P. D. Dunbabin, 'The "Revolt of the Field": the agricultural labourers' movement in the 1870s', *Past and Present*, v. 26 (1963) pp. 69, 90–3. W. Hasbach, *A History of the English Agricultural Labourer* (1908) pp. 277ff. Joseph Arch actually advised the labourers in his union to accept reductions of wages, because he thought the farmers' plight to be severe. RC1879, QQ. 58562, 60506.

70   *SM*, 22, 29 November, 27 December 1878.

71   Rider Haggard, *Rural England*, v. 2, pp. 148, 161, 169, 228–9, *Tariff Commission*, paras. 552, 566, 815, 857. A. Wilson Fox, 'Agricultural Wages in England and Wales during the last half century', *JRSS*, v. 66 (1903), reprinted in W. E. Minchinton (ed.), *Essays in Agrarian History* (1968) v. 2, pp. 129–32, 184, 190–1. *SM*, 9 January 1891. RC1893, Wilson Fox, p. 139.

72   *SM*, 22 March 1872. There were in fact 5000 fewer acres of potatoes sown in 1873 and 1874 than there had been in 1872.

73   *SM*, 16 May 1879.

74   *SM*, 31 August 1883, 22 August 1884, 28 August, 3 September 1885, 20 August 1886.

75   *SM*, 21 November 1884, 6 November 1885 (Alford notes).

76   *SM*, 18 January 1894.

77   *Royal Commission on Labour, The Agricultural Labourer, vol. i, part vi, Report on Lincolnshire*, by Edward Wilkinson, C6894 (1893) pp. 42, 107.

78   *Report on the Decline of the Agricultural Population 1881–1906*, Cd. 3273 (1906) pp. 33–4.

79   See *SM*, 25 October 1889, letters appealing to farmers to remove barbed wire during the hunting season from E. P. Rawnsley and Lord Yarborough. LAO, 2NEL 5/1, February 1885.

80   RC 1893, QQ. 36298–9, 36304–5.

81   RC 1879, Q. 60270.

82   *SM*, 9 August 1872.

83   *SM*, 1 August 1873. Also *SM*, 10 July, 14 August 1874, reports of well-timed purchases of reapers enabling farmers to carry on harvest despite striking labourers.

84   *Agricultural Gazette*, 14 September 1885.

85   *Report on the Decline of the Agricultural Population of Great Britain 1881–1906*, pp. 8–9, 88. G. Smith, *The Land of Britain, part 69, the Fens* (Land Utilisation Survey, 1937) p. 39. Collins, 'Agriculture', p. 405.

86   RC1893, Wilson Fox, pp. 90–1, 117, 118, 120 121. LAO, Scorer Farm 1/20, and 2/1ff.

87   RC 1893, Final Report, p. 88. See also F. M. L. Thompson, 'Agriculture since 1870', *VCH Wiltshire*, v. 4 (1959) p. 114.

88   RC1893, Wilson Fox, pp. 84ff, Minutes of Evidence, QQ. 36326–9.

89   W. H. Wheeler, *History of the Fens of South Lincolnshire* (1896), pp. 416–17. *Agricultural Gazette*, 19 October 1885. *Tariff Commission*, para. 815.

90   RC1893, Hunter Pringle, pp. 25–8; Wilson Fox, p. 139. RC1879, Appendix to Minutes of Evidence, p. 113, and see QQ. 6879–86.

8

WHAT BECAME OF HIGH FARMING?

By the 1870s many farmers were 'farming high'. They had invested in the new techniques of intensive mixed farming that were seen in Chapter 6. The market conditions seemed to encourage them. Prices for cereals during the middle decades of the 19th century, if not rising strongly, were certainly not falling. The market for meat was showing growth over the medium term. Falling prices for agricultural produce in the final quarter of the century represented the first major challenge to the equilibrium of this type of farming. With cereals and wool taking the greatest falls in price this was bound to put pressure on farming systems centred upon arable. The question that springs to mind, then, is whether the high farming upon which the farmers of Lincolnshire had built their reputations was able to adapt and survive into the 20th century, or whether farmers decided to retrench. To answer that it is necessary first to see how the crops grown and the stock kept changed during these years, the record of which can be observed in the annual agricultural statistics.

Corn farming under pressure

The coincidence of the markedly lower prices for cereals with the run of poor seasons effectively delayed their impact on farming systems. Encouraged to believe that a return to average seasons would restore equilibrium, many farmers tended to assume that they should hold tight and weather the storm rather than make any changes to the balance of their husbandry. The misfortune for many farmers in Lincolnshire and other predominantly arable regions was that by the time the average seasons reappeared their capital reserves were too low. If the extent to which cereal-growing was under pressure was for the moment disguised by wet seasons, nevertheless, pressure there was, and as the years passed it became clearer. The evidence of the different rates of change in prices was there. Cereals, especially wheat, and wool were decreasingly profitable compared to livestock products. It was not simply that prices were falling. Costs of production for cereals seem to have been stubbornly unchanging, despite reductions in rent and other costs. Both Royal Commissions collected sample figures for the costs of growing wheat and barley, and there was almost no difference between them, as shown in Table 7.

There were some immediate, short-term reactions prompted by the poor seasons in the late 1870s. Most marked was an increase in bare fallow as farmers left land to recover from the excessively wet seasons, reaching 3¼ per cent of the total acreage in the first years of the 1880s compared with the usual 1½ to 2 per cent. On heavy clay soils this change could be much greater. At Claypole, in the western vale, fallow was 7 to 8 per cent in the 1870s, but reached more than 15 per cent in 1881.[1] Even here the bad years brought but a relatively short-lived increase. After 1885 bare fallow almost everywhere had returned to a more normal extent.

The agricultural returns show some evidence that the poor seasons had some effect on the sowings of cereals, but this was slight, and very local in extent. The longer-term fall in prices persuaded farmers to grow less corn. Change was cumulative rather than rushed, and relatively modest. The acreage of corn crops in Lincolnshire declined by 11 per cent between 1875 and 1900, from 631,000 acres to 562,000 acres, compared with a decline of 24 per cent for England and Wales. Other eastern counties had greater reductions than Lincolnshire: 15 per cent in Cambridgeshire, 29 per cent in Essex, for example. It was still common in many parts of Lincolnshire in the 1890s to have corn crops growing on about half the arable acreage.

Commentators on agriculture complained that the farmers of Lincolnshire were clinging to an established practice. In 1880, a writer in the *Retford News,* arguing that farmers should turn to meat, thought that farmers apparently preferred the 'less profitable, though more professional pursuit of corn-growing'.[2] Another writer from East Lincolnshire claimed, 'It is on his wheat crop, though partly perhaps

Table 7 The cost of growing wheat and barley on the Wold and Fen

	Wheat		Barley	
(a) 1879–80	*Wold*	*Fen*	*Wold*	*Fen*
Rent & tithe	£1 16s 0d	£2 0s 0d	£1 16s 0d	£2 0s 0d
Rates & taxes	5s 0d	5s 6d	5s 0d	5s 6d
Seed	18s 0d	12s 6d	18s 0d	10s 0d
Manure	£2 0s 0d	£1 0s 0d		£1 0s 0d
Cultivation	£1 5s 0d	£1 7s 6d	£2 0s 0d	£1 7s 6d
Labour	10s 0d	12s 6d	10s 0d	12s 6d
Sundries	8s 0d	5s 0d		5s 0d
Total	£7 2s 0d	£6 3s 3d	£5 9s 3d	£6 0s 6d
(b) 1893–4				
Rent	18s 8d	£1 6s 0d	18s 8d	£1 6s 0d
Seed	8s 9½d	10s 0d	10s 6d	10s 0d
Cultivation	£1 14s 10d	14s 6d	£1 5s 2d	14s 6d
Reaping, threshing, delivery	£1 2s 11d	£1 3s 0d	£1 4s 5d	£1 3s 0d
Weeding	1s 0d	5s 0d	1s 0d	5s 0d
Rates & taxes	3s 5½d	7s 0d	3s 5½d	7s 0d
Manure	£1 5s 0d	10s 0d		10s 0d
Cake	12s 0d	10s 0d	16s 0d	10s 0d
Interest & depreciation		15s 0d		15s 0d
Sundries	12s 0d		12s 0d	
Total	£7 0s 10d	£6 0s 6d	£5 11s 2½d	£6 0s 6d

Sources: RC1879, Second Report of S. B. L. Druce, pp. 57–9; RC1893, Wilson Fox, pp. 142–3

from old tradition, that the farmer bases his chiefest expectations.'[3] Farmers themselves could assist in spreading such perceptions: 'A Great Sufferer' declared in 1894 that wheat was 'the chief product of the land, and the most important to the community at large'.[4]

Cereal growing was far from unchanging, however. The acreage of wheat fell by more than 50 per cent (52.8 per cent from 1875 to 1895). There were times during the 1880s when the rate of decline slowed, but by the 1890s the price differentials between the grains had so narrowed that farmers took another look at the place of wheat. Sowings fell sharply. Nearly half the fall in the acreage of wheat occurred in the four years from 1892 to 1895. As a result, whereas in 1875 it was quite common for 20 per cent of the agricultural land in a parish to be growing wheat, by 1900 this was a feature only of the Fens, with Billinghay the solitary parish returning more than a quarter of its land under wheat.

In his evidence to the Richmond Commission J. B. Lawes said he expected the acreage of wheat to contract, but that of barley and oats to increase.[5] That is precisely what happened in Lincolnshire. While wheat declined, between 1875 and 1895 there was an increase of 15.9 per cent in the acreage under barley, and a 24.2 per cent rise in the cultivation of oats. Clearly, farmers were trying to maintain the basic structure of their systems, and by substituting barley or oats for wheat they were able to achieve this in fair measure. Over much of the northern Wolds, the Cliff, Heath, Kesteven plateau, and some parts of the clay vales substitution of one grain for the other was so complete that the combined acreage of the three principal cereals was little changed in the 1890s compared with the 1870s. In the Fens, Marsh, and southern Wolds the combined acreage had fallen by up to a third.

Wheat's paramountcy among the cereals had been dislodged. Farmers now sought justifications for growing it beyond its value as a cash crop. It was not that wheat was no longer an important cash crop. For Frederick Scorer at Bracebridge sales of wheat still yielded 21.9 per cent of his total receipts in 1892-93, compared with 19.2 per cent in 1880-81. A farm on the middle Marsh records wheat as 25 per cent of receipts in 1879 and 22 per cent in 1892.[6] By the 1890s, however, farmers were beginning to free themselves from a dependency on wheat. One who farmed 800 acres at Folkingham, in his contribution to the Tariff Commission at the turn of the century, said that, whereas wheat had once been his main crop, its pre-eminence had been abandoned in favour of growing anything that would pay.[7] A similar freedom is apparent in the accounts of Herbert Carter of Holbeach. In 1892 sales of wheat earned him £1,192, 34 per cent of total receipts, whereas in 1895 only £60 came from wheat. The following year wheat accounted for 10 per cent of receipts.[8]

Among other reasons farmers gave for adhering to wheat, one was that it formed an essential part of the rotation in order to maintain the quality of the soil, especially where there was strong soil. It was said that on clays the only alternative to wheat was to grass down, and certainly in many parishes in the clay vales the acreage of wheat declined relatively little.[9] The value of the straw was the second main reason for continuing to grow wheat. With the price of the grain at an unprofitable 30s a quarter, 'if it were not for the usefulness of the straw on the farm very little would be sown', wrote one farmer to the _Stamford Mercury_. Straw remained so essential for thatching and bedding that in 1894 'we have not quite given up growing wheat despite the low prices'.[10] The straw could sometimes be a useful source of income, with prices at about £1 per ton, rising to £2 10s to £4 in a dry year such as 1893. In that year many farmers in the Fens were said to have profited by selling straw. Not everyone could do that, for the landlord's permission was usually required to sell straw off the farm, and it was not lightly granted. However, by the 1890s some farm agreements were being endorsed with permission to sell straw and hay. As well as using straw on the farm, the grain might be used as animal feed. This, however, was less a reason for continuing to grow wheat than a case of making the most of a bad job, and substituting loss-making wheat for purchased cattle feed.[11]

With the decline of wheat in the 1890s, barley became the main arable crop of Lincolnshire and remained so down to 1914. This was against the national trend: there was a fall of 23.8 per cent in the acreage of barley in England and Wales between 1875 and 1900. Nor was an increased cultivation of barley the universal experience in the eastern corn-growing counties. In Essex, for example, the great extent of heavy clays made such a change difficult, and the acreage of barley fell by more than a quarter.

It was on the light uplands of the Wolds and the Heath, where grain of best quality could be grown, that big increases in the acreage of barley were to be found. In the 1870s barley was already more important than wheat in parts of the Wolds, and this trend continued. By the 1890s barley was 'acknowledged to be the best-paying crop' for the light-land farmers.[12] It had become dominant in the northern Wolds: 'it is very noticeable that barley is becoming more and more the favourite corn product with North Wold farmers. Wheat and oats together only about equal the quantity of barley grown.'[13] It was the good fortune of the farmers of the Wolds and Heath that they were able to grow barley of the highest malting quality. While the major brewers were going abroad for barley of middling quality, to the detriment of farmers in many parts of England, the barley of Lincolnshire, Norfolk, and Suffolk remained highly prized and of high price. Farmers on the light lands had a very healthy trade supplying barley to the brewers of Burton and the major firms of maltsters. One farming family with about 2,500 acres was sending 2,000 quarters of barley a week to the major brewers during the autumn and winter delivery period.[14] Trade with such large-scale and discriminating customers had its ups and downs, but over all it proved very worth while for farmers in these areas. Even in some of the clay vales, especially where soils were of mixed composition, and in the Fens there were increased sowings of barley, mainly in the years of lowest wheat prices, although it was acknowledged to be a 'risky crop'.[15]

Oats generally produced better results on rich and strong soils. They were more versatile as a feed crop, so where prime malting barley could not be grown, oats were often preferred. Farmers in the clay vales, in the Fens, and in the mixed-soil parishes of the southern and central Wolds turned to oats rather than barley as a replacement for wheat. In the Isle of Axholme oats were preferred to the extent that they were substituted for both wheat and barley. In price, oats were 'probably as remunerative as any crop', and there was little to choose between oats and barley.[16]

The patterns of cropping were changing, but Lincolnshire remained primarily an arable county. To the outsider this could seem perverse. A landowner resident in the south of England, dismayed at his tenant's lack of enthusiasm for converting land to pasture, wrote in a letter that a nation-wide increase of two million acres of pasture between 1874 and 1884 'seems to prove to me that the consensus of farming authorities is in favour of a great decrease of arable and an increase of pasture, and what is considered good policy by so widely extended a body of experienced men is worthy of serious consideration'. But, he added, 'I do not know what amount has been laid down in Lincolnshire.'[17]

The expansion of livestock farming?

'The breeding, rearing and fattening of farm stock ... must be the chief business of farmers of the future' a reporter from south Lincolnshire wrote in the *Mark Lane Express* in 1877. A year earlier, Edmund Turnor, addressing a ploughing meeting, suggested that farms should become more and more 'beef and mutton factories' as a means of combating foreign competition.[18] His words were not falling entirely on deaf ears, for already farmers were realizing the increasing value of livestock farming. Although they had been noted as being unenthusiastic about cattle, Lincolnshire farmers were keeping more. Numbers of cattle continued to grow throughout the period of the Great Depression. The increase in the totals recorded at the June census between 1875 and 1900 was 23 per cent for Lincolnshire; for England and Wales the increase was 15 per cent. Even so, the density of stocking for cattle in Lincolnshire remained below the national average, and the county's farmers continued to need some persuasion that cattle were worth the trouble, especially when beef prices started to fall as well as those for wheat. In 1892 a farmer complained in a letter to the *Stamford Mercury* that, 'Hitherto we have looked to our stock to pull us through – now that source of hope is at zero'. In 1894 a writer from Spalding wondered which was worse, 'growing wheat at 25s per quarter or making beef and mutton for 6d per lb'.[19]

Despite the doubts, and the difficulties in financing any expansion of livestock farming, farmers were taking their stock more seriously. 'It is quite certain that a farmer of arable land cannot make it pay without stock,' a correspondent from Grantham wrote in 1886.[20] The greatest change was in the place of cattle within mixed farming. As grain prices fell, farmers were cutting down on the expenses of growing corn, and this could include a reduced application of manure. This was happening even on the Wolds, where William Frankish said he was applying four or five hundredweight of manure to the acre instead of the eight or more of earlier years.[21] The role of livestock as suppliers of manure for the wheat fields was being reduced. Instead, cattle came to be valued for their own sake. When grain prices reached their lowest in the 1890s, the roles were even reversed. Wheat in these years was grown as much for the straw and fodder as for the sale value of the grain. One of the accounts collected by Wilson Fox for the Royal Commission, from a farm of 320 acres in Lincoln Union, shows how the importance of cattle in mixed farming was growing, as the proportion of income from cattle increased from 19.5 to 24.2 per cent of total receipts between 1885-86 and 1893-94. Similarly, Herbert Carter at Holbeach gained 9.4 per cent of his income from cattle in 1887. By 1900 cattle provided 20.8 per cent of his income.[22]

Pasture could play an important part in the expansion of cattle farming. There were 110,000 acres more pasture in Lincolnshire in 1900 than in 1875, an increase of 19 per cent. That was, however, rather less than the 25 per cent increase for the country as a whole. Most of the new pasture in Lincolnshire was in the form of permanent pasture rather than grasses in rotation. The additional acres came through a slow and piecemeal process. Rarely did farmer or landlord undertake large-scale conversion to pasture. Instead one or two fields were laid down to grass as need arose. When they wanted to expand their cattle farming some farmers in Rippingale petitioned Lord Aveland in 1879 for more pasture for grazing and mowing.[23] Elsewhere, grassing down was a means of dealing with land that was difficult to work, such as fields of clay liable to flood, or hilly lands. Parishes in the southern Wolds, where land is steeply undulating, showed a greater increase in pasture than the rest of the Wolds. Changes in the acreage of pasture were relatively slight in the clay vales, where many parishes already had more than 45 per cent of their acreage under permanent pasture in the

1870s. For quite opposite reasons, the rich-soiled districts of the Fens and Isle of Axholme helped keep the county average for arable high. A benefit for the landlord was that grass on mixed farms could usually command a higher rent. On a wold farm at Tathwell in 1878 the grass land was valued at 38s to 50s per acre, arable at 30s to 42s; and a farm four miles from Market Rasen was on offer in 1899 at 25s per acre for the arable, 32s for the grass.[24] The relative amounts of grass available accounted for much of the difference here, for in parts of the county where grassland was more plentiful there was not quite the same differential.

Expansion of livestock husbandry was not dependent on additional pasture. The practice of intensive feeding continued apparently with little change. Numbers of cattle increased at a rate faster than the increase in the acreage of grass. An enquirer after a farm in Lincoln Clay Vale in 1889 was advised not to expect the grass land to feed bullocks without the use of cake.[25] Farm accounts show little change in the proportion of expenses going on bought-in feeds. With the prices of oilcake and maize falling by at least a third between the late 1870s and the early 1890s, the farmer was getting more for his money. Even when feed prices began to rise in the 1890s, farmers could substitute home-grown, unprofitable cereals. One north Lincolnshire farmer commented in 1895, 'Never did I give the animals on my farm more hand food and never had I less cake bills to pay … my grain is unsaleable and I must use it.'[26] A consequence of this was that more attention was paid to buildings suitable for cattle housing. The extensive equipping of farms with cattle shelters and feed preparation buildings that had already gone on during the mid 19th century meant that new buildings were not necessary everywhere. Even so, there was strong demand for additions and adaptations to allow livestock farming to expand.[27] In particular, one of the trends was to provide more covered yards for the stock. One of Lord Ancaster's tenants laid things on heavily to make his case, but his was a common cause. 'Beast always lose money,' he claimed, 'the reason is there is no accommodation to keep them warm … the corn trade is no good, therefore we want all the accommodation possible to make stock pay.'[28] Good buildings were valued at least as much as, if not more than pasture. A prospective tenant for one of Lord Monson's farms of 900 acres in 1880 proposed that the landlord should turn much of it to pasture, but in the end decided that draining 100 acres and repairs to the buildings would be more suitable.[29]

The margins of price between store stock and fatstock narrowed. Although they continued to buy in stock in autumn to feed over winter for resale in the spring, farmers increasingly turned to breeding, often fattening their stock as well. Estate papers bear witness to such developments, with their records of farmers' needs for buildings for rearing calves. In areas traditionally used as feeding grounds, the Fens and the Marsh, the change to breeding was marked. One of the large farmers in the Fens at the end of the century, who kept about a hundred fatstock cattle, said he now bred two-thirds of the stock.[30] Cattle were still brought down from the Wolds to marshland and fen grazing during the summer, with the result that numbers of cattle in these areas held up well. The practice, developed in the south of England, of bringing stock to maturity younger spread throughout Lincolnshire in the 1880s and 1890s. Cattle were being fattened for sale at 16 to 20 months old rather than 2½ years as had previously been usual. By 1900, 44 per cent of all cattle in Lincolnshire were less than two years old, compared with 39 per cent in 1875.

The Lincolnshire Red Shorthorn remained the dominant breed of cattle, found on large and small farms alike throughout the county. The foundation of the Lincolnshire Red Shorthorn Association in 1895 put the seal on the work of all those, mainly large farmers in the north of the county, who had developed the breed since the middle of the 19th century. These farmers were now able also to benefit from a growth in demand for breeding stock from overseas. Substantial numbers of beasts were being exported by 1900. Numbers were not recorded until 1904, but from then until 1914 exports of Lincolnshire Red cattle amounted to 774, the main destination being South America.[31]

One of the aspects of livestock farming that did not expand was dairy farming. Lincolnshire is not, perhaps, an area most naturally suited to dairying. The same, however, could be said of Essex, where dairy farming did expand, while Derbyshire, at a similar distance from metropolitan markets, was also a dairying county. Farmers in

Lincolnshire tended to blame the railway companies for not offering special low rates for the carriage of milk, as happened in some other parts of the country. This was certainly so, but there was greater inducement for the Midland Railway to offer low rates to London from Derbyshire, where dairy farmers were already to be found in some numbers, than it was for the Great Northern in Lincolnshire where dairying was hardly practised at all.

The number of cows in calf or in milk in Lincolnshire was greater by one third in 1900 compared with 1875. The general expansion of breeding herds accounted for much of this. There was growing local demand for milk, and for the minority who did take up dairying there could be success in supplying the local towns. Wilson Fox found a number of thriving businesses supplying dairy products to Lincoln, Gainsborough, and Grimsby. There were also some successful co-operative marketing and processing organizations, such as the Sutton-on-Sea and District Farmers' Company.[32] Those who took up dairy farming usually found it profitable, either as the main source of income or as an invaluable part of mixed farming. This was the case with one of Henry Chaplin's tenants who, the agent said, would have been bankrupt without his dairy.[33] The winner of the farm prize competition in 1907, John Evens of Burton-by-Lincoln, turned to dairying in 1885 on his holding of 930 acres. He was a founder member of the Lincolnshire Red Shorthorn Association who was noted for his quality breeding stock. He converted from beef to dairying to supply the market at nearby Lincoln, using the same pedigree stock. He is probably the farmer referred to anonymously by Wilson Fox as one who turned losses of £850 for the three years from 1878-79 to 1880-81 into profits averaging nearly £200 per year. There were others who demonstrated that the Lincoln Red could be a dairy beast, such as the Scorers of Nettleham. In the Fens more smallholders took up selling butter in their local markets, although it was usually not of high quality.[34]

While cattle farming was advancing in steady if unspectacular fashion, sheep farming suffered setbacks from the combined effects of disease and low prices. The optimism about sheep farming prevailing in the early 1870s was overturned within a few years. The numbers of

sheep in the county fell by 25.4 per cent between 1875 and 1900, twice
the decline of 12.6 per cent experienced in England and Wales as a
whole. Epidemic outbreaks of liver rot and foot and mouth disease had
spectacular results. The severest and most widespread outbreaks were
between 1879 and 1881, a by-product of the wet seasons. Nationally it is
estimated that six million sheep died or were slaughtered. In this county
numbers were 300,000 fewer in 1882 than they had been in 1879. For
individual farmers the losses could be severe. Some lost their whole
flock. William Frankish on his 2,000 acre farm in the Wolds lost 650
lambs and 500 ewes worth, he estimated, £800.[35] One of Henry
Chaplin's tenants, farming nearly 800 acres, lost 80 sheep in 1878, 90 in
1879 and 121 in 1880, and another farmer of 1,500 acres near Louth
said that in three years he lost £1,500 from disease in cattle and sheep.
In January 1881 it was reported that several large graziers in south
Lincolnshire had no sheep left after having to rid themselves of
diseased stock.[36] On top of all this came further outbreaks of foot and
mouth disease lasting almost the whole of 1883. Restrictions on the
movement of stock were found irksome and 'a greater calamity than the
disease itself', as 'A Suffering Farmer' declared.[37] They often meant that
farmers unable to take their stock to market fell into arrears of rent
through lack of ready money.[38]

Losses to the county's flock suffered at this time became
permanent. Lack of capital to replace stock was often cited for this, and
it was certainly important in the short term. Poorer returns from sheep
farming had a more lasting effect. The price of wool was falling heavily,
and the price of Lincoln wool by more than most types. Landlords
received cries of distress from their tenants: 'wool makes such a bad
price now and it used formerly to pay the half year's rent', wrote one.[39]
There was the alternative source of income from mutton. Here the
problems were for the grazier because the margins between the cost of
purchasing store stock and selling fat became less certain. A writer from
the Spalding area set out the problem: 'Another drawback to the grazier
in this part of the county is the land is not adapted to breeding, and as
the value of store stock is proportionately dearer than fat … the margin
is so small in the value of store and fat stock that graziers cannot see a
profit in them.'[40]

The result of these difficulties was a marked decline in sheep feeding by lowland graziers. Numbers of sheep in the Fens dropped dramatically, by about 50 per cent, between the 1870s and the 1890s. Boston May Fair went into decline. In 1874 the show of sheep was described as small at 17,000, but by 1895 only 7,000 were brought for sale.[41] Many farmers in the Fens were giving up sheep altogether. There was no incentive for them to carry on with grazing when potatoes offered better prospects. Herbert Carter was one who went this way. After deriving about ten per cent of his gross income from sheep in the late 1880s, he was earning nothing from them by 1900. The same change affected the Marsh and clay vales, although to a lesser extent, as more farmers there persevered with sheep. Some were still gaining a large part of their income from fat sheep. Farmers from the Wolds continued to use grazing in the Marsh, although they were as likely to rent pasture now as sell the stock to a grazier. By the late 1880s, 'the system of keeping old sheep has almost died out in several parts of Lincolnshire'.[42]

In the sheep breeding areas numbers held up far better. The Wolds, especially, became the area of greatest concentration of sheep. 'Large flocks of fine Lincoln, long-woolled sheep are bred and fed on turnips and grass seed,' reported Wilson Fox to the Royal Commission.[43] Farmers here increasingly went in for fattening their own stock. They were producing fodder in sufficient quantity to sustain the move. In addition, they were able to take advantage of trends in the market for mutton which favoured stock brought to early maturity, at one year instead of two. They had the option of selling animals as stores when the market was favourable, and they also had the income from the wool clip. This flexibility led William Frankish to conclude that sheep had paid the best, once he had recovered from his losses of 1879-80.[44] For some there was the market in pedigree breeding stock. The Lincolnshire Longwool breed, although in England kept little outside its county, gained reputation throughout the world during this period as one of the best longwool breeds. The breed's status was enhanced with the founding of the breed association in 1892. A market developed for breeding rams, mainly for export to Australia, New Zealand, and South America, where they were used for cross-breeding with merino and other local sheep. This trade enabled farmers to sell at prices higher than the average in the market. When Messrs Thorpe of Nocton in 1885 realized an average price of 62s 8d a head for their sheep, mainly for export, the *Stamford Mercury* declared that the 'the great cloud of depression ... must surely be lifting'.[45] By the 1890s rams were fetching prices in the hundreds of guineas, and in 1897 the first sale at 1,000 guineas was achieved. This was Riby Squire from Henry Dudding's celebrated flock. His annual sales became showpiece events. The other leading breeders of Lincolnshire Longwools, including John Turner of Ulceby, and R. & W. Wright of Nocton, were at the forefront of the expanding pedigree trade. In 1897, 5,561 Lincoln rams were exported.[46] Trade on this scale could not be confined to the celebrated breeders and a broader range of farmers was able to take a share. The Dixon farms at Holton thus sold 37 rams to Canada in 1889.[47]

While breeding stock was being sold for high prices, the Lincoln's supremacy was being challenged in its own county. The breed's disadvantage was that it was primarily a wool producer, and it was wool, especially long wools, that had fallen most in price. Farmers in Lincolnshire began to look seriously at other breeds, especially the Down breeds, that were more suited to meeting the demand for early maturity. A report on Partney sheep fair in 1885 noted that farmers were showing interest in the Hampshire Down to cross with the Lincoln. Two years later, such half-breds were 'in a decided majority' at the fair.[48]

Diversification in the Fens and Isle of Axholme

During this period farming in the fenland began to take advantage of the richness of the soils to create new types of arable farming in response to market demands for vegetables and fruit. There was no going back on the expansion of arable that had taken place in earlier decades. The acreage of wheat was reduced drastically as the price fell, and this resulted in some increase both of permanent and rotation grasses. This was, however, more to rest the land than to introduce a pastoral regime, for livestock farming was not taking the place of the wheat. Numbers of sheep fell dramatically, and the modest increase in the numbers of cattle was insufficient for them to represent the future well-being of the area's agriculture.

Instead, it was new arable crops that took the place of both wheat and sheep. By far the most important was the potato, and this will be treated in more detail below. As well as the potato, other fruit and vegetable crops were being introduced. By the 1930s several of these had become of some importance. Not all the introductions were successful. Attempts to revive the cultivation of flax, once a feature of the Fens, made little progress. Sugar beet, though much canvassed, was a crop whose time had not yet come.

Total acreages of the new crops were small, and fluctuated as growers experimented with different crops. Their economic significance, however, was great, and their range was wide, including carrots, onions, asparagus, cabbages, and marrows. Cabbages were despatched from the fenland railway stations to the markets of the North and Midlands. By the end of the century as many as 50 to 60 wagonloads a day could be recorded from Swineshead station at the height of the season. Cauliflowers and broccoli were new to the Fens in

Fig. 22 Carting celery in the Isle of Axholme, on the farm of Mr A. Horbury, at Haxey in 1938
Source: Museum of English Rural Life

this period, but several farmers took them up in conjunction with their potato-growing. These crops were often grown under contract for industrial purchasers, such as Crosse & Blackwell.[49]

One of the most prominent of these vegetable crops was celery, the cultivation of which increased greatly from the 1880s onwards. It was grown mainly in the Isle of Axholme, where it came to rival potatoes in importance. Some growers in parts of the Fens around Boston and Swineshead also took it up. It was expensive to grow, often costing £25 an acre, and, like potatoes, could be very risky, succumbing to frosts and heavy rain. On the other hand returns could be very high, an average crop producing £30 an acre, good ones up to £70. The high costs meant that the crop was mostly in the hands of large growers, though there were dealers and agents who undertook to grow celery on small owners' lands without taking a full tenancy.[50] Of similar importance in parts of the Fens was mustard. Good profits could be made, although it was a speculative crop because the market was confined to the few manufacturers dominated by Colman's of

**Fig. 23 Packing celery in the Isle of Axholme, on the farm of
Mr A. Horbury, at Haxey in 1938**
Source: Museum of English Rural Life.

Norwich. In a year of good harvest, when their demand was soon met, the farmer could lose heavily. This perhaps explains the fluctuations in income from mustard in Herbert Carter's accounts. In some years in the 1890s he was receiving about £500, in others nothing at all, and in 1900 as much as £2,000.[51]

The cultivation of fruit and flowers was another expanding business of this period. The total acreage of orchards in Lincolnshire was 1,142 in 1875 and 2,256 in 1900. Returns of the acreage of small fruit, such as raspberries, were first collected in 1887, when the total stood at 350 acres. That was probably an underestimate, for the following year's return was 750 acres. By the end of the century, fruit growing had further expanded to between 1,600 and 1,700 acres under small fruit annually. Most parishes in the county had an acre or two of orchard or small fruit, but the main development was again in the Fens, where there were some quite large acreages. Both Spalding and Swineshead, for example, recorded about 100 acres each of orchard and small fruit in 1900. There were some large fruit farms, such as one at Long Sutton, which employed 400 seasonal workers for strawberry picking in 1894. Fruit-growing here was an extension of the much larger industry around Wisbech over the county border in Cambridgeshire.[52]

Bulb growing had been started in the 1880s by some Spalding businessmen who began to cultivate on a larger scale bulbs that some of the local gardeners and smallholders had been growing as a bit of a sideline for sale to London seedsmen, such as Veitch & Barr. More growers began to grow bulbs and flowers during the following decade. Among them was Herbert Carter, whose accounts show him selling snowdrops and daffodils in the late 1890s. The introduction of new varieties of narcissus that lent themselves to forcing encouraged the development of the industry. So, too, did some increases in price: double daffodils, for example, rose from 6s to 20s per 1,000 in the 1880s. By 1905 there were about 300 acres of bulbs and flowers around Spalding.[53]

Vegetables and flowers were grown as field crops on farms rather than as horticultural crops. The acreage returned as market gardens in Lincolnshire did increase from 500 acres in 1875 to 1,500 acres in 1900. Almost all of these were supplying local towns. The county's distance from the major cities that provided both a ready market for the produce and a supply of manure precluded the development of a real horticultural industry.

The result of these developments was that the fenlands fared better in depression than most parts of Lincolnshire. Guy's Hospital was typical of landowners in not having to take any of the farms on its south Lincolnshire estate in hand, and the reductions of rent, at 28 per cent, were more modest than on their estates in other parts of England.[54]

Lincolnshire and the potato

Potato growing was well-established in Lincolnshire by the late 18th century. There was already a good trade to London, and many farmers in the Fens and Isle of Axholme grew a few acres of potatoes. By the 1830s there were some farmers with a more serious interest in the crop. At Fen House Farm, a medium-sized farm at Dorrington, by the mid 1830s potatoes were coming to rival wheat as income generator. On the warplands of the Isle of Axholme the potato soon became a major crop, for many the major crop. On some of the best soils here farmers would grow little but potatoes and wheat, although elsewhere intervening crops of barley, beans, oats, and onions extended the rotation. Some of the largest farmers in this area had as many as 250 to 300 acres of potatoes, for which they bought cow and horse manure from Hull, Leeds, and Sheffield to contribute towards the heavy applications of manure that the crop needed.[55]

The Great Depression led to a marked increase in potato growing. By 1914 Lincolnshire had become one of the major growing areas of the country, and in subsequent years Lincolnshire and potatoes were to become inextricably linked in the popular mind. At the same time the centre of production in the county shifted to the Fens.

For large numbers of farmers in the late 19th century potato growing became one of the most important and profitable parts of their farming. The acreage under this crop in Lincolnshire increased by nearly 58 per cent between 1875 and 1900. Though the 64,000 acres in the later year only represented 4.2 per cent of the total area of crops and grass in the county, it is the size of the increase that carries the weight.

The potato had achieved an importance out of proportion to its acres. So great was this development that, by the inter-war period, the Holland division of the county was producing one-sixth of the whole country's potato crop.

The potato was a localized crop. In 1875 it was grown in the fenland parishes around the Wash and in the Isle of Axholme. By 1900, although there were other places now growing potatoes, the concentration in those two regions had become even more marked. Rider Haggard found the Isle of Axholme 'one of the few places which may be called ... truly prosperous in the agricultural sense ... chiefly because of its assiduous cultivation of the potato'. In the Fens potatoes were 'the salvation of the district agriculturally', for 'all farmers who stuck to corn-growing went to the wall, and it was only those who put part of their farms under potatoes in time that have been able to hold their heads above water'.[56] It was not, however, necessarily a choice between corn and potatoes, for much of the increased acreage of potatoes came not at the expense of cereals, but from ploughing up pasture.[57] This was held to account for the decline of sheep grazing in the Fens, although that might be to confuse cause with effect.

The potato became so popular during the late 19th century that by 1900 some parishes in the Fens had nearly a quarter of their agricultural land under the crop. Potato growing was beginning to spread further afield, first into parishes adjoining the Fens, in the southern Marsh, for example, and into those parishes which ran down from the Kesteven uplands and Heath to the fen edge. But, in addition, the potato was now being grown in small quantities in nearly all parts of the county and beginning to gain significance in places where the land was not at first sight suited to the crop.

The potato was a risky crop. It was costly to grow. About £15 per acre was a figure often quoted, though it could be more. Rents were high for potato land, and were hardly affected by the downturn of the Great Depression. It was an intensive crop, with the ploughing, planting, ridging, weeding, and lifting all demanding of labour. The wages bill, therefore, was high. Expenditure on labour was regularly 30s to 40s per acre, and could reach £3 to £4. Inputs of manure, both of farmyard manure and artificial fertilizers, were great. Spending of £3 per acre on artificial fertilizers was not unusual by the 1900s.[58] Yields could vary greatly. Disease could decimate the crop in some years, resulting in returns of no more than 2 to 3 tons of poor-quality potatoes per acre. On the other hand, yields could be very good, such as the bumper crop of 1885, which yielded 7.3 tons an acre according to the official statistics. Prices fluctuated greatly, too, in very strong reaction to supply and demand in the market, and more in line with the traditional pattern of a high price following a poor crop. About £5 a ton was a good price in the late 19th century, but prices could fall to 25s to 35s per ton. Growers, therefore, could lose badly in some years. The local press liked to rebuke them when they did. 'The exceedingly fickle crop must never be largely trusted to again,' trumpeted a writer from Moulton as the rotten crop of 1876 was being lifted.[59] Farmers were not deterred by such sentiments for the simple reason that the potato was more likely to pay than most others. In 1887 at Spalding it was said that with prices generally so low the only crops likely to pay the grower were barley and potatoes.[60]

Despite all the fluctuations, good livelihoods could be made from this crop, with returns of £30 to £40 an acre in good years.[61] Potato growing rapidly developed into a big business. Selling the crop was conducted mainly through commission agents acting for merchants in the cities. Fenland growers sold mostly to London. Manchester was the principal destination for potatoes grown in the Isle of Axholme. The trade had built up rapidly following the opening of the Manchester, Sheffield & Lincolnshire Railway to Gainsborough in 1849.[62] Some of the crop was sold through Doncaster market and on to the industrial towns of the West Riding. It became common to sell potatoes as a growing crop at a price per acre. This guaranteed a price to the grower, and, with yields liable to fluctuate wildly, seemed a prudent course to adopt. In the 1870s the price was £20 to £25 an acre, declining to £11 to £17 per acre in the 1880s. During the 1890s the acreage price was rising again above £20. As well as selling crops in the ground, there were farmers who let fields to merchants to crop with potatoes. These practices, however, declined during the First World War, and died out shortly afterwards.[63]

**Fig. 24 Lifting potatoes in the 1930s. A horse-drawn
potato-raising plough is followed by workers with their baskets**
Source: Museum of English Rural Life

Potato growers up to the 1870s concentrated on the
old-established basic varieties, such as rocks and flukes. Regent was
introduced during the mid-19th century, and by the 1870s was featuring
regularly in farmers' accounts. It was, however, liable to rot in wet
seasons, and the incentive to find varieties resistant to disease was
strong. Many varieties were introduced during the last quarter of the
century, and larger farmers, at least, were quick to take up some of
them. Suttons brought Champion to the market in 1876. By March
1878 the Duddings at Garthorpe were buying 100 sacks of Champion
seed.[64]

Lincolnshire growers and seedsmen played a part in the
development of new varieties. Charles Sharpe, seedsman at Sleaford,
introduced Sharpe's Victor in 1891 and Sharpe's Express about 1901,
the latter becoming one of the leading varieties of early potato, and still
grown. Of greater renown is the King Edward. This was established in
the market by J. Butler, who farmed at Scotter. He bought up all the
stocks of a potato called Fellside. This had been bred in

Northumberland in the 1890s and passed on to a grower at Snaith, Yorkshire, who in turn found no use for them. Butler took over the stock and demonstrated the power of a strong brand name with the rechristened variety.[65]

The potato was well suited to cultivation by the smallholders of the Fens and the Isle of Axholme, who were able to employ their family labour on it. Many did take it up successfully, and it came to produce up to a third of their incomes, but the bulk of the trade passed into the hands of large-scale growers.[66] The large farmers had more capital, enabling them to withstand losses, and to expand when bad seasons exhausted the reserves of smaller growers. They were better placed to deal with the merchants who bought the crop by the acre. Some vast enterprises in potatoes thus developed. There were farms of 300 to 400 acres in the Isle of Axholme growing little more than potatoes and wheat. Thomas Dudding at Garthorpe was deriving about a fifth of his income from potatoes throughout the 1870s and 1890s. Most notable of this new breed of large-scale potato-grower was William Dennis, of Kirton in the Fens, who built up a business that farmed 4,000 acres by the turn of century, of which more than a third was under potatoes in most years. In 1904 he despatched 1,993 wagonloads of potatoes from Kirton station.[67] Dennis himself was an embodiment of the relative ease of entry into this developing business, for he started his career as farm worker, then worked for a potato merchant before starting to grow on his own account.[68]

The 1,993 wagons despatched by William Dennis in 1904 went to 250 places in Britain, but the main markets for Lincolnshire potatoes continued to be London from the Fens and Manchester from the north of the county. In the Fens, where railway lines were quite sparse, distance from a station put many farmers at a disadvantage. Those with small acreages especially complained that the time spent on the road to a station seven or eight miles away was costly. As potato growing expanded there were several proposals for new local lines. The great volume of traffic did mean that railway companies were more accommodating to the farmer than they were over the carriage of milk from Lincolnshire. The companies found it worth quoting special rates, running special trains at the height of the season, and offering free carriage to the station for distances up to three miles.[69]

The end of High Farming?

High farming as it had developed in the mid-19th century was essentially a system of the light uplands. The Great Depression represented the first serious challenge to the sustainability of that system. The Wolds farmer's was a finely balanced system designed to produce the maximum from naturally unproductive soil, and it was not easy to alter this balance, especially on the arable. 'If the Wolds farms cannot be farmed as they are now they must go out of cultivation,' Wilson Fox was told.[70] When Wilson Fox writes in his report of large flocks of long-wool sheep, yard-fed cattle, and the land producing excellent crops of barley it appears that nothing had changed. The four-course system was adhered to as much as possible on the Wolds with only slight changes, such as the substitution of oats for wheat. Sir Daniel Hall visited a farm typical of this practice, 'a very good example of the old style of farming', where only corn and meat were sold off the farm, all else being consumed and returned to the soil.[71] The light-land system came through this period remarkably well. The farmers were saved because there were still markets for some of the products of Wolds farming. Barley for malting could be substituted for wheat as a main cash crop. Mutton could take the place of wool, the farmer picking up the grazier's profit as a result of earlier maturing stock. With increased beef production, the practice of economy, and the support of substantial rent reductions farming here could be quite successful, even prosperous, while making the minimum of adjustments to its management. On the light uplands of the Heath there were other adjustments to farm management. The Norfolk four-course system came to be transformed into a five- to seven-year cropping, depending on the length of the seeds break, as a result of more importance being accorded to peas. They were used to provide nitrogen for the soil, instead of buying so much cake to feed to sheep. At the same time they could earn revenue by being sold to the northern towns, and by the 1890s marrowfat varieties were being grown especially for these markets. Sheep remained an integral part of this system, eating off the roots and stocking the rotation grass. But the income from their meat and wool was now more important than their manure, as artificial fertilizers were preferred.[72]

Elsewhere there were many changes to farming practice in response to changed circumstances. Some had their beginnings before the coming of bad seasons, falling prices, and depression. These were changes made gradually, especially until about 1885. After that they became more marked, partly it seems because hopes that agriculture was passing through a temporary recession had been abandoned, and partly because a new generation was entering farming more ready to take up new practices. In principle four- and five-course cropping remained the rule down to the end of the century.[73] However, in order to replace unprofitable wheat with more paying crops, these systems were considerably modified. One of the simplest alterations, already touched upon, was the extension of rotations by leaving temporary grass down for an extra year or two. A similarly straightforward change was to substitute oats or barley for wheat in the five-course rotation. This might produce a sequence such as seeds, oats, barley, turnips, barley, an example of a course of sowing by one of the tenants on the Heneage estate between 1887 and 1891. Established rotations also came to be broken down a little by the sowing of successive crops of corn (that same tenant on one of his fields grew oats followed by turnips, barley, oats, wheat), and by sowing catch crops of, for example, mustard seed in place of wheat. 'A man who has not broken his course of farming in the last ten years could not have done,' explained one Kesteven farmer to Wilson Fox.[74]

Changes such as these were seen by some as representing a retreat from the high farming developed during the mid-19th century. Farmers were less concerned with maintaining intensive inputs than with economy, especially on labour, and reaping more immediate returns. Leaving land down in temporary or permanent grass was often done to save the cost of labour, which disappointed the protagonists of grassland who expected immediate large increases in the number of stock kept.[75] The failure of farmers to take up some of the innovations of the period was also seen as a sign of waning enthusiasm for intensive management. A case in point was silage, which failed to catch on despite the enthusiasm of a few individuals.[76] Lincolnshire farmers were deterred by the high cost of building silos, so that 'the system of making silos does not appear to be favourably regarded about here'. In 1889 there were only 17 silos in the county.[77] Similarly, despite the number of wet seasons, experiments with grain-drying machinery were very limited.[78]

That did not mean that farmers were not investing in new equipment and techniques. Mechanization continued the trends of earlier decades, as several of the innovations of the 1860s and 1870s were taken into general use. The most notable advance was in the mechanization of the cereal harvest. Reaping machines began to come into general use in the early 1870s, partly in order to save labour at the time of the labourers' unrest. In 1872 it was reported: 'Reaping-machines are continually arriving at Mr Edward Smith's, the agent at Brigg, who appears to have extensive orders for such implements.' Reapers were noted to be frequently used in the harvests of the following years, although at Long Sutton in 1873 it was said that 'many farmers abstain from using them as long as they can obtain a sufficiency of hands to do the required work'.[79] But the machines became established: by 1887 many farmers were cutting the whole of their corn with them. Self-binding reapers were starting to appear by then, and within the following fifteen years became the principal harvesting machine. The machines were restricted in usefulness when storms left crops laid, and they spread more slowly in the Fens because of the large number of small farmers who could not afford them.[80] A similar movement happened with the hay harvest. Mowers had been an introduction of the late 1850s, but their spread into almost universal use came during these later decades. Along with them came new types of swath turner, horse rakes, and elevators for stacking. Steam ploughing, carried out by contracting firms such as the Brigg Steam Cultivation Company, continued to have its importance in areas of heavy soil.[81]

The use of artificial fertilizers had become an accepted part of the county's agriculture during the mid century. By the late 1880s and 1890s the advantages of their use became greater, especially the benefit of economy. 'With artificial manure at one-fifth the cost of farmyard manure I have been able to grow as much corn, but not quite as much straw as on the farm where all has been consumed on,' explained one large farmer to Wilson Fox. Because of such advantages the use of superphosphates became very common. Some new types of fertilizer were introduced, notably basic slag, which was valuable on newly sown grasslands.[82]

While farmers were anxious to reduce spending, it is clear that they were not putting parsimony above all else. They were looking for productive expenditure, and thus purchases of feed and fertilizer remained high on many farms. Feed bills of 20s or more per acre continued to be common on farms on the Heath and in the south-west of the county. As the 20th century opened this was still the amount one farmer at Folkingham was spending on feeds for his pedigree cattle. The same was true of fertilizer. There was a tenant of Lord Monson's paying out 33s an acre on manures in 1883, while another farmer at Tathwell, on the Wolds, quoted his combined bill for cake, manure, and sundries as 43s 6d per acre in 1884.[83] Other farmers, however, sought to reduce the amount of feeds and manures they bought and to use home-grown feeds in their place. Some increases in the prices of feeds in the 1890s encouraged that line of thinking. On the whole, however, prices for feeds and fertilizers were falling throughout this period: nitrate of soda fell in price by about a third between 1875 and 1895, guano by a half. Farmers were getting more for their money, and for many, therefore, consumption altered very little.[84]

Although William Frankish thought that 'the more highly a man farmed the more he lost', there remained a strong belief in the efficacy of high farming. A farmer from Holbeach held the view that 'with low farming small yields have resulted, and market prices ruling so low, the produce has not made sufficient to cover expenses … store stock have been purchased very dear and sold when fat very cheap'. He contrasted this with the high farmer who got good crops and was 'able to meet the markets better'. Similarly, some farmers at Spalding told Wilson Fox, 'All farm very highly here as the only chance of salvation.'[85] A result was that commentators generally believed that standards of husbandry were being kept up. This was a matter of some subjective judgement, of course, and Wilson Fox, who collected most of the information available, was presented with a variety of views ranging from the Earl of

Ancaster who thought farming was worse than it had been ten years previously, to the Earl of Yarborough's agent, who said that the land had never been in better condition. Most comments were favourable and can be summed up by the words of a farmer in the Louth area, this time to the Royal Commission on Labour: 'Though the area of good farming steadily diminishes, Lincolnshire and Yorkshire are still splendidly farmed on the whole.' There was support for this from the limited extent to which land was allowed to fall out of cultivation. In the agricultural returns for 1881, 2,575 acres out of a total of 1,498,673 acres were stated to be uncultivated arable land. Though this figure may not have been strictly accurate because of problems of definition, it amply demonstrates the minuteness of the quantity of the land involved.[86] When Wilson Fox investigated the county he again found no evidence of land having been abandoned, and little having been left to tumbledown grass.[87] Wilson Fox concluded that north Lincolnshire was rather better farmed than the south, partly because farms were larger and tenants had more capital, and partly perhaps because there were more unorthodox rotations in the south.[88]

By the later 1880s and 1890s farmers were gradually changing the nature of their intensive farming. Instead of basing it simply on high gross input to gain high returns, they came to try to make more efficient use of their inputs. The highly integrated farming system of the Heath as described by Sir Daniel Hall exemplifies the changes that had taken place. Farming was not quite so 'high' in the sense that it depended less on the input of vast amounts of purchased cake. But farmers had cash crops on about half their arable, while sheep and cattle, and sometimes hay and straw, produced further income.[89] Similarly, the systems that have been described as developing in the Fens and Wolds each in different ways represent attempts to achieve an efficient balance of high input and high output of cash products. The clays remained at a disadvantage because of their very high cost as arable lands, and Hall found them relatively poorly farmed.[90] For the entrepreneurial farmer there were ample opportunities in this period, as, with low rents, it became possible to build up sizeable businesses.

In a sense, therefore, agriculture was being pulled in two ways during the Great Depression, and farmers were faced with a choice between extensive, low-cost farming and what was gradually becoming a more efficient, intensive, high farming. The farmers' choice depended greatly upon their individual circumstances of wealth and location, but to most the pull towards high-output farming was the stronger.

Notes to Chapter 8

1   Figures for acreage and numbers of stock, whether expressed as numbers or percentages, in this chapter are derived from the annual agricultural returns.
2   *Retford News*, 26 June 1880.
3   *Agricultural Gazette*, 5 March 1883.
4   *SM*, 23 March 1894.
5   RC1879, QQ. 57642–3.
6   LAO, Scorer Farm 2. RC1893, Wilson Fox, p. 120.
7   *Tariff Commission*, para. 856.
8   LAO, HD65/64.
9   *Tariff Commission*, para. 812. PRO MAF 68.
10   *SM*, 3 January 1890. *Agricultural Gazette*, 5 November 1894.
11   RC1893, QQ. 14621, 14493, 14519–20, 61483. *SM*, 17 November 1893. *Tariff Commission*, para. 812. LAO, THIMBLEBY 5/W/7.
12   *SM*, 9 February 1894.
13   *SM*, 19 September 1890.
14   Select Committee on the Corn Averages, QQ. 676, 708–9.
15   F. I. Cooke, 'Report on the Farm Prize Competition in Nottinghamshire and Lincolnshire in 1888, class I', *JRASE*, v. 49 (1888) p. 524. LAO, HD65/64.
16   *Tariff Commission*, para. 863. *Agricultural Gazette*, 5 March 1883, 6, 27 September 1886. *SM*, 21 August 1891.
17   LAO, Higgins 4/4, Claythorpe farm, 15 December 1888.
18   *SM*, 24 November 1876. *Mark Lane Express*, 15 January 1877.
19   *SM*, 7 October 1892, *Agricultural Gazette*, 5 February 1894.
20   *SM*, 24 September 1886.
21   *Tariff Commission*, para. 865.
22   RC1893, Wilson Fox, pp. 118, 122. LAO HD 65/64.
23   Alan Straw, 'The Ancholme Levels North of Brigg: a history of drainage and its effect on land utilisation', *East Midland Geographer,* no. 3 (June 1955), pp. 40–1. LAO, 9ANC 2/C/3/8.

24 LAO, BS13/1/7/5; DIXON6/5/1. *SM*, 21 September 1883, 5 December 1884, 24 September 1886.
25 LAO, DIXON 6/5/1, 10 December 1889.
26 *Agricultural Gazette*, 21 January 1895.
27 RC1893, Wilson Fox, pp. 13ff. P. S. Barnwell and C. Giles, *English Farmsteads 1750–1914*, (1997), pp. 57–62.
28 LAO, 9ANC 2/B/3/4, 19 March 1901.
29 LAO, MON 25/13/18, Toynbee to Monson, 20, 23, 27 February 1880.
30 *Tariff Commission*, para. 565.
31 Mona Skehel, *A Taste of Lincoln Red* (1995), pp. 5, 10, 12, 89.
32 RC1893, Wilson Fox, pp. 99, 100, 125.
33 LAO BS 13/1/13/34b.
34 W. H. Hogg, 'The Farm Prize Competition', *JRASE*, v. 68 (1907) pp. 172, 176. Skehel, *A Taste of Lincoln Red*, p. 35. G. E. Collins, 'Lincolnshire Red Shorthorns', *JRASE*, v. 75 (1914), p. 38. W. H. Wheeler, *History of the Fens of South Lincolnshire* (1896) pp. 410–11.
35 RC1879 QQ. 49289–96. *Agricultural Gazette*, 17 January 1881.
36 RC1879, QQ. 49289–96. Frankish's total flock was about 1,000 (*Tariff Commission*, para. 862). E. L. Jones, *Seasons and Prices* (1964) p. 87. *SM*, 26 September 1879, 17 June, 28 October 1881. *Agricultural Gazette*, 17 January 1881. LAO, BS13/1/1/1, 13/1/1/37.
37 *SM*, 12 October 1883. Complaints may have been partly owing to the Government's not introducing a ban on imported livestock nor compensation for slaughtered animals as farmers desired. See A. H. H. Matthews, *Fifty Years of Agricultural Politics* (1915) p. 239. R. J. Olney, *Lincolnshire Politics 1832–1885* (1973) pp. 226–7.
38 LAO, 9ANC 5/1/7/4.
39 LAO, 2HEN 2/4/75, 2/2/27; 9ANC 2/B/3/4; BS13/1/13/78.
40 *Agricultural Gazette*, 27 November 1882, 31 May 1886.
41 *SM*, 8 May 1874, 10 May 1895.
42 Thomas Stirton, 'Report on the Farm Prize Competition in Nottinghamshire and Lincolnshire, classes 2 and 3', *JRASE*, v. 50 (1889), pp. 53–4, 59.
43 RC1893, Wilson Fox, p. 129.
44 *Tariff Commission*, para. 863.
45 *SM*, 13 March 1885.
46 C. E. Howard, 'Lincoln Longwools', *Lincolnshire Magazine*, v. 2 (1934) p. 319. G. E. Collins, 'Agriculture', *VCH, Lincolnshire*, v. 2 (1906), pp. 413–15.
47 LAO, DIXON 6/5/1 (29 May 1889).

48   *SM,* 23 September 1885, 5 August 1887. Collins, 'Agriculture', (1906)
      pp. 413–14.

49   E. A. Pratt, *The Transition in Agriculture* (1906) pp. 112–14, 123. Wheeler,
      History of the Fens of South Lincolnshire, pp. 402–3. John Page, 'The Sources
      of Supply of the Manchester Fruit and Vegetable Markets', *JRASE,* v. 41
      (1880) pp. 477–80. *Royal Commission on Labour: the agricultural labourer, vol. 1,
      part 6, Report on Lincolnshire,* by Edward Wilkinson, [C6894] (1893) p. 106.

50   Pratt, *The Transition in Agriculture,* pp. 125–6. Wheeler, *History of the Fens of
      South Lincolnshire,* p. 402. H. Rider Haggard, *Rural England* (1902) v. 2,
      pp. 192, 195. RC1893, Hunter Pringle p. 16. LAO, 2TGH 1/50/7.

51   Wheeler, *History of the Fens of South Lincolnshire,* pp. 403–5. LAO,
      HD65/64. *SM,* 28 October 1887. *Agricultural Gazette,* 22 October 1894.
      Pratt, *The Transition in Agriculture,* pp. 43–7. *SM,* 8 September 1893.

52   Charles Whitehead, 'Fifty Years of Fruit Farming', *JRASE,* v. 50 (1889)
      p. 167.

53   Pratt, *The Transition in Agriculture,* pp. 74–6, 81–2. E. C. Eagle, 'Some
      Light on the Beginnings of the Lincolnshire Bulb Industry', *Lincolnshire
      Historian,* no. 6 (Autumn 1950) pp. 220–9. G. W. Leak, 'The Bulb
      Growing Industry', *Lincolnshire Magazine,* v. 1 (1934) pp. 113–14. LAO,
      HD 65/64. W. E. Bear, 'Flower and Fruit Farming in England', *JRASE,*
      v. 59 (1898), p. 312. A fuller account of the bulb and flower business is
      given in Chapter 10.

54   G. M. Robinson, *Agricultural Change* (1988), p. 135.

55   Museum of English Rural Life, FR LIN3/1/1. J. C. Wallace, 'The
      Development of Potato-growing in Lincolnshire', *JRASE,* v. 115 (1954)
      p. 60.

56   Rider Haggard, *Rural England* v. 2, pp. 204–5. *Tariff Commission,* paras.
      548, 813.

57   Wallace, 'The Development of Potato-growing in Lincolnshire',
      pp. 60–1.

58   *Tariff Commission,* para. 813.

59   *SM,* 27 October 1876.

60   *SM,* 26 August 1887.

61   Rider Haggard, *Rural England* v. 2, p. 207. *SM,* 24 September 1886, 24
      April, 6 November 1891.

62   Roger Scola, *Feeding the Victorian City: the food supply of Manchester
      1770–1870* (1992) pp. 109–10.

63   Wallace, 'The Development of Potato-growing in Lincolnshire',
      pp. 62–3.

64   LAO, 3Dudding. Sir John Russell, *The Farm and the Nation* (1933) p. 42.

65   R. N. Saloman, *The History and Social Influence of the Potato* (revised edn. 1985) pp. 169–70. T. P. McIntosh, *The Potato* (1927) p. 26.

66   Select Committee on Smallholdings, PP, xii (1889) p. 351. RC1893, Wilson Fox pp. 171, 173–4. A. D. Hall, *A Pilgrimage of British Farming* (1913) pp. 91–2.

67   Pratt, *The Transition in Agriculture*, p. 208. Ruby Hunt, 'Portrait of a Village: Kirton', *Lincolnshire Life* (February 1969) pp. 48–9.*Tariff Commission,* para. 548ff. Hall, *A Pilgrimage of British Farming,* pp. 92, 113.

68   Wallace, 'The Development of Potato-growing in Lincolnshire', p. 61.

69   Collins, 'Agriculture', p. 405. A. J. Wrottesley, *The Midland and Great Northern Joint Railway* (1970) p. 103. *SM,* 20 July 1883, 27 December 1889, 2 May 1890. L. Jebb, *The Small Holdings of England* (1907) p. 30.

70   RC1893, Wilson Fox, p. 158.

71   Hall, *A Pilgrimage of British Farming ,* pp. 99–100.

72   *Ibid.,* pp. 94–7. The rotation described here was peas, wheat, roots, barley, seeds for up to three years. *SM* 23 September 1892.

73   RC1893, QQ. 36109–16. *SM,* 4 May 1894. Stirton, 'Report on the Farm Prize Competition in Nottinghamshire and Lincolnshire classes 2 and 3', pp. 50, 58, 70.

74   RC1893, Wilson Fox, p. 159. *SM,* 4 May 1894. LAO, 2HEN 2/4/82.

75   RC1893, QQ. 36298–9, 36304–5. W. J. Malden, 'Recent Changes in Farm Practices', *JRASE,* v. 57 (1896) pp. 32–3.

76   Such as John Swan of Lincoln, who gave evidence to the *Private Ensilage Commission,* Minutes of Evidence, QQ. 1–104.

77   *Agricultural Returns, 1889. SM,* 24 September 1886, 20 July 1888. Nigel Harvey, *A History of Farm Buildings in England and Wales* (1970), pp. 184–7.

78   *SM,* 2, 30 September 1881.

79   *SM,* 16, 30 August 1872; 8, 15, 22 August 1873; 11, 18 August 1876.

80   *SM,* 26 August 1887, 7 September 1888, 2 August 1889, 28 July 1893. Wheeler, *History of the Fens of South Lincolnshire,* p. 413.

81   M. E. Turner, J. V. Beckett, and B. Afton, *Farm Production in England 1700–1914* (2001) p. 93. *SM,* 27 June 1884. *Mark Lane Express,* 24 April 1882. *Agricultural Gazette,* 9 May 1881. LAO, DIXON 22/7/11/17; NEL XIX/11; THIMBLEBY 10/2/1. Wheeler, *History of the Fens of South Lincolnshire ,* p. 413. Stirton, 'Report on the Farm Prize Competition in Nottinghamshire and Lincolnshire classes 2 and 3', p. 51.

82   *SM,* 9 May 1873, 27 March 1891. LAO, 2HEN 2/2/21; DIXON 6/5/1. RC1893, Wilson Fox, p. 159.

83   LAO, BS13/1/13/75; MON25/13/18, 7 October 1883. RC1893, Wilson Fox, pp. 122–3. *Tariff Commission,* paras. 648, 861, 865.

84   *The Agrarian History of England and Wales, vol. VII, 1850–1914,* ed. E. J. T. Collins (2000) pp. 2102–3. *Agricultural Gazette,* 23 January 1893, 26 November 1894.
85   W. E. Bear, 'The Survival in Farming', *JRASE,* v. 52 (1891) p. 269. RC1893, Wilson Fox, p. 40. See also the report of corn yields in 1892 being light 'except on highly farmed land', *SM,* 19 August 1892.
86   RC1879, Second report of S. B. L. Druce, p. 60.
87   RC1893, Wilson Fox, p. 39.
88   RC1893, Wilson Fox, pp. 37–40, 150–1. *Royal Commission on Labour, the Agricultural Labourer, vol. i, part vi, Report on Lincolnshire,* by Edward Wilkinson, C6894 (1893), p. 42.
89   Hall, *A Pilgrimage of British Farming 1910–1912,* p. 96.
90   *Ibid.,* p. 98.

9

RECOVERY, WAR AND DEPRESSION, 1896–1930

In 1894 the price of wheat reached its low point at 22s 10d per quarter. An end to the depression in agriculture seemed to be in sight as wheat prices began to climb, reaching 34s a quarter in 1898. Prices at Lincolnshire markets were consistently below the national average. At Lincoln in 1894 the average for wheat was 22s 3d per quarter, and at Louth as low as 21s 11d. Even so the change of trend also affected the county, and prices here in 1898 reached about 33s a quarter for wheat. It was a hesitant recovery, however, for prices fell back again quite sharply between 1899 and 1901, and remained at about 27s to 28s for wheat until 1906–07. Thereafter they kept above 30s a quarter until 1914. Not all prices followed the same course as wheat. The price of Lincoln wool remained depressed in this period, with the exception of some rallies in the mid 1890s, around 1906 and immediately before the war, and was consistently lower than wool from the Down breeds. Things were no better for fatstock. The price of Lincoln sheep showed little change in the first decade of the 20th century. Cattle prices were rising: the agricultural returns record a 20 per cent increase in price for fat shorthorn cattle for the ten years from 1905 to 1914.

As the new century opened these rather ragged price changes left the general economic climate sufficiently depressing for Rider Haggard to find nearly every farmer to whom he spoke pessimistic, and he was struck by such things as 'the ruinous fall in the price of wool' causing problems 'which the agriculture of this county finds it very difficult to bear'. This state of affairs seemed to continue for the next decade. Cereal prices had certainly risen since the 1890s, but in 1910 they were still only about the same as in 1880, while the rising costs of cake,

manure, and labour were very apparent. Harvests were often not all that
bountiful. Robert Toynbee reported of 1897, 'There is, I think, no
doubt some improvement in the price of wheat as compared with the
last two or three years; but on the other hand the yield in this County is
spoken of as being much under an average, and there will be little, if any,
improvement in the return per acre. In other crops, as well as in the
price of meat, things remain much as they were, and I am afraid ... the
present position of the Farmer is [not] much better than it has been for
many years past.'[1] These were the conditions which prompted the
formation of the Lincolnshire Farmers' Union.

The balance of farming in these circumstances showed little
change. The graph of acreages for all the main crops between 1900 and
1914 is almost flat. Sowing of wheat followed the movement of prices
out of the depths of the mid 1890s, and by 1900 it had recovered to
175,288 acres for the whole county. In 1914 the total was still 175,001.
There were fluctuations from year to year, in particular a sharp fall in
1904, but over all there was no great change. Other arable crops show
similar changes from year to year, but with no strong trend. In livestock,
numbers of sheep showed some hesitant recovery, but then fell back
below one million in the years immediately before the war. Total
numbers of cattle rose gently, by 9.2 per cent over the years from 1900
to 1914. After the changes brought about by the Great Depression a
rather uneasy equilibrium was being established.

The movement of rents showed similar uncertainty. They started
to rise again during the late 1890s, but not in a wholesale manner. The
Heneage estate typifies the trends. Between 1898 and 1903 rents on
many farms were adjusted slightly upwards, but just as many tenants
had rents reduced, by up to three shillings per acre.[2] Lord Ancaster also
managed to increase the rents on some of his farms, but the complaints
from tenants continued. One, whose rent had been increased from
£100 to £130, wrote in 1904 to ask for his old rent to be restored,
because 'seasons, etc. have been entirely against that class of land'. His
request was granted. Another importuning tenant informed Lord
Ancaster's agent in 1901 that 'I find this year rents are being reduced
more than ever ... what with the advance in labour, the high price in
cake & manure and the low price in corn...'.[3] Agents were inclined to

agree. One acting for a marshland estate wrote to the owner in 1905 that 'there is nothing so very grand about farmers' prices and profits even now, altho on the whole we may be in slightly better financial condition than last year'. This agent doubted whether he could easily reduce remissions of rent.[4]

These continuing problems have meant that it has been common to extend the period of the Great Depression to 1914, and beyond. Gavin McCrone wrote of a 'vicious spiral' of depression affecting British agriculture from the 1870s onwards. As agriculture contracted in the face of falling prices in the late 19th century, so investment declined and the ability to respond to further price falls after the First World War was weakened. According to this view there was no stability in British agriculture before the Second World War. Although there is much to support that description, the course of agricultural change in the first half of the 20th century was rather more complex, even in the arable counties, such as Lincolnshire, where the effects of falling prices in the 1920s were sharply felt.[5]

Despite all the problems, there were signs of a real change in farming's fortunes as the new century began. Farmers were beginning to make money again, and the fact that they were able to persuade landlords to keep rents low helped. Even Rider Haggard could not avoid some signs of hope. The Isle of Axholme was 'the most prosperous place that I had hitherto found in England'. The arable farming of the Marsh was also doing well. Charles Tindall, former bailiff to William Torr and now working in estate agency for a number of institutional estates there, told him that the best and most businesslike of farmers could now expect returns of 4 to 6 per cent on their capital. There had been a distinct improvement since 1896, he thought, although 1901 had been a very poor year, especially for sheep farming, with the prices of wool so low.[6] G. E. Collins, writing on agriculture for the *Victoria County History*, noted how painful it had been for the older type of tenant to adapt to changed circumstances. However, he was far more optimistic about the circumstances and prospects for agriculture. The farmers who were careful and had adapted themselves to the conditions could make a living. In character, these farmers were likely to be different from the generation that had gone before, being men of 'simpler tastes, fewer wants and perhaps more practical knowledge'.[7] Collins was writing a few years after Rider Haggard, when most prices were starting to rise again. It is from this point, 1906, that J. R. Bellerby, in his broad study of agricultural incomes, suggested that farmers were starting to make a decent living again. His ratio of farm to non-farm income recovered from its low of 36 per cent for 1892–6 to 47 per cent for 1906–10 and 55 per cent by 1910–14.[8] Not all of Lincolnshire's farmers shared in this upturn, but the examples already noted, to which can be added the potato growers of the Fens, show that many did. As prices continued to rise in the years to 1914 there was a general renewal of hope that the corner really had been turned.

The formation of the Lincolnshire Farmers' Union

The Lincolnshire Farmers' Union gave the appearance of having been formed almost spontaneously. A group of nine farmers gathered at the Blankney Hunt Show at Harmston on 31 August 1904 agreed that there should be a union of farmers, and pledged an initial financial subscription. They called a meeting in Lincoln on 2 September, which attracted a considerable gathering at which agreement was reached to form a Lincolnshire Farmers' Union. There were 95 founder members.[9]

Of course, it was not quite as straightforward as that. The origins of the union lay in the continuing difficulties faced by agriculture at the turn of the century. There had been rumblings in farmers' circles for some time about the lack of political weight carried by agriculture, and the need for organization to change that state of affairs. One of the arguments deployed in the founding of the Lincolnshire union was that farmers 'through their lack of combination have suffered acutely in the past'.[10] At the beginning of the Great Depression the Farmers' Alliance had been founded, and it lasted until 1888. One of Lincolnshire's landowners, and former Member of Parliament, the Earl of Winchilsea, put forward a scheme for the formation of a National Agricultural Union embracing all farming interests – landowners, farmers and labourers – in 1892. This union never really attracted the whole-hearted support of any of the interest groups. After an uncertain existence it transformed itself into a constituent of the Agricultural Organisation

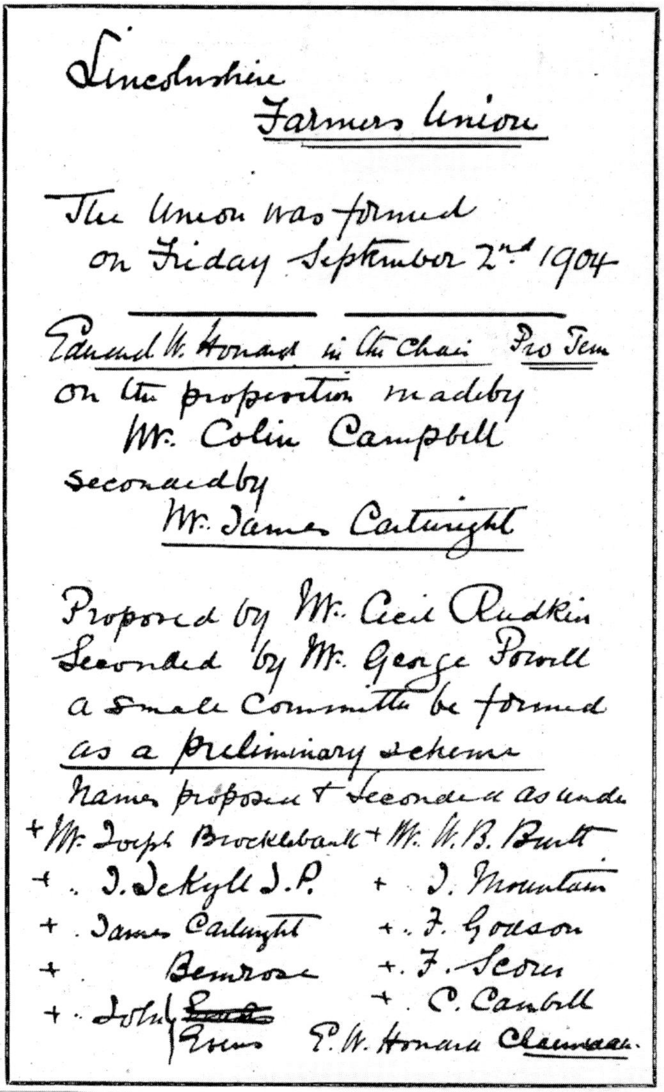

Fig. 25   The founding committee of the Lincolnshire Farmers'
Union elected at the inaugural meeting in 1904
Source: Farmer and Stockbreeder, 12 January 1931

Society in 1901. Meanwhile farmers everywhere were still feeling the need to defend their interests. Some local farmers' associations were formed, for example in Lancashire.[11]

With all these antecedents, when E. W. Howard, a member of one of Lincolnshire's most well-known farming families, spoke at a meeting in Market Rasen in 1901, he was likely to receive a sympathetic hearing. Economic conditions were continuing to go against farmers, and, therefore, it was time, he said, for farmers to join together to defend their interests: 'We have a perfect right to demand with the rest of the nation's subjects a living wage. We must co-operate into a united body called the British Farmers' Union.'[12] Although a few more years were to pass before it came into being, Howard's speech proved to be one of the starting points in the foundation of the Lincolnshire Farmers' Union. Howard became one of the founders of the union and its first secretary, while Colin Campbell was the president. Once established, the new union grew rapidly. By the time of the annual general meeting on 29 January 1909, membership had reached more than 4,000.

The Lincolnshire Farmers' Union had been founded for the 'purpose of watching over and defending matters affecting farmers', and it encouraged other counties to follow in forming their own unions. These efforts bore fruit with the foundation in 1908 of the National Farmers' Union, in which several Lincolnshire men took leading positions, including Colin Campbell as president. The national headquarters remained at Lincoln until 1919. The National Farmers' Union grew rapidly in membership. There were 10,000 members in 1909, six months after the union was formed. Five years later there were 22,000. Lincolnshire remained a stronghold for the union, with two large branches. In 1925, by which time national membership had reached 104,000, the Lincolnshire County Branch had 3,635 members and the Holland Branch 1,800. Their combined membership was exceeded only by the Somerset branch.[13]

From the outset the Lincolnshire Farmers' Union had political aims. Its successor, the national union, enlarged upon them. Ambitious parliamentary programmes were proposed in the early years, nearly all of which achieved little. Yet the instincts of the union were correct.

Agriculture in the 20th century was entering a new phase of political activity and state influence. Governments were already doing more before the Lincolnshire union was founded. The trend had been set in motion through the Royal Commissions appointed during the Great Depression. Arising partly from their recommendations, legislation affecting agriculture quietly began to build up. Agriculture was given its own department of government in 1889, the Board of Agriculture, with Henry Chaplin, squire of Blankney, as its first President. Measures such as the Agricultural Holdings Acts, derating of agricultural land and legislation to promote smallholdings followed. None of this was the return to protection for which many farmers in Lincolnshire had longed, and it seemed very tame and limited in effect. Nevertheless, the political environment in which agriculture operated was now changing and in their early awareness of that the founders of the Lincolnshire Farmers' Union were true pioneers.

The First World War

The early months of the First World War followed a traditional pattern. Demand for the produce of home agriculture immediately revived; in turn, the prices on markets, still free, started to rise. Prices of cereals rose steadily during the autumn of 1914. At Lincoln market wheat was 37s 6d a quarter in the week ending 1 August. By the beginning of December it had risen by nearly 14 per cent to 42s 8d. The price of barley rose by a similar percentage, and oats by 29.4 per cent from 19s 9d to 25s 7d. Cereal prices continued rising during the following weeks. By the following year the gazette average price for wheat, at 52s 11d a quarter, was 51.3 per cent above the average for 1914, oats were 44.2 per cent higher, and barley 37.4 per cent. The trend continued. As part of its policy of encouraging increased production of cereals, the government introduced guaranteed minimum prices of 60s a quarter for wheat and 38s 6d for oats in 1917. Market prices comfortably exceeded that, even when the government's buyer, the Wheat Commission, was empowered to set a maximum price. The official average for wheat in 1917 was 75s 9d a quarter. Expressed as an index, taking 1913–14 as 100, by 1917–18 the index for cereals had reached 234.[14]

Table 8 Acreages sown to cereals during the First World War

	1914	1915	1918
Wheat	175,001	219,803	224,117
Barley	201,170	163,344	180,870
Oats	117,718	133,154	141,216

Source: Agricultural Returns

The rising prices had immediate effect on corn-growing. Lincolnshire farmers, in common with those throughout the country, responded by sowing more wheat. An additional 363,000 acres were sown to wheat in England in 1914–15, and the result in Lincolnshire is shown in Table 8. The total acreage in the county under the three main cereal crops of wheat, barley and oats increased from 493,889 acres in 1914 to 516,301 acres the following year. Wheat saw the greatest increase, by 25 per cent, and the acreage of oats increased by about 13 per cent. The acreage of barley, however, fell, and it can be seen even from the figures in Table 8 that farmers were switching their cereal cropping from barley, which was beginning to be a problem crop as restrictions were introduced on brewing, to wheat and oats, for direct food use. Only a small amount of the increased cropping of wheat was coming from ploughing up pasture. With similar responses by farmers throughout the country, those responsible for the nation's food supply were disappointed. Farmers appeared to be cashing in on the higher prices, while hanging on to the acres of pasture they had built up during the past few decades. After a poor harvest in 1916 and with difficulties maintaining supplies from overseas, the government finally took direct action to encourage greater production of cereals and potatoes. With the Corn Production Act of 1917 a ploughing-up campaign was introduced. The late start to the campaign limited its impact, and in Lincolnshire the acreage sown to wheat in 1918 was not much greater than in 1915, while barley had started to pick up again.

Potatoes was another crop to be favoured by wartime conditions. The price index figure rose from 113 in 1914–15 to 247 in 1918–19.

Increased demand for potatoes, of course, suited Lincolnshire farmers very well. Their response in terms of planting the crop was initially modest. In parts of the Fens there were fewer acres under potatoes in 1915 than in 1914. Over the whole course of the war, however, the acreage rose by almost 25 per cent for the whole county between 1914 and 1918 to reach 102,000 acres. This expansion encouraged the development already started before the war, of spreading potato cultivation out from the Fens into other areas.

The ploughing-up campaign was intended to bring about a substantial increase in arable land, reclaiming many of the acres that had been turned to pasture during the Great Depression. 'Back to the seventies' was the slogan of R. E. Prothero, President of the Board of Agriculture. Successes were claimed for the campaign. The Commissioner for Lincolnshire, Rutland, Nottinghamshire, and the Soke of Peterborough announced in the spring of 1918 that on estates totalling 9,800 acres only 2½ per cent of land remained under pasture. W. Dennis & Sons reported that they had turned about 1,000 acres of grass to arable.[15] However, the total effect was less spectacular, limited by the late introduction of the policy, and farmers' continuing reserve about what they might be committed to. Permanent pasture in Lincolnshire in 1918 was lower by 8.6 per cent compared with 1914. Not surprisingly perhaps, the greatest proportional decline, of 17.2 per cent, was in Holland, where fenland farmers were more welcoming of the opportunity to exploit the cropping potential of their soil.

While arable farming was boosted by wartime demands, livestock husbandry was less favoured. Meat, a relatively inefficient way of converting crops to human food, was given lesser priority, especially after government started taking a more active role in food management. Fodder and feed were in very short supply throughout the war. Overseas supplies were severely disrupted. Home-grown hay was being requisitioned by the army as soon as war began to feed the horses that had also been requisitioned – to protests at the disruption to the harvest. Home-grown grains were also limited in supply as the Ministry of Food ordered milling ratios to be raised to increase the proportion going to human consumption. Even barley which would have gone to livestock was taken for bread flour. Although roots had to assume a

Table 9   Financial Results on a Kesteven Farm, 1913–27

1913	£ -157 15s 0d*	1919	£2556 3s 11d	1925	£ 529 3s 5d
1914	£ 366 1s 6d	1920	£2298 12s 3d	1926	£ 92 10s 2d
1915	£ 619 6s 1d	1921	£2160 16s 4d	1927	£ -11 1s 1d*
1916	£1702 4s 8d	1922	£1269 0s 1d		
1917	£3152 6s 5d	1923	£ 241 10s 10d		
1918	£2966 3s 1d	1924	£-181 1s 2d*		*Loss

Source: F. J. Prewett, *Progress in English Farming Systems I: milk production on arable land* (1929) p. 13

greater importance, this was not marked in the acreage returns for Lincolnshire. There were too many other pressures on the arable. Livestock farming, then, was facing great difficulty. Sheep in particular suffered badly. A report early in 1918 that difficulties in obtaining cake from manufacturers were holding back sheep was typical of the many problems. Numbers of sheep in Lincolnshire had been recovering during the years immediately before the war, but now they fell back sharply. After reaching just short of 1,100,000 in 1910, numbers of sheep dropped to 822,122 in 1915, and continued to fall throughout the war and beyond. By 1937 numbers were down to 536,000. Numbers of cattle were maintained, fluctuating around the 250,000 they had been before the war, although there were similar difficulties in maintaining beef production. 'Fat beef in north Lincolnshire is not being produced, nor are fat pigs, as the Controller's Orders have successfully stopped that. His policy is producing a scarcity.' These restrictions on the supply of feed, and other control orders, were felt more sharply in the later years of the conflict and contributed to a decline in the number of pigs.[16]

The rising prices and revived demand brought on by the war were enough to give farming's financial position a much healthier appearance. Farmers now found they could earn profits that they had not known for many years. Peter Dewey's calculations of British farming profits show returns of 2 per cent on capital in 1914 reaching

10.6 per cent in 1917.[17] These results were achieved largely by the fact that costs rose by much less than prices and incomes. Rent in particular was held down and barely changed throughout the war. Other costs rose. Labour was more expensive by 66 per cent in 1918 over 1914, much of the increase coming after the government introduced minimum wages in 1917. Most of the farmer's purchases rose greatly in price. Linseed cake had been 151s 9d a ton in June 1913. Five years later it was 380s a ton. Other feeds, fertilizers, and implements all rose in price considerably. The effect on the farmer's accounts was less than it might have been, however, because all of these, and labour, were in such short supply that he simply could not get hold of them. Table 9 shows how these changes in fortunes affected one farm in south Kesteven, taking returns from 1913 to the late 1920s. Corn was the principal arable crop, and there was a good dairy trade.

Wartime profits came at a price, of course. One was the introduction of greater state controls, not all of which were appreciated. 'Farmers are continually receiving forms', commented the north Lincolnshire correspondent for the *Agricultural Gazette* as farming was being drawn into the world of bureaucracy. Along with the ploughing-up campaign in 1917 came the county war agricultural executive committees, into whose hands execution of the policy was placed. The new committees for the parts of Lincolnshire, reconstituted from non-executive bodies set up in 1915, got to work in the autumn of 1917, sending out their orders specifying fields of pasture and meadow to be broken up for arable cropping. Their authority could over-ride cropping patterns and rotations established in tenancy agreements. With the concentration on increasing production of wheat and potatoes, farmers found themselves being ordered to alter their arable cropping to increase the acreage of wheat at the expense of barley and to some extent of oats. Several minor crops, especially some of those in the Fens, such as mustard, were discouraged. Conversely, others among the lesser crops were promoted. Onions was one; flax, which had military uses, was another. In 1917 the government decided to encourage flax production in order to make up for the loss of overseas supplies, mainly Russian. They took over a disused flax mill at Pinchbeck. A meeting of farmers was held at Spalding in January 1918, and most of those attending agreed to grow flax, some offering as many as 50 acres.[18]

The most irksome official control was the provision for a minimum wage for agricultural labourers. This was to remain a contentious matter for some time after peace returned, as will be seen shortly. With or without minimum wages, labour was the greatest problem facing farmers throughout the war. It was in short supply and expensive. Military service took many men away from their farms. In the initial burst of enthusiasm that saw thousands join Kitchener's army in the autumn of 1914, men were encouraged to go. The Earl of Ancaster was one who sent a circular to his estate employees guaranteeing to hold their jobs open for them on their return from the army. It was not only the armed forces that took men away. In Lincolnshire the construction of airfields had a marked effect on local labour supply. As time went on, with no speedy end to the war, there was greater reluctance to lose workers. Farmers now pleaded with the authorities to be allowed to keep their men, and the workers were likewise keener to avoid conscription.[19] They were supported by the war agricultural committees, one of whose roles was to help alleviate labour shortages. In the spring of 1917 the government made a concession: no full-time agricultural worker was to be called up unless the local committee gave its consent. Large numbers of men were exempted from military service under this provision. The Lindsey committee issued 2,160 certificates of exemption in the first three months of 1918. However, heavy losses on the western front in early 1918 led to the abandonment of agricultural exemption.[20]

The shortage of labour could vary from area to area. The Holland division of the county was reckoned to have been less denuded than many others, partly because of the many small farms, while many of the large intensive agricultural businesses of the area managed to retain a good proportion of their labour.[21] To help make up for the loss of regular workers, several irregular sources of labour were deployed. Women from village and town in considerable numbers, and children, came to help. The government drafted in prisoners of war and soldiers on leave, and after the ploughing-up campaign was started their numbers were increased. None of this extra labour supply was completely without problems. Accommodation could be in short supply, especially in the Fens. Here, there were examples of soldiers refusing to stay when the farmer could only offer a shed for sleeping quarters. The Women's Land Army was founded in 1916 as an attempt to create a supply of more regular volunteer workers. The timing of school holidays was rearranged in Lindsey to enable schoolchildren to help with haytime and potato harvest. Their labour was not thought suitable for the cereal harvest.[22]

The war introduced many farmers to tractor power. There were tractors available before the war. Lincolnshire's engineering firms had been involved in some of the stages in their development: the Hornsby-Akroyd oil engine and caterpillar tracks, for example. Practical working tractors had arrived with the Ivel model in 1903, followed by the Saunderson and others. There were some in Lincolnshire, but their numbers were still small by 1914. The war greatly increased their numbers, chiefly through state-sponsored mechanization. The

Fig. 26 The threshing machine arrives at a farm in Middle Rasen, 1916. Threshing contractors usually worked within cycling distance of their homes
Source: North East Lincolnshire Libraries

government bought about 500 tractors during the first two years of war, distributed around the country by the war agricultural executive committees. Some tractors were also brought on to farms by military contracts to bale hay. In these early years a wide variety of types of tractor, and the associated implements, was employed. Not all were equally reliable, but they did give many farmers their first real experience of tractors. In 1917 the government decided to standardize and ordered 5,000 Fordson tractors. Under the ploughing-up campaign, the war agricultural executive committees retained control of a high proportion of the new tractors. As part of the continuing stream of publicity about the successes of the campaign, weekly notices were published of the work accomplished by tractor power. Typical was the announcement that during the week ending 29 March 1918 the Bourne unit, of 9 tractors, had cultivated 566 acres and ploughed 5 acres.[23] The Ministry also ran a monthly ploughing competition, the object not to plough the best furrow, but the greatest number of acres. As well as tractors, the government ordered over 100 sets of steam ploughing tackle from John Fowler & Co. of Leeds. Several of these steam ploughs came, new or second-hand, to the Fens, to the benefit mainly of peacetime potato production, for by the time many of these orders were fulfilled the war was close to its end.

If the Edwardian years had brought modest but steady recovery, the rapid changes during the war had added a surge. Farming in 1918–19 appeared reasonably comfortable, with profits undreamed of for many years. However, farmers approached peace with caution. Their union in its dealings with government was calling for a 'permanent' settlement for agriculture, to which the response was the appointment of another Royal Commission, in 1919, followed by the Agriculture Act of 1920. That seemed a promising start, but not enough to convince many farmers: the acreage of permanent grass was already starting to rise again by 1921.

The post-war depression

A press report of January 1921 noted that north Lincolnshire farmers were 'disappointed at having to take less than 95s per quarter' for wheat. It had been as low as 80s in December. 'If these prices, hours of labour and other expenses continue, wheat cannot continue to be produced,' the reporter concluded.[24] Clearly, economic reality was reasserting itself after the war. Prices for agricultural commodities fell rapidly in the early 1920s as free markets were allowed to resume, both at home and internationally. As supplies returned to normal the British government was able to abandon rationing and wartime controls. First to go were controls on meat and fatstock in December 1919, followed by milk and dairy produce in February 1920. Cereals were the last to be freed, in an episode that went down in farming's folk history as the 'Great Betrayal'. The guaranteed prices introduced in 1917 had been renewed by the Agriculture Act 1920. The following year the Act was repealed. At the time there was hardly a protest from farmers. Their concerns lay elsewhere. Ruling prices were then still higher than the guaranteed minima, farmers were more bothered about the activities of the Wheat Commission in trying to enforce maximum prices, and even more bothered about the Act's provisions for minimum wages. It was only later that farmers generally came to realize what had been taken away and to see the repeal as betrayal.

With free markets prices were bound to come down from the artificial heights reached during the final stages of the war. If 95s a quarter for wheat was a disappointment in early 1921, it soon seemed untold riches. The official Gazette price of wheat for 1921 was 71s 6d per quarter. From 1923 prices were quoted by the hundredweight, and the average for that year was 9s 10d, about 42s by the former measure. That was a very poor year, and wheat for the next few years hovered around 11s to 12s per hundredweight, before falling sharply again from 1929. Wool prices fell dramatically after controls were lifted. In July 1921 prices of Lincoln wool were only a third of what they had been twelve months previously. Most other farm products fell in price by between a third and a half from their position in 1918–20. That still left many of them higher than they had been before 1914, and they stabilized for the rest of the 1920s, until the international slump in 1929 brought renewed falls.

Stable prices in the mid 1920s brought little comfort to many of Lincolnshire's farmers. The sharp falls in price affecting their prime products of wheat, barley, and wool immediately after the war had been enough for the bottom to drop out of their businesses, for the depressions of the 1920s and 1930s were primarily in arable. The extent to which arable farming was at a disadvantage was shown in the Ministry of Agriculture's price indexes. Set at 1936–38 = 100, the values in 1938 put arable products at 93, compared with 104 for livestock, and 111 for fruit and vegetables.[25] Reports from around the country at this time all emphasized the difficulties for arable farming. Of the Cotswolds it was written in 1939, 'No area in the country has suffered more from the effects of the farming depression since the last war.'[26] Many of the Essex clays went out of cultivation again, to be left until they were reclaimed at the beginning of the next war. Arable-farming Lincolnshire shared in these difficulties, and in particular the light-soiled uplands did so, as will be seen shortly. That is not to say that livestock farming was trouble free. Lincoln wool prices fluctuated widely during these two decades, but for the most part were similar to those that prevailed before 1914. The specialist trade in breeding stock fell off as well. In most years the sale of Lincoln rams was not what it had been before the war. A purchase of 384 rams by the Russian government in 1936 was an exception to the general trend.[27]

Besides falling prices, the second major problem for post-war farmers was that their costs had got out of control. In particular, labour costs became a very sore point. It was seen in Chapter 7 how difficult it was for farmers during the Great Depression to keep the labour bill down. Now it was even harder. Before the war wages had been rising with the general upturn in the economy, and they continued to do so as war began. The Corn Production Act 1917 introduced minimum wages, controlled by Wages Boards, and the Agriculture Act 1920 renewed this measure. The minimum was first set at 25s a week in 1917. That compares with average weekly rates for ordinary labourers in 1914 of 16s 6d in Lindsey, 15s in Kesteven and 18s in Holland. The official minimum was increased by stages until it was 46s in August 1920. That was for a working week of 48 hours in winter, 50 in summer, which was considerably less than the 60 hours common in summer before 1914. Farmers everywhere loathed the controls, and Lincolnshire's farmers were as vociferous as any in their complaints. A reporter from north Lindsey writing in the *Agricultural Gazette* in 1919 bemoaned the fact that 'rising wages and a reduction of hours threaten to make farming impossible. As it is we are only doing necessary work, and such things as hedges, dykes, roads, etc. are much neglected.' Farmers cut back on labour if they could: 'one man spared means £140 per year', commented one. It was this conviction that agriculture was being strangled by labour controls that caused farmers to press for the return of a free market. 'Why not let corn and labour find its own level, and all have cheap food again? The sooner the better for all,' wrote an east Lincolnshire correspondent for the *Farmer and Stockbreeder*. The repeal of the Agriculture Act abolished the wages regulations. For many this was a cause for much rejoicing, for the implications of the simultaneous removal of the price guarantees were less immediately apparent.[28]

However, the pressure of labour costs did not abate. With repeal of the regulations wages fell rapidly. Despite this farmers were not satisfied that they had labour costs down to an equilibrium, and their continued pressure for further reductions introduced rancour between employer and worker. There were a number of disputes. Early in 1922, for example, the 60 to 70 men at the farms of W. Dennis & Son at Deeping St Nicholas were on strike for several weeks. At issue were working hours. Dennis's wanted their men to work 54 hours a week in March and April for 34s.[29] Further disputes followed in 1923, though none in Lincolnshire were as bitter as the one in Norfolk that spring. The attention attracted by that dispute ensured that the Labour government of 1924 enacted the Agricultural Wages (Regulation) Act. It brought back minimum wages and the wages boards, and they were to stay. The boards pushed wages back up slightly. The new minimum set for Lincolnshire was 36s a week. The downward pressure on wages continued, but the boards managed to hold rates steady. They did have to negotiate reductions sometimes. Renewed depression following the Wall Street Crash of 1929 especially prompted further wage cuts. The Lincolnshire wages boards agreed in 1931 to a reduction of the minimum wage by 2s a week to 30s for a 53-hour week. For the farmers this was still not enough, and there were campaigns for the wages boards to be abolished.[30]

With prices falling once more, the familiar cycle of rebates and reductions in rent started again, and continued with renewed vigour after the financial crash of 1929. Estates were selling land and more farmers were owners of land, but the movements of rent retained their impact and significance. In early 1932 Sir Berkeley Sheffield of Normanby Hall was making rebates on his tenants' rent of 25 per cent. The following year the Earl of Ancaster offered rebates of 20 per cent. On the Yarborough estates rebates introduced in the late 1920s were still being made in 1934, by which time they were of 25 per cent.[31] Farms of all sizes were affected. The smallholders of Holbeach Crown Colony were petitioning their landlords, the Ministry of Agriculture, for a reduction in rent in March 1930, because of 'the severe losses resulting from the prevailing depression in agriculture'.[32] While the question of wages had the highest profile, economies in other areas were being pursued by most farmers. Expenditure on the construction and repair of buildings dropped markedly. Unlike during the Great Depression, few new farm buildings were built after the First World War. For several years investment in implements and machinery was modest. Other casualties of these times included the Kirkstead Agricultural Society, wound up in 1930 as agricultural depression reduced the numbers attending its shows.[33]

A further examination of Table 9 (see above p. 188) shows the extent of the change in fortunes after the end of war. The early 1920s produced a downturn as sharp and as penetrating in its effects as the late 1870s. Any excess profits generated by the war years were quickly wiped out. Capital was drained away just as much as during the late 19th century. By 1931, farmers' capital, it was reckoned, had declined by 50 per cent since 1924. Many farmers found themselves in a vicious circle, short of capital to invest in labour-saving implements, and then burdened with the wages of the workers they had still to employ. This was one reason why the numbers of farm workers in Lincolnshire fell by only 2 per cent between 1921 and 1931, a much lower rate of decline than before 1914 (Table 2, p. 43 above). Some stability was regained during the later 1920s, but after the Wall Street Crash in 1929, the spiral went downwards again, reaching its full depths in 1931–32. Farmers were leaving the industry. Bankruptcy remained a small part of the total numbers giving up, but the national change in the number of bankruptcies among farmers from 5,900 in 1921 to 7,321 in 1932 demonstrates the trend. After 1932 things began to improve, although many farmers, especially on smaller farms, were still losing money in the later 1930s.[34]

With arable farming under intense pressure, cultivation and production quickly returned to its pre-war pattern. The number of acres sown with wheat in the county had already fallen back to pre-war figures by 1924. Over the period from 1918 to 1931 there was a fall of 28.8 per cent in the acreage of wheat. The acreage of oats was similarly 24.2 per cent lower in 1931 than it had been in 1918. This was a decline of longer-term duration, however, for the horse population, which consumed most of the oats, was now in decline. By 1939 the area sown to oats was down a further 15.7 per cent. The acreage of barley declined by 21.6 per cent between 1918 and 1931. Some of the land taken out of cereal cultivation was returned to grass: permanent pastures and rotation grasses increased in acreage by 11.5 per cent in this period. In districts of heavy soil much arable was allowed to go to grass. The Fens went against this trend and became even more heavily concentrated on arable, increasing the production of potatoes, sugar beet, vegetables and fruit. These will be considered in more detail in the next chapter.

Light-land farming under pressure

The inter-war depression hit all arable farming hard, but was a disaster for light-land farmers. The Lincolnshire Wolds were described in the early 1920s as 'an economic white elephant'.[35] Sharp falls in the prices of cereals and wool knocked the bottom out of sheep–corn husbandry. Not even the barley which had helped the farmers of this area during the 1880s and 1890s could be relied on now, for beer consumption dropped by about 50 per cent between the wars and with it the demand for malting barley. The acreage of barley in Lincolnshire, 201,000 acres in 1914, had declined to 101,300 by 1937.

Light lands across the whole of England were affected badly. The established sheep–corn husbandry of the southern downs gave way to alternate husbandry to save labour, involving long grass leys, which were stocked on the short term with 'flying flocks' of sheep. Often these were of hill breeds, such as Cheviot, or cross-breds, in preference to the Down breeds. There was increased permanent pasture and in areas difficult to cultivate land was left more or less uncultivated and weedy.[36] On the downs of Hampshire, Wiltshire, and Berkshire dairying was another activity to which farmers could turn.

The light lands of Lincolnshire suffered as badly as anywhere. The weakness of the market for sheep, and for long-woolled sheep in particular, had a devastating effect. John Bygott, in the early 1920s, thought that 'In a sense the sheep map is an index of the agricultural methods employed in the Wolds and the Heath, where the four-course rotation ensures that there shall always be considerable areas under turnips.'[37] Farming in the Wolds in the 1930s, reported A. G. Street, was still a 'sheep and turnip' business.[38] The northern Wolds were where several of the best pure-bred flocks of Lincoln sheep were to be found, good for the breed's survival and for the shows, but a problem in the economic conditions. Little appeared to have changed. Frank Hoyle, a farmer at Kirmington, gave voice to traditional views when he told a reporter from *Farmers' Weekly* that the livestock on his farm had a subsidiary role as 'muck-making machines'. This, indeed, was the problem with the Wolds, and to a lesser extent the Heath: finding ways of adapting to new conditions was proving very difficult. The farmers here did not have recourse to all the means of dealing with the problems that were open to those on the downs of southern England.

Change, however, did come. Its extent varied considerably according to the nature of local soils. Where soils were poor, in parts of the central and southern Wolds, for example, there were problems. This land did not lend itself to change from the sheep–barley system and there was 'tenacious resistance to change'. In the 1930s much of this land fell back into a very poor state of cultivation.[39] On what Makings called the 'good wold' of the northern Wolds there were greater opportunities to vary the pattern of farming and to break away from the orthodoxy of sheep–barley husbandry on a four- or five-course rotation. Use of artificial fertilizers enabled new crops – sugar beet, potatoes, and vegetables – to be introduced. This did not happen before many farmers had been forced out of farming, the innovations being left to newcomers acquiring land cheaply. Frank Hoyle at Kirmington was less traditional than his comment about the role of livestock makes him seem. He actually moved to the Wolds in 1931, where he adapted the arable regime to include more potatoes and many minor crops, such as savoys, carrots, and red cabbage, all of them very successful. Others like that included Ralph Godfrey, who took a farm at Melton Ross in 1932, to add to his land in the Trent Valley, and started growing potatoes there.[40]

Arable remained dominant, 75 per cent or more of the acreage of most farms. Wheat was now usually the principal crop following the decline in the market for barley. The Wheat Act of 1932 had the effect of reinforcing this change. As likely as not, barley followed wheat in the rotation. New crops were nearly always cash crops: potatoes and sugar beet thus substituted for turnips. Peas for human consumption were another crop that was more often grown now, sometimes under contract to processors, while the other vegetables played valuable supporting roles. Farmers here might have held on to traditional views on the role of livestock, but their management of livestock was changing. It was less usual to breed sheep now. Instead stores were bought for over-wintering and summer flying flocks were becoming more common. As a result the total numbers of sheep on the Wolds fell. Cattle feeding was also less popular. However, on many farms the effect of these changes was not to diminish but to maintain the contribution of livestock to the farm's income.

One who adopted many of these techniques was A. A. Spilman, farming 700 acres at Kirmington in the mid 1930s. The four-course of the sheep–corn system had been replaced by a mixed six-course rotation. This enabled new cash crops of potatoes and sugar beet to be introduced in order to maintain maximum output from arable farming. All the crops of the farm were sold. Malting barley was still an important crop, and 250 acres were sown to it. The potato acreage of 90 allotted him by the Potato Marketing Board was set with King Edwards and Majestics. Spilman employed livestock to help maintain the soil's fertility, and they were fed on purchased proprietary feeds. His emphasis was on winter stock, with some additional flying flocks in summer. In the autumn 140 steers, mainly Lincoln Red, 600 Hampshire Down-Lincoln cross lambs and 250 store pigs were bought in to over-winter.[41]

The Lincoln sheep's reign as the supreme breed of these districts came to an end. The breed became 'the despised and rejected of sheep' as demand for small sheep told against the Lincoln's virtues of bulk, slow maturity and a great fleece.[42] Prices for sheep were falling, but those for Lincoln sheep fell more heavily. Lincoln rams at Sleaford fell from £10 5s 8d to £3 10s between 1930 and 1932, while the Hampshire Down price fell from £8 8s 2d to £6 13s.[43] Export sales of breeding stock were also badly affected. Annual reviews of the sheep breeding trade in the 1930s reported poor trade for longwools in general and Lincolns in particular, while the Down breeds were doing much better. Outbreaks of foot and mouth disease had imposed restrictions on overseas trade in livestock in some years. Even when the ports were open, sheep breeders in Argentina were importing fewer rams from Lincolnshire. They had locally bred Lincoln stock, and bought some Lincolns from New Zealand. Only 50 Lincoln rams were sold for export in 1935. By that time several leading breeders were abandoning the Lincoln. Clifford Nicholson, champion breeder at the Royal Show in 1919 and winner of many other prizes with his Lincolns, began to sell his flock for export from 1928 onwards, and gradually replaced it with Romney Marsh sheep. Shortly after the Second World War the sheep of the Heath and Cliff were said to be mainly Suffolk or Oxford crosses. On the Wolds the Lincoln still held its own, but, with only 44 registered pedigree flocks in 1947 compared with 330 in 1901, its existence was becoming less secure.[44]

The experience of light-land farming on the Cliff and Heath was similar. Arable remained dominant, and as with the north Wolds the opportunities to widen the basis of cash cropping were taken. At Sudbrook, near Ancaster, R. G. Simpson, moving in from Scotland in 1936, brought in a number of practices from his home country, including the Clydesdale horses he employed. Potatoes were his principal new cash crop. In this he shared with many other farmers of the district. The yield of 7 tons an acre could hardly compare with the 10 tons or more on the Fens. The quality, however, could be good, and 'limestone Edwards' could command a premium in the market. Grown at minimal cost, potatoes were profitable on a crop of good quality.

Mostly main crop potatoes were grown, but some growers were successfully introducing early varieties in the late 1930s.[45]

The state to the rescue?

Relationships between farmers and the government in the 1920s were not the most cordial. Farmers were generally dissatisfied with their treatment. The compiler of the farm notes from north Lincolnshire for *Farmer and Stockbreeder* in 1926 commented: 'We have heard a good deal of what the Government is going to do for the farmers – lending money to drain the land. This is not what we want. Farmers need something to enable them to make ends meet and not to have to sell our barley at 32s or 33s per quarter and oats at 26s.'[46]

At heart, most farmers were protectionists, especially in arable-farming areas such as Lincolnshire which had borne the brunt of the foreign competition in cereals since the onset of the Great Depression. At that time some farmers had campaigned actively for tariffs. William Frankish was one, who joined Joseph Chamberlain's Tariff Commission. Most put up with the present political reality of free trade and hoped for other means of support.[47] This was the line generally followed by the Lincolnshire Farmers' Union and its national successor from its foundation into the 1920s.

Meanwhile the farmers' attitude to government developed into ambivalence at best, with a strong line of scepticism. They liked the idea of support from government, but they maintained a hearty suspicion of state activity. This had already surfaced in the last quarter of the 19th century in the attitudes of Lincolnshire farmers to statutory regulation of tenant right. The same happened with the Corn Production Act and the Agriculture Act. Guaranteed prices for cereals were welcomed. However, farmers were not always comfortable with the consequences of state intervention. They railed against the state controls introduced during the First World War: the powers of the agricultural executive committees, penalties for bad farming, and most especially direction over wages. The continuance of some controls after the war if anything strengthened farmers' feelings against 'farming from Whitehall'. Many called for a return to a free market in agricultural produce, and were not entirely upset at the repeal of the Agriculture Act.[48] Once it had gone, however, the vocal among Lincolnshire's farmers added their voices to the protests at Lloyd George's not keeping his promise of 1920 to maintain support for farming. As prices fell during the early 1920s discontent grew. Not even the introduction of a subsidy for sugar beet could erase the mutual suspicion which characterized relationships between farmers and government in the aftermath of the repeal of the Agriculture Act. Farmers continued in their dislike of state intervention, especially the workings of the wages boards, while grumbling that the government was not doing more to help lift them out of the depression.

Even with governments that were generally non-interventionist by inclination, some measures intended to help farmers suffering from depressed economic conditions were introduced in the 1920s. A subsidy for growing sugar beet was introduced in 1925 specifically to help arable farmers in the eastern counties. Results were dramatic, and will be examined fully in the next chapter. Measures to promote efficiency in marketing were introduced with the Agricultural Products (Grading and Marketing) Act of 1928 which encouraged grading of produce to agreed standards. Produce so graded could be sold under the 'National Mark'. These were voluntary schemes, and of the products of Lincolnshire farming only eggs were affected. Loans for improvements were made available, principally under the Agricultural Credits Act 1928. Although the commentator quoted above might have despised them, many farmers in Lincolnshire did take up these loans. Long-term loans granted under this Act to farmers in the county amounted to £687,215 by 1934. This was the second highest amount awarded to any county, because, reported the *Farmers' Weekly*, Lincolnshire had been one of the greatest sufferers in the depression. The average amount borrowed was £4,000, and the loans were for sixty years.[49]

Compared with either protection or price support, these measures perhaps were rather modest in their contribution to renewal in farming. For the most part, success in the inter-war years was to come by farmers seizing new market opportunities, to which we turn in the next chapter.

Notes to Chapter 9

1   H. Rider Haggard, *Rural England* (1902), v. 2, p. 241. LAO,
     MON25/13/18, 13 December 1897.
2   LAO, 2HEN2/2/64.
3   LAO, 9ANC 2/B/3/4, 2/C/1/3.
4   LAO, Misc Don 157.
5   Gavin McCrone, *The Economics of Subsidising Agriculture* (1962) pp. 173–4.
6   Rider Haggard, *Rural England,* v. 2, pp. 200–1.
7   G. E. Collins, 'Agriculture', *Victoria County History, Lincolnshire,* v. 2 (1906)
     pp. 405–6.
8   J. R. Bellerby, *Agriculture and Industry Relative Income* (1956) p. 56.
9   Michael Fenton, *Farmers and Farming in Lindsey 1900–1914* (1978) p. 28.
     Tom Tiffin, *The Origin of the Farmers' Union* (1949) pp. 9ff.
10   *Lincolnshire Chronicle,* 17 September 1904.
11   *The Agrarian History of England and Wales, vol. VII, 1850–1914,* ed. E. J. T.
     Collins (2000) pp. 329, 664, 667, 680. A. H. H. Matthews, *Fifty Years of
     Agricultural Politics* (1915) pp. 379–80. Alistair Mutch, 'Farmers'
     Organizations and Agricultural Depression in Lancashire, 1890–1900',
     AgHR, v. 31 (1983) pp. 26–36.
12   *Farmer and Stockbreeder,* 12 January 1931, p. 66.
13   *British Yearbook of Agriculture 1908–9* (1908) p. 126. *NFU Yearbook* (1926).
     B. A. Holderness, 'Agriculture', in *Twentieth Century Lincolnshire,* ed. Dennis
     R. Mills (1989) pp. 58–9. G. Cox, P. Lowe, and M. Winter, 'The Origins
     and Early Development of the National Farmers' Union', *AgHR,* v. 39
     (1991).
14   *Royal Commission on Agriculture* (1919), Minutes of Evidence, I, appendix,
     p. 5.
15   *Farmer and Stockbreeder,* 4 March 1918.
16   *Agricultural Gazette,* v. 87, 7 January 1918, p. 9.
17   Peter E. Dewey, 'British Farming Profits and Government Policy during
     the First World War' *EcHR,* 2nd ser., v. 37 (1984) pp. 374–8.
18   *Agricultural Gazette,* v. 87, 21 January 1918, p. 60, 25 November 1918,
     p. 466.
19   Alan Armstrong, *Farmworkers: a social and economic history 1770–1980* (1988)
     p. 161. Pamela Horn; *Rural Life in England in the First World War* (1984)
     pp. 30, 81.

20   John Sheail, 'The role of the war agricultural executive committees in the food production campaign of 1915–1918 in England and Wales', *Agricultural Administration*, v. 1 (1974) p. 150.

21   RC on Wages and Conditions of Employment, 1919, v. 2, reports of investigators, XXI, Lincolnshire (Holland), para. 28c.

22   Horn, *Rural Life in England in the First World War*, pp. 105, 175.

23   *Agricultural Gazette*, 8 April 1918.

24   *Farmer and Stockbreeder*, 31 January 1921.

25   B. R. Mitchell and H. G. Jones, *Second Abstract of British Historical Statistics* (1971) p. 190.

26   B. J. Fricker, 'The Agriculture of Gloucestershire', *Journal of the Bath and West of England Society*, 6th ser., v. 14 (1939–40) p. 20.

27   Summaries of the export trade annually in *Farmer and Stockbreeder Year Book*.

28   *Wages and Conditions of Employment in Agriculture. General Report*, Cmd 24 (1919) p. 207. *Agricultural Gazette*, v. 90, 1 September 1919. *Farmer and Stockbreeder*, 14 February 1921. Edith Whetham, *The Agrarian History of England and Wales, vol. 8, 1914–1939* (1978) pp. 140–1.

29   *Farmer and Stockbreeder*, 20 February 1922, p. 436.

30   *Ibid.*, 17, 24 August 1931. Armstrong, *Farmworkers: a social and economic history 1770–1980*, p. 183.

31   *Farmer and Stockbreeder*, 8 February 1932, 18 July 1933, 14 May 1934.

32   *Ibid.*, 24 March 1930.

33   *Ibid.*, 3 March 1930.

34   *Ibid.*, 17, 24 August 1931. J. H. Smith and P. R. Richardson, *Farming in the Lincolnshire Limestone Areas 1936 to 1947* (University of Nottingham, 1950) p. 79.

35   John Bygott, *Eastern England* (1923), pp. 171–2.

36   See *Farmers' Weekly*, 17 September 1937, p. 23.

37   Bygott, *Eastern England,* pp. 251–2.

38   A. G. Street, *Farming England* (1937) p. 84.

39   S. M. Makings, *Lincoln Wold Farming* (1939) p. 32. L. Dudley Stamp, *Land Utilization Survey of England, parts 76–77* (1942) pp. 473, 482–3. H. R. Fell, 'Two Notable Lincolnshire Farmers' *JRASE*, v. 152 (1991) p. 40.

40   *Farmers' Weekly*, 18 March 1938, pp. 32–3. Fell, 'Two Notable Lincolnshire Farmers', pp. 36–46..

41   Allan Knox, 'The East Midland Counties', in *Regional Types of British Farming*, ed. J. P. Maxton (1936), p. 109. *Farmers' Weekly*, 24 June 1938, pp. 32–3.

42   J. A. S. Watson, *Rural Britain Today and Tomorrow* (1934) p. 66.

43   *Farmer and Stockbreeder*, 26 September 1932.

44 *Ibid.*, 1 July 1947, pp. 1,412–15. *Farmer and Stockbreeder Year Book* (1936) p. 139. Fell, 'Two Notable Lincolnshire Farmers', p. 37.
45 *Farmers' Weekly*, 24 June, 29 July 1938. Knox, 'The East Midland Counties', p. 108.
46 *Farmer and Stockbreeder*, 15 February 1926, p. 355.
47 R. J. Olney, *Lincolnshire Politics 1832–1885* (1973) pp. 188–92.
48 *Farmer and Stockbreeder*, 3 January, 14 February 1921.
49 *Farmers' Weekly*, 6 July 1934.

10
NEW FARMING 1925–1940

The pressures on farming during the 1920s were immense. There was necessarily retrenchment. However, just as had happened in the depression of the late 19th century, before long signs of new growth began to appear. New farming businesses were being built up, new patterns of husbandry were being developed, many based around livestock and potatoes. The high farming tradition was far from finished, as mechanization and technology played an increasing part in agricultural operations. In some areas of activity state assistance made a real difference, especially during the 1930s.

New farming, new farmers

As the experience of farming on the light lands of the Wolds and Heath showed, many of the practices that had become established by the end of the 19th century were becoming difficult to maintain. New patterns of farming were needed in the 20th century. As often as not it was a new generation of farmers that was responsible for their introduction. This was a feature that emerged during the Great Depression and continued into the inter-war years. New men came into farming during the 1880s and 1890s who had not lost capital in the late 1870s and 1880s; they often had made money in commerce and industry which they were able to invest in farming. The founders of the bulb-growing business around Spalding were a prime example: many of them entered farming from merchanting trades in the town.[1] Their approach to the business of farming reflected this background, which in turn encouraged that feeling among observers, noted in Chapter 2, that an old order was passing. The Royal Commission on Wages and Conditions in Agriculture in 1919 commented, 'Though the old traditions and prejudices are still tenacious in many parts, the best Lincolnshire farmer is today essentially a businessman.'[2]

That spirit which had brought new men into farming in the late 19th century continued. The inter-war period was a time when entrepreneurs could take advantage of low costs, especially low prices for land, and were able to expand their farming significantly. Some very large enterprises were built up quickly. Clifford Nicholson started with a 500-acre tenancy in 1912, at Horkstow at the northern edge of the Wolds. By 1939 he had 9,000 acres based on the Wolds and at Willoughton on the Cliff. Ralph Godfrey at Melton Ross, from a start on a farm of 140 acres in 1918, had reached 3,500 acres in 1939. Both men attributed much of their successes to having kept a tight grip on costs, especially labour. Nicholson, at least, was also slow to invest in new machinery. They abandoned many of the established practices of the area, hence Nicholson's disposal of his Lincoln sheep. Both looked for new crops at low cost, especially potatoes. This was the one crop that had a ready and profitable market throughout most of the 1930s, and was now grown widely beyond the Fens. Godfrey had 700 of his 3,500 acres growing potatoes in 1939.[3]

For farmers to succeed during the 1920s and 1930s, a fairly strong measure of specialization seems to have been almost a necessity. Investigators for the Royal Commission on Wages and Conditions of Employment in Agriculture 1919 noted that 'in Lincolnshire the old traditions have been so largely shaken that, wherever it is possible and a pioneer has been forthcoming, specialist crops have been introduced'. The forms of mixed farming remained largely intact, but farmers were increasingly concentrating on their livestock, or potatoes, or one of the niche markets. The Royal Commission on wages cited the growing of carrots on the light sands round Moortown and Roxby on the edge of the Ancholme clay vale as an example of such specialization.[4]

Livestock farming

For most farmers the way ahead came to be to concentrate more of their efforts on livestock. In the early 1920s the evidence of prices was not perhaps so clear. The Ministry of Agriculture's price indexes, based on 1911–13 = 100, stood at 141 for fat cattle in 1926, 157 for sheep, and

164 for wheat. The balance tipped in favour of livestock during the next couple of years, and when prices fell further after 1929, it was the price of wheat that fell sharply while livestock declined more gently. By 1931 the price index for wheat was 76, but for cattle it was 122 and for sheep 133. There was no doubt now about the benefits of livestock. The input side of livestock was also advantageous, for costs of purchased feeds were low and for Lincolnshire's arable farmers the use of home-grown cereals represented a considerable saving. Feeding regimes along high farming patterns could be maintained at fairly low cost. Livestock management was more economical of labour, bringing another important element in the accounts under greater control.

Livestock assumed greater importance in farming throughout England and Wales, and this was no less true of most of Lincolnshire. The big exception was the Fens, to which more detailed examination will be given later in this chapter. Outside the Fens, almost all the noted successful farmers of the inter-war years relied heavily on livestock. On the Kesteven limestone, for example, by 1936–39, livestock enterprises accounted for between 44 and 54 per cent of total farm receipts. This was a proportion considerably lower than for many other eastern counties. Research carried out by Cambridge University on farms in the region from Huntingdonshire to Essex showed 68 per cent of gross farm receipts already to be coming from livestock by 1930–31. The difference between these counties and Lincolnshire was that sugar beet and, especially, potatoes had a greater share of the honour. Even so, the need for livestock was undoubted. Potatoes and sugar beet were more important in the farming of the Lindsey limestone, but here, too, livestock accounted for approximately 38 per cent of receipts by the late 1930s.[5]

With an increase in livestock farming came a renewed emphasis on pasture. Peace in 1918 was followed by an immediate return of the ploughed-up land to pasture, indeed with interest, for permanent pasture in 1925 was almost 40,000 acres greater than it had been in 1914. Pasture continued to increase during the 1930s, though at a lower rate. By 1939 the combined acreage in Kesteven and Lindsey was 12.8 per cent greater than for 1918. The Fens being exceptional again, it is as well to leave Holland out of this reckoning. Lincolnshire was never

Fig. 27   Over-wintering cattle on Mr J. Popple's farms
at Hallington, 1935
Source: Museum of English Rural Life

going to become a pastoral county, but these changes had brought the
proportion of pasture in the total returned acreage of these parts to
almost 40 per cent. Although there was a greater emphasis on livestock,
the numbers recorded in the agricultural returns did not rise as much as
might have been expected. Sheep, in particular, continued to fall in
number, a reflection of the difficulties facing light-land agriculture
discussed in Chapter 7. Despite an increase by 9.2 per cent between
1936 and 1939, the sheep population of Lincolnshire in the 1930s was
no more than a third of what it had been in the 1870s and two-thirds
that of 1914. It is possible that the use of short-term flying flocks of
sheep meant that some escaped record in the June census, but that was
unlikely to alter the general trend. There was no strong trend in the
cattle population during the 1920s and 1930s. Taking only the parts of
Kesteven and Lindsey again, numbers fluctuated within a range of

about 30,000. Despite the success of farmers such as Harold Bowser (see below), numbers of cattle in the Fens declined considerably.

Much of the livestock farming continued along established lines. Winter stores and summer pastures remained common practice in the management of cattle. The strengths of the Marsh for its pastures and as a breeding ground of herds of Lincoln Red cattle remained, and in some respects were reinforced. The Popple brothers, who farmed at Hallington and Winterton, demonstrated this on a large scale. On their 2,000 acres they maintained a large herd of Lincoln Red cattle, supplemented by Irish stores bought in for over-wintering.[6] There were alterations to established practice as well, and many of the farmers from Lincolnshire who featured in the series called 'Successful Farming' run by *Farmers' Weekly* during the mid 1930s exemplified that. Nearly all of them were making their farming pay by increasing their interests in livestock. Emphases differed: one might go for pedigree stock, another fattening cattle, another a dairy herd. They were likely also to have a second string by growing a specialist crop.

William Todd, of Little Ponton Grange, was a breeder of mainly pedigree livestock. In 1935 he had 50 Shire horses, 700–1000 Hampshire Down sheep, and 60–80 Shorthorn cattle. He also had a small herd of Lincoln Curly Coat pigs. With each of these he was a successful prize-winner at regional and national shows. He sold breeding stock throughout the world. He also bred recreational horses for hunting, jumping, and riding. His other major cash crop was the wool clip. Two-thirds of his 1,100-acre farm was pasture. The arable was sown to barley, oats, turnips, and green food for sheep keep.[7] Pedigree stock also featured at the 700-acre Scothern Manor, on the clays below the Cliff, farmed by John and James Walker. Pedigree Lincoln Red cattle and Lincoln Longwool sheep were bred. A flock of Hampshire Downs was kept for early lambs. The next major line was dairying, producing grade A milk for sale in Lincoln, six miles away. This business was so important that the management of the farm was constituted as Scothern Dairy Co.[8]

Harold H. Bowser farmed 772 acres in the Fens, and demonstrated that livestock could still hold a place of importance amongst the intensive arable farming of this area. Most of his land conformed to the fenland arable pattern: 250 acres of wheat and 200 acres of potatoes. However, Bowser also developed what he called sidelines into major contributors to the balance and success of the farm. These included a large breeding herd of Essex pigs, a large stock of Lincoln Red cattle for baby beef, and Percheron horses for breeding.[9] Another farmer in the Fens who kept more livestock than many in this area was Mrs Walker of Ash Tree Farm, Spalding. Her father had been a noted breeder of Shire horses, which she kept up to some extent, but in 1925 she started a pedigree herd of Aberdeen Angus cattle, and built this up into a substantial stock. The main herd was 35 head, but with additional stock, mainly Lincoln Red, taken in for summer, she could have up to 100 head. Cropping on this 300-acre farm was mainly of potatoes, with wheat, some beans for canning, and mustard in addition.[10]

A farm that had started to develop along these lines just before the First World War was in south Kesteven, the subject of the first in the series *Progress in English Farming Systems* published by the Agricultural Economics Research Institute. This farm, of 558 acres in the 1920s, had been taken in hand in 1913 and managed as a partnership between landlord and bailiff. It was turned into a specialist dairy and corn farm with 111 acres of the total in pasture. The arable was cropped intensively, with cereals as cash crops, and roots and legumes as feed for the dairy herd of more than 80 head. Applications of manure were heavy: dung for the roots, artificials for the cereals. Upholding some of the precepts of high farming, expenditure on artificials averaged about 16s per acre each year, four times the national average. Profits, after allowing for interest on capital and management at 30s per week, were impressive. In the years from 1922 to 1927 returns averaged 13 per cent on capital.[11]

As some of the examples already quoted show, dairy farming was beginning to move out of the margins of Lincolnshire agriculture. There was even some investment in milk processing, such as a cheese factory which opened at Grimoldby, in the Marsh, in 1934. Dairying grew in importance, for example, in the largely pastoral western clay vale. Usually milking strains were introduced into herds of Lincoln Red, but some farmers went over to a true milk breed. Although farmers

Fig. 28 Bottling milk on the Culverthorpe dairy farm in the 1920s
Source: Museum of English Rural Life

were finding growing markets for milk now, dairying in Lincolnshire
was still not going to rival that of neighbouring counties. Dairy herds
were rarely larger than 20 to 30 cows. Markets were still predominantly
local, so most dairy farming continued to be near to Lincolnshire's own
towns. Farmers on the grazing lands of the inner Marsh were increasing
their dairy herds, serving Grimsby and the coastal resorts. A few
Lincolnshire dairy farms built up trade beyond their immediate district.
One example that expanded rapidly during the 1920s was Culverthorpe
Dairy Farms in south Kesteven. Started after the First World War by
Gen. Adlercron, owner of Culverthorpe Park Farm, weekly sales of
1,600 gallons of milk had been reached by 1927. By this time also, a
shop had been opened in Nottingham as trade expanded beyond the
nearby towns of Grantham and Sleaford. The farm was one of the first
in Lincolnshire to adopt machine milking, in 1923, and the business was
incorporated in 1926.[12]

**Fig. 29 A Lincolnshire Curly Coat sow at the
Lincolnshire Show of 1930**
Source: Museum of English Rural Life

The lesser branches of livestock farming showed marked increase. Pigs had always been something of a Lincolnshire speciality. Their numbers had always fluctuated greatly from year to year, a consequence of their short gestation period. They had, in any case, rarely been treated as a serious part of the farming, but rather as a useful adjunct for eating scraps, for supplying the household and some extra income. Some farmers started to take pigs more seriously during the Great Depression, but the effect on numbers had been slight. Now, however, there was real growth as many more farmers turned to pigs as more than a sideline. Numbers went up from 139,300 in 1925 to 208,000 in 1937. There were still short-term fluctuations, as a change in price could quickly be reflected in numbers. This could make pig-keeping a risky proposition, but the market was expanding also, and some farmers found it worth putting in the effort of management.

The increase in numbers was most marked in Holland, for in arable-dominated fenland pigs were the main livestock. They were cheap and easy to manage, for they used up surplus produce, waste potatoes and sugar beet. Conditions were similar in the Isle of

Axholme, where the pig market at Epworth was reopened in April 1931.[13] The importance of pigs in both of these districts demonstrates that they were an easy business for the small and middling farmer to build up. For W. H. Owen, with 120 acres at Bridge End, Horbling, pigs accounted for 90 per cent of the livestock side of the farm. Owen started farming this holding in south-west Kesteven in 1919. His output was mainly wheat and pigs. His accounting control was as meticulous as that of the more celebrated farmers featured in the magazines, and this enabled him to make a profit most years.[14] Besides the smaller farmers, there were some more specialist pig units being set up, such as one at Wroot in 1934, with 250 pigs. In addition, some of the noted farmers of large acreages now paid more attention to the pig. Harold Bowser, with over 700 acres, included a good herd of pigs among his stock. He turned to the Essex as his favoured breed in 1932, in place of the Lincoln Curly Coat. He was part of a general trend, for in the midst of the expansion of pig farming the Lincoln Curly Coat breed started the decline that, despite several attempts to revive its fortunes, ultimately led to its extinction. In 1934 for the first time there was no class for the breed at the Lincolnshire Show, its place being taken by the Essex. Mostly, Lincolnshire's farmers, as almost everywhere in the country, turned to the more productive Large White, 'the blue-eyed boy of the pig World'.[15]

Poultry farming also expanded greatly. This was a movement that had begun during the Great Depression, mainly amongst smallholders in the Fens, who had taken up egg production on a commercial scale. Numbers of all types of poultry in the county doubled between 1921 and 1939 from 1.4 million to 2.8 million. Most were hens kept for their eggs. This was another of the enterprises of W. H. Owen at Horbling, for example. Producers in a wide range of circumstances across the county took up eggs, often on a small scale. Cheap motor transport was one of the facilitating agents for this, as for many of the specialized farm products. Regular collections of produce were made by lorries calling at the farms. There had been from times past a few farmers in the Fens who kept geese for the London market, and to supply upholsterers with feathers. Poultry meat, however, remained a minor product, and the number of ducks, geese, and turkeys actually fell.[16] Both pig and poultry farming spread into the Wolds, these being among the few new enterprises not handicapped by the natural poverty of the soil. They were also able to use the grain grown on the farm.[17]

Arable farming

While wheat was on the decline, and livestock assumed greater prominence, the arable farmer had two positive areas of development in potatoes and sugar beet. Lincolnshire and the potato became even more inextricably linked, as the expansion of the crop that had gone on before the First World War continued unabated. The connection between Lincolnshire and the potato was etched into popular perceptions, for, until the plastic packs in the supermarket came to dominate, in greengrocers up and down the land the 'Lincolnshire best' sign was a common sight.

The problems associated with potatoes were just as great as ever. In particular, disease could almost wipe out a crop: it did in 1931. Prices

Fig. 30 Planting Majestic potatoes near Spalding in April 1938
Source: Lady Nevile

fluctuated wildly: the short crop of 1931 resulted in the officially recorded average price for the year reaching £8 9s per ton, but two years later it was down to £3. But the fact remained that this was one of the few crops from which farmers could be reasonably sure of a profit, in good years a very handsome profit. It had a relatively secure market: although consumption per head of the population was starting to decline, population growth meant total consumption was still rising, and there was almost no competition from imported supplies. To the hard-pressed arable farmer the potato was, therefore, a most attractive crop, and it was no wonder that it became the principal cash crop throughout much of Lincolnshire. The county was by far the largest producer of potatoes in the country, accounting for about a quarter of the total acreage in England and Wales by the end of the 1930s. Expansion of potato production was such that this proportion had

**Fig. 31 Riddling, weighing, and bagging potatoes the old way,
with hand riddles, on the Nocton estate of Smiths Potato Crisps
in February 1937. Behind are two of the wagons
used on the estate's light railway**
Source: Museum of English Rural Life

increased slightly since the mid 1920s. The example of the 'limestone Edwards', already noticed, demonstrates the way in which farmers outside of the crop's heartland in the Fens were taking it up. In parts of the outer Marsh there was an increase in the acreage of arable, principally for potatoes. The acreage growing potatoes increased between 1918 and 1939 by 14.3 per cent for Lincolnshire as a whole, much of this in the 1930s. In the early 1930s a new market opened supplying potatoes for the Smiths Potato Crisps company. Crops were grown on contract, Smiths specifying the Dutch variety Muizen. After Smiths bought the Nocton estate to supply most of their needs, contracts with other growers declined.[18]

Sugar beet offered new opportunities as the one new crop to which many farmers in Lincolnshire, including those outside the Fens, could turn. Its merits as a cash crop for the root break in the rotation had been canvassed since at least the 1870s. There were then proposals to build a factory at Long Sutton to process locally-grown sugar beet. A good deal of interest was aroused by this, and at least one of the county's seedsmen was encouraged sufficiently to offer sugar beet seed.

Fig. 32 Sugar beet being cleaned and despatched to the factory at Bardney, October 1934
Source: Museum of English Rural Life

It all came to nothing, however. Pennells dropped sugar beet from their seed catalogue in 1878, and all further attempts to get the crop into regular cultivation before 1914 failed.[19]

Interest in sugar beet did not go away. After the First World War Lincolnshire farmers were prominent among those who campaigned to have the excise duty on home-grown sugar reduced or removed altogether.[20] Interest, however, did not extend to growing the crop in any quantity. In 1920 there were only 162 acres in the whole county. Four years later, the acreage had increased to 4,538. Expansion might have continued in this way, but in 1925 much stronger stimulus came from the government. A subsidy was introduced for the growing of beet, together with support for sugar factories. Immediately the acreage sown to sugar beet increased. The county's total was 7,189 acres in 1925, and 16,320 in 1926.

The subsidy was intended to support the arable farmers of eastern England, and it was here that most of the crop was grown. In the four counties of Lincolnshire, Norfolk, Suffolk, and Cambridgeshire two-thirds of the total acreage of sugar beet in Great Britain were grown. By 1932 the acreage in Lincolnshire was 43,620 and this rose to 71,566 acres in 1934. The expansion of sugar beet growing

Fig. 33 The scene at the factory when the lorries arrived
Source: Museum of English Rural Life

was linked closely with the development of the sugar processing industry. Growers were generally under contract to one of the factories, usually one within about twenty-five miles distance from their farm. Factories at Spalding, Bardney, Brigg, and Newark were the major purchasers of Lincolnshire growers' beet, and their expansion was the determinant of the expansion of the acreage. The beet-lifting season, concentrated into a few weeks in the autumn, became a new peak in the agricultural cycle for farmers engaged in this business. Deliveries to the sugar factories at Bardney and Spalding were being made at the rate of about 2,000 tons a day during the height of the season in October 1934. In that year the value of the crop to Lincolnshire's farmers was reckoned to be about £1m.[21]

One of the benefits of sugar beet for mixed and arable farming was that established rotations could be maintained. Sugar beet was regarded as the saviour of the root break in arable rotations. In some light-land areas beet was the third most important crop after wheat and barley by the mid 1930s, although elsewhere potatoes and oats surpassed it. As well as its value as a cash crop it could be fed to stock. The common practice was to leave beet tops to be fed off by sheep, and sometimes by cattle. Beet pulp was also fed to cattle, taking the place of turnips. So important did this new crop become that in Kesteven up to one-third of the arable acreage could be under roots, nearly all sugar beet and potatoes. Turnips and mangolds had not disappeared from the rotation, but in most years of the 1930s there were fewer acres of them than of sugar beet, and they were declining. In some areas, especially in Kesteven, the traditional root crops were ceasing to be grown by the end of the Second World War.[22]

The dynamic fenlands

The fenlands were exceptional in almost all respects. They stood out, not only in Lincolnshire, but in the farming of the nation, as a success story. The whole area of the Fens, extending from southern Lincolnshire across Cambridgeshire and the Isle of Ely into western Norfolk, remained one of the most intensively farmed areas in England. 'The Holland Division of Lincolnshire,' commented S. L. Bensusan in the late 1920s, 'though utterly lacking in beauty, was full of life, activity, and, I think, wealth.'[23] Another commentator referred to the Fens as being more of a horticultural than an agricultural area by the 1930s: 'extensive horticulture' he thought perhaps described it as accurately as intensive farming.[24]

The Fens were almost entirely arable. Potatoes were the principal crop and the 'chief topic of conversation'. The extension of the acreage that had started in the Great Depression continued. In the Holland division of Lincolnshire, ploughing up during the First World War had taken the acreage to over 50,000. The following few years the acreage fluctuated, dropping sometimes to its pre-war figure, but by 1939 there were 58,139 acres under potatoes in Holland, an increase over 1918 of 15.5 per cent. In that year the acreage of potatoes exceeded that for wheat by 9,000, and took up nearly one-third (30.1 per cent) of the total arable of the division.[25] Early and maincrop varieties were grown, each in fairly distinct districts. The early crops were grown around Boston. Here the best fields were reserved for potatoes, growing them year after year for as long as the land could stand it. A green crop was grown in summer after the early potatoes were lifted. Sometimes this was a green manure crop for ploughing in before winter. Cauliflowers, spring cabbage, and broccoli might be grown, these having the added benefit of being cash crops. Even the best fields could not take permanent monoculture. Eel worm could become increasingly a problem. Rotations, therefore, would be extended, at least for a while. Wheat was usually sown after the potatoes, with peas, beans, or clover in the third year. This practice was also followed on those fields that were not suitable for continuous potato-growing.[26]

King Edward and Majestic were the most commonly grown maincrop varieties in the 1930s. In the maincrop district a reasonably definite rotation, extending over six or seven years, was followed, such as potatoes, mustard, wheat, potatoes, wheat, clover/green manure, potatoes. Crops of sugar beet, peas, beans, and oats would be inserted into that pattern, while additional crops of potatoes might be taken from good-quality fields.[27]

Potato growing continued to be intensive in all its operations and its employment of men, equipment and manures. Fenland potato growers generally chitted their seed before planting, the chitting houses then often doubling-up as tomato houses over the summer. Preparation of the land for potatoes generally involved deep ploughing, to 10 or 12 inches, sometimes deeper. Steam ploughs were often used. Nearly three-quarters of the steam ploughing sets in Lincolnshire were in the Fens.[28] All the farmyard manure available was used for the potato crop. In addition, 10 to 15 cwt per acre of artificials were applied to early potatoes, 12 to 20 cwt per acre for the maincrop. Spraying against blight was universal. Bordeaux mixture (copper sulphate and lime) had been introduced to the Fens in 1901–02. Soon its use was common, applied as a spray or as a dust. In 1914 potato growers persuaded Holland County Council to use statutory powers for the control of contagious diseases in animals to restrict movements of potatoes in order to prevent the spread of black scab.[29]

Farmers invested heavily in up-to-date equipment, but even so, many operations continued to be manual. Planting, lifting, and riddling were the most concentrated of these. The many seasonal peaks in potato cultivation caused heavy demand for casual labour. The use of gangs remained a strong feature of fenland farming as a prime means of meeting this demand. School holidays were timed to fit in with some of them, especially harvest, so that schoolchildren could be employed for some of the work. Potato ploughs and rotary spinners were used for lifting the crop, but gathering the tubers was still done by hand throughout the 1930s.[30]

Wheat was the main cereal of the Fens. It cropped heavily on this rich soil. In the 1920s, the average yield for wheat in Holland, 21.5 cwt per acre, was nearly 4 cwt greater than the average for Kesteven. In a good year, usually with a dry summer, exceptionally heavy yields could be gained. The harvest of 1933 was one of the bumper crops, giving an average yield of 24.8 cwt per acre in Holland. Another good year was 1921. Wheat was grown now at least as much for its straw as for its grain. On these rich soils the straw could become weak and lodging could be a problem. For that reason many farmers continued to use sail reapers into the 1930s rather than the binder, although 'not from choice but from necessity, as the fen farmer is exceptionally keen on the most modern and up-to-date implements'.[31] Oats was the second cereal crop. Barley was now very little grown.

Mustard grown for seed was a major crop by the 1930s. The largest acreage in the country was in Holland. Most was grown under contract to Colmans. It was a risky crop, as poor conditions at harvest could severely damage it. Many farmers preferred to harvest by hand in order to get it in as good a condition as possible. Contract farming was expanding to supply the fruit and vegetable canning industry. Many of the canners and dried vegetable processors had factories in Boston, Spalding, Peterborough, Kings Lynn, and other local towns. One of the earliest of these, for dried peas, was built at Heckington in the 1890s. Peas were the main vegetable crop. One farmer of 4,000 acres was cited as having more than 1,000 acres under peas in 1934.[32] There were 21,256 acres of peas in Lincolnshire by 1939, only about one-third of which were in the Fens, for they had proved invaluable as a cash crop in other areas as well, especially on the Wolds and Heath. After peas, the principal vegetable crops of the Fens were beans, cabbage, and cauliflower, and carrots in parts of Lindsey. The 2,286 acres of small fruit grown there in 1939 made Holland the sixth largest county for this crop in England. South Lincolnshire's fruit growing came as an extension of the fruit-growing area based on Wisbech. Most of the crop went to canning at Boston, Spalding, Wisbech, and Kings Lynn.[33]

S. L. Bensusan thought that 'the system in vogue is very modern' in fenland farming. As much sugar beet was grown as possible. In some parts the farming took on more the nature of a market garden, with bush fruit and orchards.[34] Large-scale horticulture as practised in the Fens stimulated adaptations to farm management and accounting. Cecil Robinson, who farmed about 700 acres, perhaps took the industrial nature of some of this farming to a logical conclusion. He organized separately the general farming, including potatoes, the large-scale market-garden crops such as fruit and bulbs. tomatoes and cucumbers, and cultivation under glass each into what he called 'departments'. Robinson, like many others, took marketing very seriously. He went as far as registering a trade mark for his farm. Not all did that, but many took care in the gathering, packing, and transport of their produce.[35]

Livestock had become a small part of fenland farming by the 1930s, with the exception of pigs. There were some, even among the larger farmers, who had no livestock at all other than the farm horses.

Less than a quarter of the area of Holland was under permanent pasture. The only dairying was for local demand, and almost all carried on by small farmers who had three or four milk cows as an additional line. Breeding herds were almost non-existent. Many farmers, however, still bought store cattle for fattening in yards over winter. The resale value of the cattle was a side benefit. They were kept solely for the manure, which was used mainly on the potato fields.[36]

Rents were as high as 50s per acre, and Bensusan thought this an incentive to intensive farming. Another mark of intensive farming was the employment of capital per acre. It was noted that, as well as being highly capitalized generally in the 1930s, fenland farming exhibited little difference in the amount of capital employed by large and small farms, whereas in other regions large farms tended to have less capital per acre.[37] This intensive and relatively prosperous farming of the Fens meant that wages were generally higher than elsewhere in Lincolnshire. After the First World War, 'George', a waggoner at Walmsgate, was enticed down to the Fens at Timberland, where his wage was £80 per year plus living compared with the £50 plus living that he had received on the Wolds.[38] Rates held up throughout this period. In 1937 the minimum established by the Holland wages board was 36s a week. The number of workers also remained stable in the Fens. Between 1921 and 1938 there was a decline of only 1 per cent in the number of farm workers in Holland, the one exception to a general downward trend.[39]

The Isle of Axholme experienced a similar expansion of market garden crops. Celery, already one of the main specialities of the area, became even more prominent as returns from cereals declined during the 1920s. By 1931 there were more than 1,000 acres under this crop. Celery was another crop that was grown under contract for canning.[40] By no means as extensively grown, red beetroot became another local speciality. It was introduced at the end of the First World War, and the Isle became the main centre for growing it. Lindsey County Council lent its support to growers' efforts at marketing schemes.[41]

Spalding and the bulb industry

By the mid 1930s the Holland division of Lincolnshire accounted for 48 per cent of the production of bulb flowers in Great Britain. There were

3,256 acres of bulbs here in 1935. The only other places with significant acreages of bulbs, in the hundreds of acres, were the neighbouring Isle of Ely, and Cornwall. More than 9,000 tons of cut flowers were despatched from Spalding each year. In addition there was a good trade in bulbs. The bulb fields had become a spring-time tourist attraction by the 1930s.[42]

This represented a very strong development in a trade that had modest beginnings in the 1880s. Within a decade quite a wide range of smallholders and farmers in the Spalding district had begun to grow a few bulbs, and the bulb-growing region was already extending into the neighbouring fens of Cambridgeshire.

Initially the trade had been entirely of bulbs for planting, but the late 19th century also saw a great increase in the demand for cut flowers. It was not long before the bulb growers were expanding into the cut flower trade, and this became the dominant part of their trade for about twenty years. Flowers from Lincolnshire were ready for market about a month later than those from the Scilly Isles. Stems of daffodils and other bulbs formed the bulk of the supply from the Fens, with small quantities of other flowers. 'In Lincolnshire the business of cut flowers has been taken in hand very seriously indeed,' wrote E. A. Pratt in 1906. There were then about 300 acres of bulbs and flowers around Spalding, and the business was expanding rapidly in the years before the First World War. The trade was, however, still a novelty, with a small number of serious growers, and other farmers using it as a sideline. A good day's loading from Spalding station then was about one ton of cut flowers. From the mid 1920s growers began to move back into the dry bulb market. The new Kirton Agricultural Institute set up a bulb research unit in 1930, and one of its studies was into the storage and marketing of bulbs. That, and the interest of the Empire Marketing Board helped further to encourage farmers in this move.[43]

The types of bulb grown varied over time. Snowdrops were probably the most common when the trade was a small-scale one, but the larger growers experienced susceptibility to disease and reduced their planting. Narcissi became the dominant crop of the 1890s. Not many tulips were grown then because Dutch imports could usually undercut the home-grown price. By 1914, however, the production of tulips was beginning to expand. Most other types of bulb, except hyacinths, were also grown, and a number of other flowers such as peonies.[44] Twenty years later, the objections to the suitability of hyacinths for this region were being abandoned as growers were being drawn into further extensions of the trade.[45]

Bulbs need rotation to produce good results, and were found to do best following a crop for which a heavy application of manure had been made and which had left the land in a good tilth. Potatoes were the ideal crop to precede bulbs, which thus fitted in well with other major crops of south Lincolnshire. They were commonly grown in a four-course rotation along with wheat, potatoes, and, by the 1930s, sugar beet.[46] Forcing bulbs under glass was becoming more common by 1914, this hitherto having been the work of market gardeners and florists close to London.

The bulb crop was sold almost entirely to wholesale merchants. The same was true of cut flowers, sold wholesale on commission. Some bulbs were sold to Dutch merchants who took them to be grown on in the Netherlands into plumper bulbs. The Dutch dominated the international bulb trade and it was not long before they were investing in Lincolnshire. By the 1930s several of the bulb farms were in the hands of Dutch growers.[47]

The development of bulb growing, wrote A. W. Ashby, was helping to create an agriculture 'to meet the needs of an industrial population'.[48] It was an activity requiring intensive applications of capital and labour. Up to £100 an acre might be reckoned as the capital required.[49] Depending on the varieties grown, it could cost as much as £100 per acre to buy the bulbs for planting. Labour needs were great. Many jobs, such as picking blooms, were done by women and boys.[50] The returns could be commensurately high. Even with such high costs it was possible for small growers to succeed, as their more individual attention to the crops could result in sales at higher prices.[51] In the late 1930s there were approximately 700 growers, most of them operating on a small scale. However, the large producers were dominant. The related growers, J. T. White & Sons Ltd and H. W. White & Son, were typical of this trend. Each farmed about 1,000 acres. Several of these growers had adopted limited liability, being among the first in farming to take this step, driven by the large capital requirements of bulb growing.

Mechanization

D. N. McHardy, one of the foremost researchers and writers on farm machinery in the 1930s, wrote in 1938 that in Lincolnshire 'the power farming technique can probably hold its own with any other district in the world. ... There is hardly any problem in cultivation or harvesting that has not been successfully handled by the machine-minded farmers of this area.'[52] Mechanization in this period meant primarily tractors. The ploughing-up campaign of the First World War prompted many farmers to start taking tractors seriously. During this time tractors began to appear in quantity. This was when the farms of W. Dennis & Sons started using tractors. By 1919, when additional purchases brought the firm's total to 19, they were looking to eliminate the horse within a few years. It was an ambition not achieved, for in the 1930s

Fig. 34 A Fordson tractor with potato ridger and Ransome cultivator, Nocton farm in the early 1930s
Source: Museum of English Rural Life

**Fig. 35 A Farmall tractor with narrow front carriage for
row-crop work. Many farmers in the Fens used this type for
their horticultural crops**
Source: Museum of English Rural Life

there remained several horses on this estate, whose ability to get on to
the wet fen could often outdo the tractor.[53] Another high-profile
advocate of mechanized farming was J. G. Henson of Boothby
Graffoe. Having started farming with his father in 1923 on 400 acres, by
the late 1930s he had 2,000 acres. His capital investment in machinery
amounted to £6 10s an acre. He was a firm believer in the value of deep
cultivation, and for this had a number of tracklaying tractors, with large
multi-furrow ploughs made by Ransomes, cultivators, harrows, rollers,
and seed drills.[54] Henson had lighter tractors and implements as well,
and even he retained a few horses.

The first attempt to quantify the extent of mechanization was a
census of tractors and a few other implements carried out by the
Ministry of Agriculture in 1937. It was conducted by questionnaire, but

returns were sufficient for reasonable confidence in the results. The number of wheeled and track-laying tractors recorded in England and Wales was 43,000; 3,800 of them were in Lincolnshire, the highest return in any county. The greatest density of tractor numbers was in the Holland division of the county, where the profits from potatoes had encouraged investment. In this survey the only other place with a similar density of tractors was the Vale of Evesham, another area of intensive horticulture.[55] By the late 1930s mechanization was clearly not only for the enthusiasts and the farmers on the scale of J. G. Henson. The importance of thorough cultivation for good crops, especially of potatoes and sugar beet, and the need for labour efficiency were drawing many farmers, great and small, to tractors.

The annual agricultural statistics started to record the numbers of tractors in 1942. The number in Lincolnshire had risen to 7,119, demonstrating that change was gathering pace. The statistics do not record change in the 1920s, but other comment says it was slow. In the recession of the mid 1920s few farmers could afford a tractor, not even in the Fens. Ploughing matches here could not introduce a class for tractors for shortage of possible entrants. It was said that some farmers went back to horses to save spending on repairs to the tractor. From about 1930 tractors began to appear in greater number in the Fens, and those who could not yet afford their own would hire a contractor's. It was the same in the Wolds, where the large farmers and contractors took up tractors in significant numbers at this time. Some sample surveys taken in the Wolds illustrate this process. In 1928 a random survey of 63 farms had 25 tractors between them. Ten years later a sample of 60 farms held 62 tractors.[56] Tractors were produced in a variety of shapes and sizes. Most farmers had a standard wheeled tractor, but in some areas, especially in the Fens, row-crop tractors were locally numerous, equipped with mounted toolbars for cultivating between rows of sugar beet, potatoes and horticultural crops. At the other end of the scale were the large tracklaying, or crawler tractors. These were used for heavy work, such as deep cultivating or hauling power binders. In the mid 1930s Fowler's Gyrotiller, a massive machine for subsoil cultivation, was operated by a few contractors in the county.[57]

Along with the tractor came other implements. The statistical record for these does not start until 1942, and even then does not always distinguish clearly those implements specifically for tractor power. However, combined with the other survey evidence, it is clear that farmers were not just adapting their old implements to use with a tractor, but taking on those designed for this power. Among the implements that were recorded in the official statistics were tractor-drawn ploughs, of which there were 7,639 in Lincolnshire. The disc harrows, although of much earlier origin, did not get taken into regular use until the use of tractors was well under way. The 639 disc harrows recorded in the 1942 returns are further indication that mechanization was taking hold. The power binder was not separately recorded in the 1942 statistics. It was, however, becoming a more common sight in the fields of the Wolds. The cereal harvest was generally late here, necessitating a concentrated effort, which acted as encouragement to mechanization. The same considerations were leading a few of those with large fields to start turning to the combine harvester by the end of the 1930s.[58]

**Fig. 36 A combine harvester on Mr Nevile's farm,
Aubourn in the late 1930s**
Source: Museum of English Rural Life

The combine harvester arrived in Britain during the late 1920s. The first one put to work seems to have been at Redbourn, Hertfordshire, in 1928. The first farmer in Lincolnshire to have one was G. H. Nevile, owner of the Wellingore estate. He bought his first combine harvester possibly in late 1928, but more probably in 1929; a year later he had another. Nevile acquired these machines in an effort to keep down labour costs on the land he was farming in hand. About the same time, in 1930 or 1931, a neighbour, Fred Coldron, the agricultural engineer at Wellingore, bought a combine which he used for contract work. G. H. Nevile's first combine harvester was a Caterpillar 38, his second an International Harvester No 8. Fred Coldron, who was a local agent for International Harvester, also had one of these.[59] Other farmers in the 1930s bought machines by Massey-Harris and Allis-Chalmers. No Lincolnshire farmer appears to have bought a combine made by Clayton & Shuttleworth, even though they were pioneers in its development and had their first machine on sale by 1929. It was used in Lincolnshire, but almost entirely in tests and

**Fig. 37 A traction engine driving the threshing machine
at Firsby, 1937**
Source: Mr G. H. Brown

demonstrations. Lord Londesborough's estate at Blankney was the base for most of these demonstrations. Sales were almost entirely overseas.

The Wheat Act provided some encouragement to farmers to invest in new machinery in the 1930s. At the harvest of 1934 there were 38 combine harvesters on farms in England. Five were in Lincolnshire, on four farms, two in the Wolds and two on the Heath. Those five cut that year 1,230 acres, 710 of them barley. There were four more combines hired out by a contractor in Lincolnshire, though they were perhaps not fully employed in 1934, cutting 357 acres between them. Those farms that pioneered the use of combine harvesters were in general highly mechanized. They had powerful tractors, necessary to pull the combine, and along with them the disc harrows, tractor ploughs and other cultivating implements. The adoption of the combine harvester progressed slowly, however: by the outbreak of the Second World War there were still no more than a dozen or so combines in the county. Most of them were at work on the large farms of the Heath, with a few more in north Lincolnshire. Farmers were going to need more convincing that the combine was going to repay its investment, when cereal prices seemed not very secure, even with the benefit of government support. These machines were costly to buy, and on top of that was the need for corn-drying equipment. Drying was essential, though, especially if, like Nevile, the farmer wanted to get barley of best malting quality. The prevailing view of the time that combine harvesters were really only suited to large fields added to the caution with which this machine was approached.[60]

Several commentators said that Lincolnshire's farmers maintained due caution about new machinery. There had been 'no undue rush' to obtain combine harvesters, noted one article. They were keen enough to get the best equipment they could, but, while profitable potato crops helped pay for many a new implement, money generally was tight. The decline in the numbers of horses kept for agriculture perhaps demonstrates this in another way. From a total of 51,736 horses in Lincolnshire in 1925, numbers fell to 39,843 in 1935 and to 36,454 by 1940. The rate of decline was almost exactly in line with that for England and Wales as a whole. If Lincolnshire was mechanizing at a faster rate than most counties, there were possibly some under-employed horses here, kept as insurance for when spares for the tractor could not be obtained or afforded.[61]

The Wheat Act and recovery

In March 1932 the government passed the Wheat Act, which offered some support to cereal growers. Very low prices for wheat in 1930 and 1931 preceded the introduction of this Act. The acreage of the crop in England and Wales slumped to its lowest recorded by the agricultural statistics, at 1,197,000 acres. Under the new Act, a guaranteed 'standard price' of 10s per cwt for wheat was set, which would be made up if the market price fell short. These deficiency payments were to be funded from a levy on wheat flour delivered from mills, a disguised though mild tariff, because most of the flour would be from imported wheat. The effect was dramatic. Almost immediately there were reports of increased sowing of spring wheat in Lincolnshire in 1932.[62] The full impact was not felt until the next year, when the autumn-sown wheat was recorded. The agricultural returns for 1933 showed the acreage sown to wheat in Lincolnshire was 27 per cent greater than it had been in 1932. The biggest difference was in Lindsey, where there was an increase of 28,000 acres, up by 31 per cent, an effect of the boost to sowings on the Wolds and Cliff. In Kesteven the acreage sown to wheat rose by 13,000 acres from 1932–33. This fillip to wheat was offset by reductions in the acreages of barley and oats which were not given any support under the new Act. The two together lost almost as much as the increase in wheat. Barley registered a particularly strong decline in acreage: in Kesteven it was 12,000 acres and in Lindsey barley lost 19,000 acres. The change in the acreage of oats was much less.

The government abandoned free trade in 1931, and this opened the way for new policies towards agriculture. There were two main lines of policy. One was the promotion of greater efficiency, through the creation of marketing boards. The Agricultural Marketing Acts of 1931 and 1933 were intended to strengthen the farmer's hand in marketing beyond the National Mark schemes. Producer-controlled marketing boards were to be given monopoly trading rights. Five of these marketing boards were established. The most important one nationally, the Milk Marketing Board, had little impact on arable Lincolnshire. The

Potato Marketing Board was a different matter. When it first was proposed numbers of Lincolnshire growers expressed concern that the county's acreage would be reduced, and that growers on the limestone would be disadvantaged under the proposed grading of potatoes. When it came to the vote, however, nearly all supported the creation of a board: in the national vote over 90 per cent of producers were in favour. The Potato Marketing Board started trading in the summer of 1934, and was the most important of the marketing boards for Lincolnshire farmers. Through its system of grading to take the smaller potatoes out of the market for human consumption when crops were large, the board was starting to protect growers from excessive falls in price by the time war curtailed its operation. Second in importance for Lincolnshire farmers was the Pig Marketing Board, intended to promote the production of pigmeat more into the mainstream of farming, and which got off to a slightly shaky start in the same year.[63]

The Wheat Act represented the second line of government policy in the 1930s, subsidy, direct or indirect, and some modest protection. In its use of deficiency payments the Wheat Act reintroduced a number of principles of the Corn Production Act of 1917 and its successor, the Agriculture Act of 1920. These principles were extended by the Agriculture Act of 1937, which introduced the guaranteed prices for barley and oats and increased the wheat subsidy.

Although the Wheat Act prompted immediate and striking changes in the growing of wheat, a quick recovery for arable farming was not forthcoming. The balance of cereal crops was altered. The production of cash crops had been stimulated at the expense of feed crops and livestock. The new Act, it was said, stimulated the production of wheat as a cash crop, while doing nothing to redress the shortage of capital in farming.[64] Market prices of cereals, meanwhile, continued to fall. Wheat reached its lowest price in 1934–35. The later 1930s, however, saw the beginnings of a hesitant recovery. From the lows of between 5s and 6s per cwt, the price of wheat rose to 7s 2d, even 9s 4d in 1937. Barley followed this upward movement, though oats offered more mixed returns.

Recovery in farming during the 1930s, therefore, was slow and faltering. Confidence was beginning to return to farming life, but there was still some way to go. Despite the encouragement offered by improving prices, good financial returns were not guaranteed. Many, probably most, farmers lost money at least once during the years 1936–39. Losses were most common in 1938 when a particularly poor harvest pulled farm incomes down. Crops, and incomes from them, were better in the other years, and livestock was now the major part of most farm enterprises. Even then, profits were rarely enough to make much contribution to building up capital. As a preparation for a possible war, therefore, the stimulus to cereal production afforded by the Wheat Act and the Agriculture Act was of undoubted benefit. Otherwise, by stimulating cash crops at the expense of fodder and livestock, it could have been regarded as a diversion from the realignment of so many farm businesses during the inter-war years – unless the government intended to create a more permanent structure of support for agriculture.

Notes to Chapter 10

1   G. W. Leak, 'The Bulb Growing Industry', *Lincolnshire Magazine*, v. 1 (1934) pp. 113–14, E. C. Eagle, 'Some Light on the Beginnings of the Lincolnshire Bulb Industry', *Lincolnshire Historian*, no. 6 (Autumn 1950) pp. 220–9.

2   *Wages and Conditions of Employment in Agriculture. General Report*, Cmd 24 (1919) v. II, Reports of investigators, XXIII, Lincolnshire (Lindsey), para. 10, p. 201.

3   H. R. Fell, 'Two Notable Lincolnshire Farmers' *JRASE*, v. 152 (1991) pp. 36–46. Mary Steele, *Lincolnshire: land, longwools and legends* (1996) pp. 170–3.

4   RC on Wages and Conditions of Employment in Agriculture (1919) v. 2, Reports of investigators, XXIII, Lincolnshire (Lindsey) para. 6, p. 200.

5   J. H. Smith and P. R. Richardson, *Farming in the Lincolnshire Limestone Areas 1936 to 1947* (University of Nottingham, 1950). University of Cambridge, Farm Economics Branch, *An Economic Survey of Agriculture in the Eastern Counties of England* (1931) pp. 26, 28, 32.

6   *Farmer and Stockbreeder*, 2 December 1935, p. 2700.

7   *Farmers' Weekly*, 23 August 1935, pp. 26–7.

8   *Ibid.*, 17 April 1936, pp. 28–9.

9   *Ibid.*, 26 February 1937, pp. 34–5.

10   *Farmer and Stockbreeder,* 27 January 1936, p. 222.

11   F. J. Prewett, *Progress in English Farming Systems I: milk production on arable land* (1929).

12   *Farmers' Weekly,* 3 August 1934. Allan Knox, 'The East Midland Counties', in *Regional Types of British Farming,* ed. J. P. Maxton (1936), pp. 100–1. H. G. Robinson, 'Company Farming and Direct Marketing', *Country Life,* v. 62, 3 December 1927, pp. 851–3.

13   *Farmer and Stockbreeder,* 16 February 1931.

14   Museum of English Rural Life, FR LIN5/2.

15   *Farmers' Weekly,* 27 July 1934, 26 February 1937. Museum of English Rural Life, FR LIN5/2. J. A. S. Watson, *Rural Britain Today and Tomorrow* (1934) p. 66. Among other efforts, a new Lincolnshire Curly Coat Pig Breeders Association was formed in 1945, but it was short-lived. The breed died out in the early 1960s. *The Ark,* v. 9 (1982) pp. 146–7.

16   Watson, *Rural Britain Today and Tomorrow,* p. 66. B. A. Holderness, 'Agriculture' in *Twentieth Century Lincolnshire,* ed. Dennis R. Mills (1989) pp. 39, 41–42.

17   S. M. Makings, *Lincoln Wold Farming* (1939) p. 31.

18   *Agricultural Statistics. Farmer and Stockbreeder,* 20 May 1935, p. 1098.

19   *SM,* 22 March, 26 April 1872. R. Pennell & Sons, Lincoln, seed catalogues, 1870s. *Tariff Commission* (1906) paras. 561–3. *Agricultural Gazette,* 12 October 1894.

20   *Farmer and Stockbreeder,* 20 February 1922, p. 414.

21   *Ibid.*, 6 June 1932, 29 October 1934, p. 2420.

22   Dennis Mills, ed., *Twentieth Century Lincolnshire* (1989), p. 334. G. B. Wells, 'Some Aspects of East Midland Agriculture: 5 Lincolnshire (Kesteven)', *JRASE,* v. 115 (1954) p. 17.

23   S. L. Bensusan, *Latter Day Rural England* (1928) p. 69.

24   J. C. Wallace, 'Fenland Farming', *Agricultural Progress,* v. 11 (1934) p. 61.

25   *Agricultural Statistics.* J. C. Wallace, 'The Development of Potato-growing in Lincolnshire', *JRASE,* v. 115 (1954) p. 60.

26   Wallace, 'Fenland Farming', p. 62. R. McG. Carslaw and P. E. Graves, 'Farm Organization on the Silty Soils of Holland, Lincolnshire', *JRASE,* vol. 99 (1938) p. 60.

27   Wallace, 'Fenland Farming', *Agricultural Progress,* v.11 (1934) p. 62. R. McG. Carslaw and P. E. Graves, 'Farm Organization on the Black Fens of the Isle of Ely', *JRASE,* v. 98 (1937) p. 52. Carslaw and Graves, 'Farm

Organization on the Silty Soils of Holland, Lincolnshire', *JRASE*, vol. 99 (1938) p. 60.

28   Museum of English Rural Life, TR 8FOW ET3/1.

29   *The Agrarian History of England and Wales, vol. VII, 1850–1914,* ed. E. J. T. Collins (2000) p. 286.

30   Wallace, 'Fenland Farming', p. 62. Carslaw and Graves, 'Farm Organization on the Silty Soils of Holland, Lincolnshire', pp. 63–4.

31   *Ibid.*, p. 63.

32   Wallace, 'Fenland Farming', pp. 62–3.

33   *Ibid.,* pp. 64–5.

34   Bensusan, *Latter Day Rural England*, pp. 68–9.

35   J. C. Wallace, 'Notable Farming Enterprises: an up-to-date farming and horticultural enterprise', *JRASE*, v. 96 (1935) pp. 100–8.

36   Wallace, 'Fenland Farming', pp. 61, 65.

37   Bensusan, *Latter Day Rural England,* pp. 69–73. Carslaw and Graves, 'Farm Organization on the Black Fens of the Isle of Ely', p. 42.

38   Charles Kightly, *Country Voices: life and lore in farm and village* (1984) pp. 49–50.

39   Alan Armstrong, *Farmworkers: a social and economic history 1770–1980* (1988), pp. 176 (quoting W. H. Pedley, *Labour on the Land* (1942), p. 6), 183.

40   *Farmer and Stockbreeder,* 8 January 1934.

41   *Ibid.,* 5 January 1936. V. Cory, 'The Development of Farming in the Isle of Axholme' *JRASE*, v. 147 (1986) p. 59.

42   *Farmers Weekly,* 1 May 1936, p. 30.

43   E. A. Pratt, *The Transition in Agriculture* (1906) pp. 74–6, 81–2. Eagle, 'Some Light on the Beginnings of the Lincolnshire Bulb Industry', pp. 220–9. G. W. Leak, 'The Bulb Growing Industry', *Lincolnshire Magazine,* v. 1 (1934) pp. 113–14. LAO, HD65/64. *Farmers' Weekly,* 1 May 1936, p. 30. A. W. Ashby, 'Bulb Growing in South Lincolnshire', *JRASE*, v. 76 (1915) pp. 110–12.

44   Ashby, 'Bulb Growing in South Lincolnshire', pp. 113–14. W. E. Bear, 'Flower and Fruit Farming in England', *JRASE*, v. 59 (1898), p. 315.

45   Wallace, 'Fenland Farming', p. 65.

46   Ashby, 'Bulb Growing in South Lincolnshire', p. 113. *Farmers Weekly,* 1 May 1936, pp. 30–1.

47   Ashby, 'Bulb Growing in South Lincolnshire', pp. 116, 119, 121. *Farmers Weekly,* 1 May 1936, p. 30.

48   Ashby, 'Bulb Growing in South Lincolnshire', p. 130.

49   *Ibid.,* p. 127. *Farmers Weekly,* 1 May 1936, p. 31.

50   James Waugh, 'Narcissus Cultivation', *Journal of the Board of Agriculture,* v. 15
      (1908–9) pp. 905, 907.
51   *Ibid.,* p. 908.
52   D. N. McHardy, *Power Farming for Crops and Stock* (1938) p. 50.
53   H. Scott Hall, *Farming by Fiat,* advertising pamphlet for Fiat tractors
      (MERL, TR MRL P2/B51).
54   *Farmers Weekly,* 3 January 1941, pp. 28–29.
55   McHardy, *Power Farming for Crops and Stock,* pp. 47ff.
56   J. H. Smith and P. R. Richardson, *Farming in the Lincolnshire Limestone Areas
      1936 to 1947* (University of Nottingham, 1950). G. K. Nelson, *To Be A
      Farmer's Boy* (1991) pp. 134, 143. Charles Rawding, *Binbrook 1913–1939*
      (1991) p. 13.
57   Museum of English Rural Life, TR FOW MP1/2, shows sales of some
      Gyrotillers to customers in Lincolnshire. One of my father's teenage
      memories is of seeing one of these machines at Firsby.
58   Makings, *Lincoln Wold Farming,* p. 6.
59   Nevile's Caterpillar 38 is preserved at the Scottish Agricultural Museum.
60   Dennis Mills, 'Early Combine Harvesters, especially in Lincolnshire'.
      Unpublished report to the Museum of Lincolnshire Life, 1993, pp. 5–8
      (MERL, D DX109). Lists of early combine harvesters compiled by Ian
      Fleming, 1994, 1997 (MERL, D DX110). R. D. Brigden, Farming in
      partnership: the Leckford estate and the pursuit of profit in inter-war
      agriculture, PhD thesis, University of Reading (2000) pp. 297, 300. A.
      Bridges and H. Whitby, *Studies in Power Farming I: Mechanized Corn-growing*
      (1936) pp. 8–9, 21.
61   G. B. Wells and A. Mann, 'Farming in Kesteven and Lindsey', *Journal of the
      Ministry of Agriculture,* v. 54 (1947) pp. 154, 157.
62   *Farmer and Stockbreeder,* 28 March 1932.
63   *Ibid.,* 1, 8 January, 5 February, 19 March 1934. *Farmers' Weekly,* 6 July 1934.
      Edith Whetham, *The Agrarian History of England and Wales, vol. VIII,
      1914–1939,* p. 247.
64   Smith and Richardson, *Farming in the Lincolnshire Limestone Areas 1936–47,*
      pp. 10, 62, 64, 86, 98–9.

11
THE SECOND WORLD WAR

The outbreak of war in 1939 immediately brought about full government control of agriculture. There was to be no waiting two or three years for farmers to respond to market trends and appeals to patriotism. The day war broke out the Minister of Agriculture in a broadcast to the nation told farmers that they should plough up at least ten per cent of their grassland to sow with wheat, potatoes, or, where necessary, crops to feed livestock. The declaration of a ploughing-up policy was a major element of wartime policy. Alongside the control of cropping came guaranteed prices and assured markets, all designed to induce and encourage farmers to increase production. The instruments of policy also quickly appeared. The county war agricultural executive committees started work; the Women's Land Army was reformed. While the Ministry of Agriculture had control of farming the Ministry of Food was established, as in the First World War, to oversee the marketing and distribution of food.

The government was quick to put its wartime agricultural policy into operation because it was prepared, not by the experience of the Great War alone, but by about three years of work in anticipation of a new war's being declared. Unease at the scale of German rearmament had prompted the Minister of Agriculture in the spring of 1935 to set up a committee, jointly with the corresponding departments in Scotland and Northern Ireland, to examine the problem of food production in time of war. The committee presented its report in April 1936 containing recommendations about the need to increase home production of food, with special emphasis on wheat, potatoes, oats, and eggs. Other studies followed, all conducted by inter-departmental committees, whose reports of January and March 1937 and April 1939 came with a steadily growing sense of urgency, and produced plans from which more definite measures could be enacted.[1]

The first of these was the Agriculture Act 1937. It extended the principles of the Wheat Act by introducing deficiency payments for barley and oats, and raising the 'standard quantity' for wheat subsidy from 27 to 36 million hundredweight. It was not, therefore, overtly a measure in preparation for war. Indeed, in introducing the Act, the government declared that it was intended to improve the prosperity of farming as it existed, based upon livestock, and not to institute the ploughing up of land for cereals that wartime would necessitate.[2] For all the public declaration, this measure was a most deliberate effort to reinvigorate the arable farming upon which much of the planning being made for food production in time of emergency depended. As a step towards restoring some of the land's fertility lost through neglect in the successive years of depression, subsidies were granted on agricultural lime and basic slag. The Act also provided for grants for the improvement of land drainage, and for a major campaign to eradicate animal disease, especially tuberculosis in dairy cows. A national veterinary service was to be set up to lead these efforts.

The Agricultural Development Act, passed in May 1939, was quite clearly in expectation of early hostilities. The scope of the deficiency payments on barley and oats was widened to make more growers eligible for subsidy. A special payment of £2 for every acre of permanent pasture ploughed up between 3 May and 30 September 1939 was to be made, an idea which had been proposed in the Ministry in 1938 but not immediately implemented. Some of the heaviest clays in Lincolnshire were ploughed up under this scheme. They included carr grasslands in the Ancholme valley, where King's College estate put 150 acres under the plough in July.[3] This Act also offered further grants for drainage, and gave the Minister of Agriculture authority to purchase and store supplies of fertilizers, primarily of phosphate rock, and 3,000 to 5,000 tractors and ancilliary equipment. These powers were granted rather late in the day, as it turned out, and war started with little feed or fertilizer in reserve, and with the procurement of tractors and machinery about half way through its course.

Locally, the implementation of government policy for agriculture was placed in the hands of the war agricultural executive committees for each county. These, too, had been established for some time in anticipation of war. As far back as 1936 a list of the principal appointments was drawn up, but kept secret even from the appointees themselves for a while to come. The committees corresponded with the county councils: in Lincolnshire, therefore, there was one each for Holland, Kesteven, and Lindsey. The committees were given extensive powers to direct farmers in their management and husbandry. They could determine which fields a farmer was to plough, what supplies he was to get, and could direct auxiliary labour to him. If they were not satisfied with a farmer's standards the committees could take over the management of his farm, and at worst have him evicted. To bureaucracy-hating farmers all of these matters could be the cause of dispute with the committees. In Lincolnshire things seem to have gone remarkably smoothly. In an article written just after the war, the advisory officers for Kesteven and Lindsey reported that ploughing-up targets were met with a minimum of official orders, and most of the orders that were issued were of a confirmatory nature. This county was spared the high-profile cases of farmers being dispossessed by war agricultural committees that afflicted some places.[4]

Causes of friction between farmer and county committee were on a smaller scale. Most were of a magnitude similar to the experience of farmer A. H. Smith of West Pinchbeck. He was fined £50 for failing to comply with an order to destroy rats, having returned the official forms with 'do not waste paper' written across them.[5] Destruction of vermin happened to be one of the administrative areas given special emphasis by the government's regime of control.[6] There had been campaigns against rats for many years, but not always well supported by officialdom. Now, however, they assumed a new prominence. They were pursued by the war agricultural executive committees with vigour, and they received greater publicity in the local and farming press. Thus, among the many articles, one appeared in the *Farmer and Stockbreeder* about the 'rat campaigns' in Lincolnshire for the two years 1939–41, which had yielded more than 250,000 kills.[7]

The National Farmers' Union enjoyed a new, closer relationship with the government, as its central organization was drawn into consultation about the implementation of policy. It was not always a comfortable position to be in, for when farmers complained about regulation and control, about the supply and quality of labour, and about shortages of fertilizers and feeding stuffs, the representatives on the union's national committees usually found themselves having to present an official line. A meeting of the Grantham branch of the union in 1941 was typical in passing a resolution critical of government arrangements for the management of livestock and their feed, and demanding greater provision for agricultural labour. The local representative on the national council had to argue that it was quite impossible for the government to accede to such demands.[8]

The ploughing-up campaign

A key component of the government's policy was the ploughing-up campaign, a revival of the policy of the First World War. Ploughing up was introduced immediately the war started, and the programme was given a stronger political and administrative direction than in the first war, with targets for the additional arable acres announced each year by the Minister.

The reclamation of derelict land was a prominent part of the ploughing-up campaign in the early years of the war. The work was directed towards repairing some of the ravages of the inter-war depression, and had considerable publicity value. Among the half a million acres that were subject to land reclamation schemes organized by the county committees were several high-profile examples. They included about 6,000 acres of Feltwell Fen in Norfolk, which had been abandoned because farmers could not afford to keep the drains in order; 3,500 acres on the South Downs, much of it land that had been earmarked for building plots before the war; and the most ambitious scheme in Montgomeryshire, where the war agricultural committee took on a project devised before the war to plough and grow potatoes on 3,000 acres of mountain land 1,000 feet above sea level. Reclamation activity in Lincolnshire was modest by comparison. The Kesteven War Agricultural Executive Committee reckoned there were between 10,000 and 15,000 acres of derelict or semi-derelict land. When it came to taking land over for reclamation, however, the committee settled for 600 acres around Norton Disney. J. G. Henson, of Boothby Graffoe, was placed in charge of this land. An experienced practitioner of mechanized farming, he applied intensive cultivation to the land, and in his first harvest he was looking forward to good crops of flax, peas, wheat, potatoes, and sugar beet.[9]

Reclamation of derelict land was but a part of the plan for increasing the acreage of arable. Ploughing up grassland was the foundation stone. The ten per cent of permanent pasture for which the Minister of Agriculture had asked in his broadcast of September 1939 to be ploughed up was shortly afterwards set more formally as a target of 2,010,000 acres, of which 1,500,000 acres should come from England and Wales. That set the pattern for the whole of the war. Each year a

Fig. 38 Mechanization was encouraged by the war agricultural executive committees during the Second World War. At one of the many demonstrations of new equipment the committees arranged, a tractor-mounted drainage plough made by Rotary Hoes is being put through its paces
Source: Museum of English Rural Life

new target was announced for the extent of the grassland to be ploughed: two million acres in 1940–41 and again in 1941–42, another million acres in 1942–43. There was considerable success in meeting these targets. By 1943 the acreage of permanent grass in England and Wales was nearly 5.3 million acres less than it had been in 1939, a reduction of 34 per cent. Results came quickly, as the subsidy for ploughing up old pasture announced in the spring of 1939 had already induced some transfer of land during that summer. During the first two years of war ploughing up of permanent and rotation grasses met the government's targets reasonably well. Thereafter things were less clear-cut. The acreage ploughed up fell well short of the target in 1942: 1,186,000 acres in England and Wales, 1,408,000 acres for the whole of the United Kingdom.

Table 10 Plough-up targets, 1939–40 to 1942–3 (acres)

	1939–40	1940-1	1941-2	1942-3
England & Wales	1,500,000	1,700,000	1,675,000	800,000
Scotland	260,000	260,000	200,000	60,000
Northern Ireland	250,000	200,000	100,000	100,000
United Kingdom	2,010,000	2,160,000	1,975,000	960,000

Source: K. A. H. Murray, *Agriculture, History of the Second World War* (1955) pp. 237, 243

Management of the ploughing-up campaign was handed to the war agricultural executive committees. Each county was allotted a quota of pasture to be ploughed. In the first year, 1939–40, the all-round figure of ten per cent was used, but thereafter account was supposed to be taken of individual areas and their suitability for growing crops in place of pasture.[10] As might be expected with Lincolnshire's being a major arable county, the ploughing-up of pasture here fell well short of the national targets. Only about 7.5 per cent of the acreage was ploughed up in the first year. Even so, the cumulative effects were not insignificant. By 1943 the reduction in acreage from 1939's total was

29.2 per cent, and ploughing up during the remaining years of war resulted in a decrease of 33.4 per cent by 1945. There was a greater than average percentage reduction in the acreage of pasture in the Fens. The returns for Holland show a decline of 38 per cent from 1939 to 1945. As this area was already almost entirely arable, the number of acres of pasture ploughed up here, 17,000, was quite modest. By contrast, the percentage of the clay vales and the marshlands of Lindsey ploughed up was less than the average. On the Heath and the Cliff permanent pasture had been a third of the total acreage in the late 1930s, and was reduced to about a fifth by the end of the war. The reductions in permanent pasture outlived the war. New regimes of subsidy helped keep the acreage of pasture in the immediate post-war years little different from that recorded in 1945.[11]

The ploughing-up campaign targeted especially permanent pasture. Initially, at least, farmers also turned over some of their rotation grasses to cereals and potatoes. The acreage of clovers and rotation grasses in Lincolnshire was reduced by 12.8 per cent between 1939 and 1941. Leys, however, remained important for the maintenance of mixed farming, especially with shortages of feeding stuffs. In addition, the pressure of maintaining intensive arable production soon had its effects on the soil's fertility and some land was returned to rotation grasses. Concern about fertility was so strong that the *Farmers' Weekly* ran a series called 'Wartime fertility' on ways in which the fertility of the land could be maintained. These articles featured prominent farmers to get the message across. Among them was J. G. Henson of Boothby Graffoe, noted proponent of mechanized farming. As well as helping bring derelict land back into condition, on his own farm he said he was keeping up his cattle numbers by careful management of all possible feeds grown on the farm, including beet tops, wheat, barley, and oats straw. Green manure crops of mustard and rape were also part of his recipe. However, the government must do its part, he said, by making available all the artificial fertilizers it could. At the opposite extreme was Capt. G. M. Wilson on the Iceni Farm estate in Surfleet. His was an organic farming system, at the heart of which was the production of compost, mainly vegetable, with the addition of manure from the small number of livestock. He had started this regime in 1931 and ten years later was producing 1,000 tons a year of compost for the farm of 295 acres producing potatoes, cereals, and horticultural crops.[12]

Maintaining fertility remained a serious problem, as shortage of feeds and fertilizers and the reduction in the number of cattle all had their effect. Farmers had to return to temporary grass, the extent of which in England and Wales increased by 346,000 acres in 1942, nearly 20,000 of them in Lincolnshire. This pattern was repeated in the following years, both nationally and in the county. At the end of the war Lincolnshire had nearly 24,000 acres more in temporary grasses than at the beginning, an increase of 19.3 per cent. In many areas of the county, including the Heath and the Cliff, the proportion of rotation grasses at the end of the war had returned to what it had been just before it started.[13]

There were many advocates for deep ploughing as a method of maintaining fertility and keeping the land in good condition. J. G. Henson was among the mechanized farmers who were keen on this. There was nothing new in deep ploughing. It had been practised for years on heavy land and in the Fens; it was one of the reasons why steam ploughing became established in Lincolnshire. The war brought renewed emphasis on deep cultivation as a preparation, for example, for potatoes, with the Ministry of Agriculture's advisory services pressing its case strongly.[14]

Having set targets for the number of acres of grass to be ploughed up, the county committees and the farmers were allowed a fair amount of leeway in determining what to sow in the extra arable. The responsibility lay with the committees to persuade farmers in their counties to produce crops that would suit the national interest, taking into account local circumstances. The government certainly made its wishes clear by public announcement about which crops had priority and setting target acreages for some of them. The emphasis was, of course, on cash crops producing food for direct human consumption. Control of the price mechanism was another means of getting this message across. The wheat price of 14s 8d a hundredweight in 1941, rising to 16s 3d in 1943, was a great improvement on the five or six shillings prevailing just before the war. Fatstock prices were held back relative to cereals, emphasizing the priorities in official thinking. By 1943–44, the price index (base 1936–37 to 1938–39 = 100) had reached 192 for cereals, excluding barley; for fat cattle it was still 154.[15]

Farmers responded by growing as many cash crops as they could. Established rotations were often lengthened and otherwise altered to increase the proportion of land going to cereals, potatoes, and sugar beet. Wheat was obviously one of the crops the nation demanded, and, taking the country as a whole, there were some impressive responses. Despite the incentives, however, the acreage sown to wheat in Lincolnshire did not rise immediately. A wet autumn in 1939 did not help matters. Only 14,000 more acres of wheat were sown in the whole of England and Wales. In Lincolnshire the acreage fell substantially. Indeed, in the first three years of war, sowings of wheat were ten to twelve per cent lower than they had been in 1939, whereas nationally there were increases in both 1941 and 1942. A government anxious about supplies of home-grown food in 1942 departed from its existing practice and announced acreage targets for all main crops for 1943, including an increase of 600,000 acres of wheat. The farmers of England and Wales responded with an increase of 889,000 acres. Lincolnshire contributed 63,000 additional acres of wheat that year, an increase of 30.5 per cent over 1942, and taking sowings well above those for 1939. Sowings eased off again, and by 1945 were back to those of 1940.

Increased acreages of spring-sown barley and oats in 1940 made up to some extent for the shortfall in the previous autumn's wheat sowing. Barley had already become rather the favoured cereal of the county, and this showed in wartime cultivation. Steadily increased sowings of the crop meant that by 1944 the acreage in Kesteven was 48.9 per cent greater than it had been in 1939; in Lindsey it was 42 per cent greater. While the established strongholds on the light lands accounted for much of this increase, there were many more acres sown in most parts of the county. Even in the Fens was this so: the returns for Holland show an almost threefold increase, but as there were only 3,442 acres in 1939, that hardly made the area a major barley producer. The acreage of oats showed greater fluctuation. After a surge in the early years of war, sowings fell back, and in most places there were fewer acres under oats at the end of the war than at its beginning. Peas became vastly more popular. Their cultivation had been increasing before the war; now greater demand for fresh and canned peas for human consumption brought about an increase in acreage by almost fourfold. This was a crop that could be taken up by farmers on almost all types of soil; for many it fitted admirably into rotations as preparation for the major crops of wheat and potatoes. With the input of fertilizer and machinery now available, peas amply repaid the effort put into them.

Potatoes was another of the crops targeted by the government, and Lincolnshire growers rose to this challenge. This was less so in the heart of the Fens, where potatoes were already so important that the scope for greatly increased acreage was perhaps more limited. The agricultural returns for Holland show only a marginal increase in the total acreage of potatoes between 1939 and 1944. The greater change in this part of the county came with the increase, by nearly two-thirds, in the planting of first early varieties, while maincrop potatoes declined slightly. Growers were turning so much to early varieties that the Holland branch of the farmers' union in 1943 passed a resolution slightly complaining that some were being ordered to grow some late crops for the government's end-of-season reserve.[16] Most of the increased acreage of potatoes came in areas where they had previously been little grown. Hence there were much greater proportionate increases in the potato acreage, in Kesteven by 91.1 per cent between 1939 and 1944, and Lindsey, where the total acreage of the crop at the end of the war was slightly greater than in Holland. As ever, the fluctuating seasons had their effect on the potato harvests: when the maincrop was being lifted in 1944 it was very wet, and it was too dry for the earlies to swell properly in 1941. There was occasional friction with the authorities responsible for purchasing the crop, leading on one occasion in 1941 to complaints in Parliament that 'thousands of tons' were left to rot because of inefficiency on the part of the Potato Council.[17] Shortage of labour was a perpetual problem in this branch of farming, which was only partially mechanized. This was particularly marked at harvest time. However, none of these difficulties did anything to alter the importance of potatoes in the county's agricultural regime, nor to alter the trends being established. The increased cropping of first earlies throughout the county continued into the immediate post-war years.

Only for a few crops were there attempts by government to set specific acreages from the beginning of the war. One of them was flax, in demand for military needs, for instance in the manufacture of parachutes. There were 4,400 acres of flax grown in England and Wales in 1939. Immediately, the Ministry demanded an increase of 10,000 acres. The following year an additional 40,000 acres in England and Wales was the aim. The result of this appeal was that the 53 acres in Lincolnshire growing flax in 1939 became 2,724 the next year. By 1944 there were 5,882 acres. The costs of processing flax made this a short-lived revival in England. By 1948 the acreage of flax had declined throughout the country; in Lincolnshire that decline was 66 per cent. Sugar beet was another crop for which more specific targets were set. By 1939, of course, this was already established as one of the major crops in Lincolnshire, and wartime demands had less immediate effect. Even so, additional sowings over the years were significant: by 1944, the peak year, the acreage had increased by 36.3 per cent.

The growing of bulbs and flowers in south Lincolnshire was sacrificed to the war effort. Growers were ordered to cut their plantings to a quarter of the pre-war acreage. The rest was ploughed up for food crops. Cereals and potatoes were most extensive, but onions was one crop introduced on many former bulb fields. The land was suited to the crop, and so were the skills of the horticultural workforce. The number of acres growing onions in Holland, 61 in 1939, had risen to 3,525 by 1944.[18]

Arable farmers received help from good harvests in most years of the war. There were disappointing results in 1941, but the following years, especially 1943, produced yields well above average.[19] Yields were good for the country generally, but arable Lincolnshire came out particularly well. In 1943, the official returns for wheat in Holland were 29.8 cwt per acre compared with an average over the preceding ten years of 25.9 cwt. Yields in the other parts of the county were similarly above average. Potatoes, likewise, produced good crops. Holland's returns for 1943 were 9.5 tons per acre compared with the ten-year average of 8.1 tons.

Livestock farming

Lincolnshire farming was naturally disposed towards the government's priorities of maximizing production of wheat, potatoes, and sugar beet in particular, and arable crops in general. When it came to livestock, milk was the number one priority of the Ministry of Food. In this there was a contrast with the First World War, when dairy production was almost ignored. The importance of milk now was such that there were proposals in 1940 that the number of beef cattle should be reduced by compulsory slaughter so that supplies of feed could go to the dairy cows. It did not come to that, but selective rationing of feedingstuffs and price incentives were used to encourage farmers to produce milk. By holding the price of calves down, farmers were encouraged to sell their milk rather than use it to fatten young stock. As the war progressed and the Ministry of Food continued to stress the need for milk, various other schemes were adopted to stimulate production. The war agricultural executive committees used their powers to persuade farmers to cull low-yielding cows and maintain herds that made best use of the feed ration. For farmers in Lincolnshire the emphasis on milk was a problem. Even here, however, the demands and encouragement of official policy were sufficient to draw more farmers into some dairy production, especially those on heavy land. South-west Kesteven was one district where dairy farming was becoming more common. There was a modest rise in the total number of cattle throughout the county over the course of the war, with the exception of Holland, where farming was becoming more concentrated on arable.

Meat production received no encouragement from government. There was some acceptance of beef, and during the final years of the war the numbers of beef cattle were allowed to increase as official thinking started to look ahead to how supplies of meat might stand once peace returned. Even so, for farmers in the prime beef fattening districts of the clay vales, the pressures of the ploughing-up campaign forced reductions in the numbers of stock kept, especially those kept over winter in yards. The national sheep population was reduced by 30 per cent during the course of the war, and there was a particularly large loss of pigmeat, as the number of pigs kept on farm holdings was cut by half between 1939 and 1945. All of this had its counterpart in Lincolnshire for, while cattle recorded a modest increase, the numbers of sheep and pigs dropped quite dramatically throughout the county. Sheep in lowland areas of the country were positively discouraged. There was a more marked decline in the numbers of sheep in the major sheep-farming districts of Lincolnshire. On the Kesteven uplands the number of sheep per 100 acres had reached as high as 74 per cent in 1938. By 1944 stocking was down to 32 per 100 acres, a drop of 57 per cent. There was a further fall to 19 per 100 acres the following year. On the Cliff in Lindsey, stocking per 100 acres declined by 41 per cent between 1938 and 1944.[20] In those areas where sheep had been of lesser importance before the war, they became almost a rarity by 1945: there were then only 2,030 in the whole of Holland. Restrictions were placed on the processing of pigmeat, so that, for example, a new bacon factory at Ruskington was not allowed to open straight away. The MP for Horncastle argued in Parliament that pig-keeping should be encouraged, as a means of using refuse potatoes. He received no support from government, however. Numbers of pigs on the farms of Lincolnshire fell by 65 per cent between 1939 and 1943, with, again, a greater decline in the Fens than in the rest of the county. There were many like Mr C. Nevile, president of the National Farmers' Union from 1942, who used to have about 200 store pigs on his farm at Skinnand, but got rid of them all.[21] By 1944 the government was becoming anxious about the state of livestock production after the war, and there was some easing of restrictions sufficient for numbers to start to rise again.

Shortage of feed was a major constraint on livestock husbandry. Imports of feed grains, oilcakes, and other fodder practically vanished as the available shipping space was allocated to cargoes deemed more immediately necessary. From the 6.2 million tons imported annually during the years immediately before the war, supplies had dropped to 687,000 tons by 1941–42, and only 156,000 tons two years later. The byproducts from imported cereals and oilseeds were more readily available, but even so the decline in the total supplies of imported feed was 85 per cent, from the 8.7 million tons average before the war to the 1.3 million tons of 1943–44.[22] Home-grown supplies became more important, therefore, and, initially at least, were encouraged by government. Acreages of fodder crops increased during the first years of the war. Lincolnshire returned an increase of 9 per cent in the acreage of turnips and swedes, and 150 per cent for cabbages and kale between 1939 and 1941. Most of this was in Lindsey and Kesteven; the acreage of turnips and swedes in Holland declined by nearly two-thirds. Thereafter these crops fell back again, in much the same way as the acreages of oats. By 1945 the acreage of turnips and swedes in Lincolnshire was 19 per cent less than it had been in 1939, though kale remained at a higher figure. Meanwhile, the ploughing up of grassland deprived the livestock farmer both of pasture and hay, while feed grains were diverted to human consumption. In 1942 the extraction rate for milling wheat was raised from 76 to 85 per cent, while between January and November 1943 barley and oats were also taken to mix in with the bread flour. Farmers had to learn to make better use of their grassland to support a relatively larger head of stock on a reduced area. Silage was one aid to this. Despite much promotion since the 1880s, farmers had not hitherto taken to silage. Now they began to take it up. The Ministry and the county committees encouraged this move by arranging demonstrations of silage making.

The government was able to claim some dramatic results in the production of food during the war. Output in the United Kingdom was increased substantially, reaching at its peak in 1943–44 a net value some 15 per cent greater than the immediate pre-war years (Table 11). These efforts also exceeded the results of the 1918 harvest when wartime measures were last in force. The figures in Table 11 show how production adhered to the government's priorities. Arable crops produced in the United Kingdom were 14.8 million tons greater than they had been in 1918, including an increase of a million tons of cereals and 3.2 million tons of potatoes. In addition, British agriculture was producing considerably more milk than it had done in the First World War, which meant that there had been a marked intensification of farming since 1939, and in comparison with 1914–18.

Table 11 Index numbers of agricultural output in the United Kingdom 1940–45 (1936–7 to 1938–9 = 100)

(a) Crops	Year					
	1940	1941	1942	1943	1944	1945
Wheat	99	122	155	209	190	132
Barley	144	150	189	215	229	276
Oats	149	167	183	158	152	167
Cereals	132	155	182	195	186	179
Potatoes	131	164	193	202	187	201
Sugar Beet	116	118	143	137	119	141
Vegetables	110	122	156	133	144	137
Fodder crops	98	127	133	135	140	132
(b) Livestock	Year (June–May)					
	1940–1	1941–2	1942–3	1943–4	1944–5	1945–6
Milk	90	88	93	96	97	100
Beef & veal	97	73	83	83	92	93
Mutton & lamb	108	89	89	79	72	69
Pigmeat	87	38	35	32	35	38
Eggs	90	75	57	51	54	63

Source: K. A. H. Murray, *Agriculture, History of the Second World War* (1955) pp. 237, 243

Labour supply

Securing sufficient labour to achieve the increases in agricultural production demanded by the war effort became one of the areas of disagreement between Lincolnshire farmers and the government. Despite greater mechanization, intensive cultivation, especially of potatoes and sugar beet, made heavy demands on labour. At the beginning of the war the Lincolnshire Farmers' Union passed a

Fig. 39 Land Girls making silage: a photograph taken at another of
the WAEC demonstrations, this one in October 1942
Source: Museum of English Rural Life

resolution calling on the government to place young farm workers on
the list of reserved occupations. The skills of the young men as tractor
drivers needed to be retained, the union argued.[23] The Ministry of
Agriculture did make attempts at the beginning of the war to retain
workers on the land by securing some measure of reservation for
agricultural workers. Those aged 21 and over were to be exempt from
call-up. These measures had little real effect. Workers were taken away
from the land by the immediate call-up of the Territorial Army, which
included about 20,000 farm workers in England and Wales, and there
were losses of men to other occupations. Within a year farmers were
grumbling about labour being insufficient in quantity and quality.
Things could not get better, as the war departments continued to press
for farming's contribution to the services. Early in 1941 it was decided
that the services would have to recruit 22,000 'non-key' men from
agriculture in the United Kingdom, 10,000 from England. Along with

this the age of reservation was to be raised to 25. The call-up was postponed until the end of the year, but that did not lessen the protests when it came. In October 1942 the minimum age for call-up was reduced from 18½ to 18. The only concessions the services were prepared to make was to postpone calling up additional men until after harvest was over.[24]

The Lincolnshire farmers felt let down and misunderstood. When the call-up of farm workers was made in 1941 there were protests from the county. One farmer, P. J. Ward, at a meeting in Lincoln declared, 'We were assured by the government that if they took any labour we should have efficient labour in its place, and efficient labour is apparently going to be the Women's Land Army.'[25] The Ministry thought it was helping agriculture by organizing extra labour for harvest, but the Lincolnshire branch of the National Farmers' Union pointed out that the county's farmers needed labour at least as much for cultivating, planting, and weeding. The Ministry seemed to think 'more of acreage than of tonnage', suggested J. Davey at a union meeting in the spring of 1943. From the Fens at the same time came a plea for extra labour for hoeing onions and work with vegetables.[26]

Relatively small episodes illustrate the differences in approach between government and farmers. In December 1940 there was concern in north Lincolnshire that the farmers would lose their accustomed supply of local female labour. Women from Brigg, Scunthorpe, and Grimsby had provided seasonal labour for weeding, pea-pulling, and potato-lifting but, because they were not in full employment on the farms, the government was likely to direct them away from farming, replacing them with Land Girls. The correspondent to the *Farmer and Stockbreeder* thought this regrettable, for the local women 'will make better all-round land-workers than the raw girls, willing as they may be, who will have to start their training from zero'.[27] Another small project of 1941 similarly revealed a gap between farming and the state. In April that year the government announced a scheme to draft agricultural workers from the eastern counties to the grassland counties of midland England. They would use their skills in arable farming to help with the ploughing-up programme in pastoral country. The idea was that this should be a voluntary scheme, but hardly anyone came forward. Only one man volunteered from Lincolnshire among the 25 from the whole of the eastern counties. By the autumn the government resorted to compulsion: 200 men of the eastern counties, from Lincolnshire to Essex, were to be transferred.[28]

Just as in the First World War, therefore, agriculture was to be heavily dependent on a range of alternative workers, a few full-time, but most casual. The government had anticipated this by forming the Women's Land Army in June 1939. Land Girls were, therefore, already being deployed during the first autumn of the war in such tasks as potato harvesting and beet lifting, while the county's colleges and agricultural stations were putting new recruits to the Land Army through courses on tractor driving.[29] The arrival of the Land Girls was not greeted with universal enthusiasm, either from the farmers or their regular workers. The meeting of the Lincolnshire Farmers' Union that wanted young farm workers to be kept from military service heard members arguing that the girls would be useless as tractor drivers. There continued to be some complaints about the quality of Land Girls for the next three years, but they were from a minority, for most farmers' objections melted away in the face of the reality of the work done.[30] There were some who joined the Women's Land Army who turned out not to be suitable for the work, but most were willing and hard-working.[31] Whether the farmers liked them or not, the girls were a far more important part of the labour force than they had been in the First World War. The national Women's Land Army had 19,000 members in August 1941. Twelve months later the number was 52,000, and the peak was reached at 87,000 in August 1943. Training organized mainly by the agricultural executive committees improved the skills of the Land Girls. The committees were the employers of many of the girls deployed in Lincolnshire. Rather than being attached to particular farms they were sent in gangs to work on potato planting and harvesting, beet thinning and lifting, and all the many tasks of the county's arable farming. These girls lived off the farms, mainly in hostels, which it was hoped would be more congenial to those not used to country life.

The only other source of regular labour was prisoners of war. Some Italians arrived in time for the harvest of 1941. By the same time the following year there were some 20,000 prisoners at work in agriculture. After the north African campaigns numbers rose rapidly to reach 50,600 in mid 1944. Like the Land Girls, prisoners were often treated with suspicion. Mr J. Turner told a meeting of the Lincolnshire Farmers' Union in 1942 that the Italian prisoners presented the farmer with three problems: 'to get them on the farm soon enough, to get them to stay long enough and to get them to work while they were there'.[32] Despite this, most farmers found the prisoners a valuable source of extra labour. Lifting and cleaning sugar beet was work often given them, for which they worked in gangs under military escort. The prisoners were valued also for other heavy work, such as draining and threshing. Very few German prisoners were employed on farms, but as the Allies advanced after D-Day, some Russians liberated from German prison camps came to work on Lincolnshire farms.[33] The war departments also released British troops on home leave to help on farms, mainly for the corn harvest.

Fig. 40 Russians freed from German prisoner-of-war camps during
1944 were brought over to work on farms in Lincolnshire and
the East Riding of Yorkshire
Source: Museum of English Rural Life

The employment of schoolchildren received official sanction. It was already a major feature of local practice for schoolchildren to be taken on to assist with certain farm tasks. The long-established timing of school holidays to allow pupils to help with the potato harvest continued, and was extended. Now this was publicized as part of the war effort. More than a thousand children in 1942 were reported to be employed on the south Lincolnshire potato harvest in October, with some being brought in from schools in the East Riding of Yorkshire. Some schools began summer work camps quite early on in the war, and as this movement grew official organization was added. At their peak in 1944 more than 67,000 schoolchildren were involved. In some counties the camps featured more strongly than they did in Lincolnshire. However, at least one grammar school in Sheffield had camps in 1942 and 1943, and other schools from the East Riding and some in Lincolnshire itself also were involved in camps.[34]

Adult volunteers, ranging from undergraduate students to factory workers, added another valuable source of auxiliary labour, especially for harvest. Ad hoc arrangements were replaced by a national volunteer recruitment organization in the later years of the war. Lincolnshire was included in the north-east region for this purpose, recruiting mainly from the urban West Riding. Harvest camps were set up across the country, totalling 200 by the end of the war, including one at Surfleet, near Spalding. Local part-timers, mainly women, and casual workers made up the final component of the auxiliary labour upon which farmers could call.

Despite the difficulties with the labour supply, the combined effects of the sources of additional labour and increased hours of work were to maintain the labour input through the war years. Data for the United Kingdom from a post-war study of agricultural output and employment suggest that the labour force held up well (Table 12). Without the Women's Land Army, the schoolchildren, and the others there is little doubt that agriculture's achievements in the war would have been poor indeed, but they did not make all the difference. For while the index of employment stood at 108 for 1943–44, for net agricultural output it was 115.[35]

Table 12 Index of agricultural output in terms of man-years

1937-9	100	1941-2	103	1943-4	108
1939-40	99	1942-3	107	1944-5	109
1940-1	100				

Source: H. T. Williams, 'Changes in the productivity of labour in British
agriculture', *Journal of the Agricultural Economics Society,* v. 10 (1954) p. 334

Costs and profits

Maintaining the input of labour, even increasing labour productivity,
came at a cost. The labour bill in United Kingdom farming rose nearly
threefold over the six years of war. In June 1940 a national minimum
wage for agricultural workers was introduced, set at 48s a week for adult
males, well above the 37s 9d average for England and Wales before the
war began in 1939. The national minimum was progressively raised to
60s a week in December 1941, 65s in December 1943 and 75s a week in
March 1945. Rates for women, youths, and for overtime were also
raised more or less in proportion. Higher rates of wages, the extensive
working of overtime, and the need for large numbers of casual workers
at peak times all contributed to the greatly increased expenditure on
labour. Long hours, and the use of shift working in order to get more
out of each day, as farmers and their staff made their contribution to the
nation's war effort, were among the developments that helped add to
labour costs. Experience varied from place to place depending on the
amount of overtime and casual employees that were needed, but
Lincolnshire surveys suggest that expenditure on labour increased
broadly in line with the national average of three times greater.[36] As a
result, labour took up a greater portion of total farm costs, rising from
about a quarter to a third.

Some other costs of farming increased markedly during the war,
especially machinery and fertilizers. Greater use of machinery was a
major contributor to the increased output of labour. From the
beginning of the war the government, claiming that tractors were then
only being used at about half capacity, set about encouraging the greater
use of tractors, and of all machinery.[37] Some concessions on fuel

rations were made, and the county executive committees were given a role in persuading farmers to take up machinery. In some respects the persuasion was unnecessary. Shortages of good horsemen and good horses were already pushing farmers towards the tractor. Mechanization was already advancing in Lincolnshire during the late 1930s. This put the farmers here in a good position at the start of the war, but perhaps less so at its end. The allocation of tractors tended to go more to those places without any, so by 1945 many of the tractors in Lincolnshire were getting a bit worn out. The number of tractors, recorded in the agricultural statistics only every other year, increased by 90 per cent in England and Wales between 1942 and 1946, whereas Lincolnshire's rate of increase was 60 per cent, from 7,119 in 1942 to 11,354 in 1946. The ploughs and other implements to go with these tractors increased in similar proportion. Numbers of tractor-drawn ploughs, for example, increased by 53.8 per cent between 1942 and 1946. Disc harrows more than trebled in number, from 639 to 2,015. Numbers of combine harvesters increased from the handful immediately before the war to 194 in 1946. Although the 589 milking machines in use in Lincolnshire in 1946 pales by comparison with, for example, in Cheshire, the increase by 111 per cent since 1942 was a strong indication of the extent to which farmers were beginning to take dairying more seriously. Transport on and around the farm was also transformed by the use not only of tractors, but of lorries and cars as well.

Demand for new machinery soon outstripped supply in a controlled market. The government became the principal supplier. The first steps had been taken before the war when, under the measures of April 1939, the government decided to build up a reserve of 3,000 tractors together with suitable ploughs. About half of the tractors, ordered from Ford in Britain, had been delivered by the time war broke out, with deliveries by then being made at the rate of 100 a day. The government continued to buy large quantities of all types of equipment throughout the war. Local supplies were limited by the fact that Marshalls at Gainsborough, along with the other British agricultural engineers, had much of their capacity diverted to military work. Several of the types of tractor and machinery most needed had in any case to be

Fig. 41 During the Second World War mechanization of the sugar
beet harvest began. This tool bar with beet-lifting shares made by
Levertons wasdemonstrated by Kesteven War Agricultural
Executive Committee at Nocton in October 1942
Source: Museum of English Rural Life

imported from America, and that meant the Ministry of Agriculture had
to fight for shipping space. The ministry's purchases were distributed
by the war agricultural executive committees. The committees
employed much of their machinery on contract hire, also providing the
skilled labour to operate it.

Meanwhile the number of horses employed on the farms was
falling rapidly. There were 37,432 returned in Lincolnshire in 1939,
declining to 31,513 in 1942 and 29,126 in 1946. All in all these figures
represent a very rapid change in the character of farming. As early as
1941, S. J. Wright suggested that on a simple reckoning of number of
tractors per thousand acres 'our agriculture is probably more fully
mechanized than that of any other country in the world'. By the war's
end there was a more general agreement that British agriculture was
among the most mechanized in the world. Farmers' expenditure on

machinery was estimated to have risen during the war by between three and five times what had it been in the late 1930s. There were still large gaps. Almost anything to do with sugar beet, for instance, had to be done by hand. A beet harvester had been a prize-winner at the last Royal show before the war, but development proceeded slowly, and harvesting this crop was not mechanized until after 1945. It was a similar story with potatoes. Planting machinery was almost non-existent in 1939. The stimulus of war brought forward new designs of planter, so that by 1945 there were reasonable numbers of these available. Even so, many acres were still set by hand. Satisfactory potato harvesters were still to be developed. Lifting the crop continued to be the work mainly of schoolchildren and other helpers following behind the potato spinners and diggers.[38]

Fig. 42 A Bettinson potato harvester being demonstrated at J. T. Caudwell's Hartley House Farm, Holbeach, September 1943
Source: Museum of English Rural Life

Farmers were using fertilizers during the war more than they had done before, despite the loss of supplies of phosphates and potash normally imported from Germany and France. In their place, for the most part, came nitrogenous fertilizers and lime produced in Britain. An index of the quantities of fertilizer used in United Kingdom farming, with 1938–39 set at 100, had risen to 287 for nitrogen by 1944–45, phosphates had reached 203 and potash 153.[39] Subsidized prices and propaganda from the Ministry of Agriculture had the desired effect, for many farmers who had hardly considered the use of artificials before, largely because of cost when their profits were low, now became converts. Although prices increased by more than 30 per cent, they were kept artificially low by a government keen to encourage use. Expenditure on fertilizers on a sample of Lincolnshire farms increased at least twofold, and often threefold between 1939 and 1945. The greater part of this was the result of increased quantities applied to the land.[40]

In contrast to fertilizers, expenditure on feeding stuffs was greatly reduced. When the war ended the nation's farmers were spending on feeds an amount less than half of the pre-war figures. Most of this change was because the large quantities of imported feeds hitherto used were not available, while reductions in the scale of livestock farming also had their effect. Rent was stable, as had been the case in the First World War. However, total farm costs increased by about two-thirds over the course of the war (see Table 15 below).

Farmers could afford these large increases in expenditure as a result of increased profits. The main contribution to greater profits was increased prices. As Table 13 shows, agricultural prices rose to a far greater extent than wholesale prices and the prices that made up the cost of living index, many of which were held down by government subsidies. Plainly this was due to governmental management of the price mechanism, which was engineered to direct farmers to those areas of food production most desired by policy, and to create total farm incomes sufficient to fund investment in machinery, fertilizers and other improvements.

Prices followed the pattern familiar in time of war, and rose rapidly. In the first two years of war agricultural prices rose by 67 per cent. Some important farm products, notably barley and oats, were left free of control for the early part of the war, and not unnaturally their prices went up spectacularly. Even controlled prices were allowed to rise substantially, partly to cover increases in farming costs, and also as an earnest of good faith that farmers would be remunerated for the extra they were being asked to produce. Several adjustments were made to prices to bring wheat to 14s 8d a hundredweight in 1941 compared with an average of 7s 9d for the period 1936–38, and fat cattle to 62s 7d per live hundredweight compared with 43s 10d, the average price for 1939. Agricultural prices increased more slowly during the second half of the war. In 1945 they were only 14 per cent higher than the point reached in 1941. Maintaining the differentials in pricing, fat cattle were held to an increase of only ten per cent for the last three years of war, while wheat's price was raised by 28 per cent. Even so, agricultural prices were kept ahead of general wholesale prices throughout the war. In 1943 the government presented the first comprehensive price review, drawn up in consultation with the farmers' unions, the precursor of what became the pattern after the war.

The receipts from sales of farm produce were bound to benefit from such favourable prices. Good yields also helped. With the exception of 1941, harvests during the war were good for all the main

Table 13 Price index numbers 1939–45 (1936–8 = 100)

Year	Cost of living	Wholesale prices	Agricultural prices
1939	104	101	103
1940	121	135	143
1941	130	150	172
1942	131	157	183
1943	130	160	186
1944	132	164	190
1945	133	167	196

Source: K. A. H. Murray, *Agriculture, History of the Second World War* (1955) p. 286

arable crops; 1942 and 1943 were especially good, 1944 about average. The returns for farmers varied greatly according to individual circumstances, but for all receipts were much higher than immediately before the war. Results from a sample of farms in Kesteven are shown in Table 14. For these principal crops receipts more than doubled. Receipts from sales of livestock showed very little change over the course of the war, a measure of the effectiveness of the manipulation of the price mechanism.[41]

Table 14 Receipts per acre from a sample of farms in Kesteven

Year	Wheat	Potatoes	Sugar beet
1939	£ 8.0	£21.7	£17.7
1940	£15.5	£23.2	£32.5
1941	£10.1	£30.5	£27.9
1942	£12.8	£41.8	£37.9
1943	£17.2	£53.7	£35.6
1944	£14.2	£43.2	£34.2
1945	£21.9	£47.6	£46.6

Source: J. H. Smith and P. R. Richardson, *Farming in the Lincolnshire Limestone Areas 1936 to 1947* (University of Nottingham, 1950) pp. 61–72

Note: Receipts are in decimalized old money

Table 15 shows the effect that the relative increases in prices and costs had upon farm income. Estimated net farm income in the United Kingdom rose by more than four times between 1938–39 and 1943–44, falling back following the poorer harvest of 1944. Not surprisingly, in view of the government's priorities for production, it was the large arable farmer who did especially well. Net income per farm for arable farms in England and Wales rose from £285 in 1937–38 to £1,545 in 1943–44. Lincolnshire farmers were no exception in having a generally profitable war. Despite the encouragement of the Wheat Act, the last years of the 1930s were difficult, with most farmers suffering at least

Table 15 Agricultural income in the United Kingdom 1938–9 to 1944–5 (in £ million)

	1938–9	1939–40	1940–1	1941–2	1942–3	1943–4	1944–5
Total receipts*	299.5	354	459.5	499	563.5	596.5	588
Total farm expenses	242	262	303	326	359.5	388.5	406.5
Net income	55.5	112.5	188	208	222.5	230.5	188
Index of net income**	97	196	328	363	389	403	329

*Value of output, plus subsidies and miscellaneous receipts amounting to no more than £12m in any one year

**Index calculated on basis of 1937–8 to 1938–9 = 100

Source: K. A. H. Murray, Agriculture, History of the Second World War (1955) p. 379

one year of loss. From the depths of 1938, farm incomes in the county climbed to a peak in 1942–43. On a sample of farms on the Heath and the Cliff, net incomes rose by 2.7–3.1 per cent between 1939 and 1942.[42] Incomes were knocked back by poorer crops in 1944, but were rising again the following year. As farmers were quick to point out, the levy of Excess Profits Tax made certain that they did not become bloated.

'For the first time since I had been farming the industry was important,' John Cherrington, a farmer in Hampshire, recalled of these times.[43] Farmers emerged from the war with not only their incomes and capital restored, but also with a new spirit of confidence. They had acquired a taste for using machines and fertilizers as never before. Moreover, it became clear that these changes were things not easily to be given up. As the war drew to its close, thoughts both among farmers and in government turned towards how to avoid a repetition of the calamitous slump that followed the First World War. Already in November 1940 the government, in promising guaranteed prices for wheat for the duration of the war, had made assurances that a healthy and stable agriculture would be supported beyond the war. It had been heard before, of course, and was doubtless greeted with a lot of cynicism, but despite the uncertainties of the approach of peace, it became more and more clear that the stage was set for a major and permanent change in British farming.

Notes to Chapter 11

1   The most recent survey of wartime agriculture and policy is contained in John Martin, *The Development of Modern Agriculture: British farming since 1931* (2000). The official history, K. A. H. Murray, *Agriculture, History of the Second World War* (1955) remains valuable. Also R. J. Hammond, *Food and Agriculture in Britain 1939–1945* (1954), Mancur Olsen, *The Economics of Wartime Shortage* (1963).

2   *Farmer and Stockbreeder,* 1 June 1937.

3   *Ibid.,* 18 July 1939, p. 1815.

4   G. B. Wells and A. Mann, 'Farming in Kesteven and Lindsey', *Journal of the Ministry of Agriculture,* v. 54 (1947) p. 156.

5   *Farmer and Stockbreeder,* 29 May 1945, p. 832. For the wider issue of enforcement of policy see Martin, *The Development of Modern Agriculture,* pp. 60–6.

6   Martin, *The Development of Modern Agriculture,* p. 37.

7   *Farmer and Stockbreeder,* 29 October 1934, p. 2423, 2 September 1941.

8   *Ibid.,* 6 May 1941, p. 918.

9   *Farmers' Weekly,* 3 January, 22 August 1941.

10   Martin, *The Development of Modern Agriculture,* p. 39.

11   The figures for acreages in this and the following paragraphs are from *Agricultural Statistics 1939–1944, and 1945–9.*

12   *Farmer and Stockbreeder,* 10 June 1941, pp. 1171, 1176.

13   *Farmers' Weekly,* 14 November 1941, pp. 29–30. J. H. Smith and P. R. Richardson, *Farming in the Lincolnshire Limestone Areas 1936 to 1947* (University of Nottingham, 1950) p. 29.

14   See, for example, Wells and Mann, 'Farming in Kesteven and Lindsey', p. 156.

15   Prices and profits are treated further below, pp. 262–5.

16   National Farmers' Union archives, Potato Committee minutes, MERL, SR NFU AD1/49, p. 380, 17 November 1943.

17   *Farmers' Weekly,* 11 July 1941, 3 November 1944. *Farmer and Stockbreeder,* 13 June 1941, p. 19.

18 J. O. Page, 'Lincolnshire Bulb Flowers', *Journal of the Ministry of Agriculture*, v. 54 (1947) p. 166.

19 *Farmers' Weekly*, 18 August 1944, p. 15.

20 Smith and Richardson, *Farming in the Lincolnshire Limestone Areas 1936 to 1947*, p. 33.

21 *Farmer and Stockbreeder*, 4 June 1940, p. 1235; 13 June 1941, p. 19; 20 January 1942, p. 99.

22 *Agricultural Statistics*.

23 *Farmer and Stockbreeder*, 28 November 1939, p. 2823.

24 Murray, *Agriculture. History of the Second World War*, pp. 82, 123, 188. *Farmer and Stockbreeder*, 23 December 1941, p. 2418.

25 *Farmer and Stockbreeder*, 23 December 1941, p. 2418.

26 *Farmers' Weekly*, 12 March 1943, p. 17.

27 *Farmer and Stockbreeder*, 31 December 1940, pp. 2662–3.

28 *Farmers' Weekly*, 10 April, 2 May, 24 October 1941.

29 *Farmer and Stockbreeder*, 19 September 1939, p. 2286, 12 December 1939, p. 2924.

30 *Ibid.*, 28 November 1939, 4 August 1942. For a similar reaction in another part of the country, see Fred Kitchen, *The Farming Front* (1943).

31 *Farmers' Weekly*, 2 May 1941, p. 43.

32 *Ibid.*, 16 January 1942, p. 14.

33 *Ibid.*, 24 November 1944.

34 *Ibid.*, 23 October 1942. Sadie Ward, *War in the Countryside* (1988) pp. 50–1. R. J. Moore-Colyer, 'Kids in Corn: school harvest camps and farm labour supply in England, 1940–50', *AgHR*, v. 52 (2004) pp. 183–206.

35 H. T. Williams, 'Changes in the Productivity of Labour in British Agriculture, *Journal of the Agricultural Economics Society*, v. 10 (1954) pp. 334–8.

36 Smith and Richardson, *Farming in the Lincolnshire Limestone Areas 1936 to 1947*, p. 44, for example, show increases 2.7 times on the Heath and 2.5 times on the Cliff between 1939 and 1945.

37 *Farmers' Weekly*, 22 September 1939.

38 Edith H. Whetham, 'The Mechanization of British Farming, 1910–1945', *Journal of Agricultural Economics*, v. 21 (1970) pp. 323–6. Smith and Richardson, *Farming in the Lincolnshire Limestone Areas 1936 to 1947*, pp. 53–5. S. J. Wright, 'Farm Implements and Machinery', *JRASE*, v. 102 (1941) p. 35. C. Davies, 'The Mechanization of Lincolnshire Farms', *Journal of the Ministry of Agriculture*, v. 54 (1947) p. 169.

39 Williams, 'Changes in the Productivity of Labour in British Agriculture, p. 336.

40   Smith and Richardson, *Farming in the Lincolnshire Limestone Areas 1936 to 1947*, pp. 52–3.
41   *Ibid.*, pp. 61–74.
42   *Ibid.*, pp. 76–82.
43   John Cherrington, *On the Smell of an Oily Rag* (1979) p. 99.

EPILOGUE

In 1947 the first Royal Show since the war was held at Lincoln. It was a huge success. Attendance figures, at 240,323 over the four days, broke previous records. It overwhelmed the local roads, which were clogged with traffic coming to the show.[1]

The show came as a great relief in the midst of continuing austerity and control, and especially following the hard times recently experienced at the hands of the weather. The long, hard winter of 1947 is notorious. The first snow fell on 22 January, and there were further falls on 36 of the days following until 13 March, when a thaw finally started. Flood followed thaw as the rivers filled with melt-water. Despite some anticipation, and removal of things to safe places, rising waters were soon sweeping away clamps of potatoes and stacks of corn, and were damaging buildings, some beyond repair. The Fens were hit the hardest, with some flood waters as much as eight feet high. Some of the fenland pumping stations were overwhelmed, but on the whole the drainage systems coped remarkably well, such was their general standard of efficiency. Many low-lying lands were still not clear of flood water in May, and waterlogged soils delayed sowing and planting. Drought then followed flood, adding further injury, with soils now baked hard. There were gaps in the potato fields; grass to feed the champion Lincoln Reds in the Marsh was not growing. The long winter and poor spring had resulted in heavy losses of lambs. Not surprisingly, the newspapers found many with long memories to declare this the worst year they had ever known.[2] The financial results of these seasons were also very poor. Farm incomes plummeted, often falling below those of the immediate pre-war years, and, as in all bad years, those with the best reserves of capital were best able to cope.

This was not the best of introductions to peace time. Farming, in common with most of British life, was still conducted under austerity conditions. Most of the items farmers purchased were still rationed.

Fig. 43 Boston market in 1946. This photograph presents a scene of
apparent timelessness despite all the changes experienced by farming
in the immediate past during the war and in the decades before that.
Source: Museum of English Rural Life

The war agricultural executive committees still controlled most of the
operations of farming. Cropping orders continued to determine the
major priorities of cultivation, and these were not very different from
those that had pertained throughout the war. The general balance
between livestock and crops remained upset in many parts of the
county resulting from the intensity of the drive for cash crops during
the war. Fertility, already under pressure during the 1930s, had been run
down in the light-soiled districts. Concerns about the rising cost of
labour were, if anything, more pronounced after the Second World War
than after the first.[3] There had been some relaxations: the imports of
feeding stuffs were starting to rise, and livestock was being allowed to
take a greater role in farming. The pace of change was, however, limited,
and many of the trends in cultivation during the war continued with
little alteration in the years immediately following the return of peace.
The growth of non-food crops was still discouraged and restricted.
Bulb growers, therefore, were faced with particular difficulties. They

were allowed fuel to heat glasshouses only on condition that three-quarters of their area was devoted to food production. Other materials were in short supply and subject to controls, while labour was difficult to obtain. The acreage of bulbs in south Lincolnshire, consequently, had hardly started to return to its pre-war extent, while the Dutch growers were getting back into full production.[4]

Yet, alongside such concerns, G. B. Wells and A. Mann, the advisory officers for the Kesteven and Lindsey divisions, a little in the manner of Philip Pusey a hundred years before them, could declare, 'It must be a long time since the county looked in better form, with ditches and hedges clean and trimmed, the land productive.' Despite the demands placed upon the land by the war, the county was not, in their view, 'farmed out'. The arable farming of Lincolnshire had certainly benefited from government support throughout the war. Mechanization had advanced, with consequent increase in productivity per man. Deep ploughing had helped maintain output through difficult times of war, contributing to the land's generally healthy appearance afterwards.[5]

Much in Lincolnshire's farming had changed in the hundred years between Philip Pusey and Messrs Wells and Mann, but some things had not, and the most important was the continuance of a high farming tradition. Recessions might enforce economies and for some those could be severe, but Lincolnshire men did not believe in stinting the land. 'Despite the bad years between the two wars, farmers were keen to farm well,' was the view of Wells and Mann again.[6] From the time that the concept had gained currency, farming high had held the stronger following among Lincolnshire farmers. Parsimony was not the route to success. The foundations laid during the mid-19th century 'golden age' proved to be remarkably strong. In maintaining this high farming tradition, Lincolnshire's farmers were helped by demand for some of their produce just when they needed it, whether it was malting barley, pedigree sheep, or spring bulbs. Entrepreneurship on the part of a number of farmers helped turn such demands to good account. But if there was one crop that underpinned investment and success it was the potato. It was uneven in its favours. It made a few farmers very rich, and they were most likely to be found in the south of the county. Even so, the influence of this crop was immense throughout most of Lincolnshire.

As the Royal Show opened at Lincoln, the Agriculture Bill was making its passage through the House of Lords. When the Bill had been introduced in Parliament in January it had been greeted with scepticism in farming circles. After all, farmers had heard this type of talk from politicians after the last war. So there was doubt that this Bill really would provide farmers with an assured future, while it certainly seemed to restrict their freedom.[7] However, as the year progressed farmers began to be more accepting of the proposals: the prospect of the continuance of financial support through farm price reviews involving the farmers' unions as partners seemed perhaps a better one than a rapid return to insolvency in free markets. As the farmers of Lincolnshire gathered at the Royal Show in 1947, then, they reflected on the upsets of the winter and spring just past, moaned about the shortages of workers and petrol, the rationing, and licences. But they might also have remembered the generally good results they had enjoyed in recent years, and the good condition of the land that the county advisors had noted, and on such foundation they could look forward to the prospect of renewed growth and development in the county's farming. As always in farming, next year would be better.

Notes to Epilogue

1   Nicholas Goddard, *Harvests of Change: the Royal Agricultural Society of England, 1838–1988* (1988) pp. 164, 171–4. *Royal Show Supplement, JRASE,* v. 108 (1947). *Farmer and Stockbreeder,* 8 July 1947, pp. 1463, 1465ff.

2   Victor Kelsey, 'The Lincolnshire Floods, Spring 1947', *Journal of the Ministry of Agriculture,* v. 54 (1947) pp. 175–8. E. J. Smith, *Black Winter: the story of the storms and floods of 1946–1947 and of the devastation on the land which followed* (*Farmers' Weekly,* 1947) pp. 35ff.

3   J. H. Smith and P. R. Richardson, *Farming in the Lincolnshire Limestone Areas 1936 to 1947* (University of Nottingham, 1950) pp. 47, 85–6.

4   *Farmer and Stockbreeder,* 1 July 1947, pp. 1416–17. J. O. Page, 'Lincolnshire Bulb Flowers', *Journal of the Ministry of Agriculture,* v. 54 (1947) pp. 166–7.

5   G. B. Wells and A. Mann, 'Farming in Kesteven and Lindsey', *Journal of the Ministry of Agriculture,* v. 54 (1947) p. 158.

6   *Ibid.,* p. 154.

7   See, for example, comment in *Farmers' Weekly,* 3, 17 January 1947.

BIBLIOGRAPHY

Abbreviations

AgHR	*Agricultural History Review*
EcHR	*Economic History Review*
JRASE	*Journal of the Royal Agricultural Society of England*
JRSS	*Journal of the Royal Statistical Society*
LAO	Lincolnshire Archives Office
MERL	Museum of English Rural Life
PP	Parliamentary Papers
RC1879	Royal Commission on the Depressed Condition of the Agricultural Interests (the Richmond Commission), 1879
RC1893	Royal Commission on Agriculture, 1893
SM	*Lincoln, Rutland and Stamford Mercury*
VCH	*Victoria County History*

Archive Collections

Lincolnshire Archives Office:
>	Ancaster estate papers (ANC)
>	Burton Scorer deposit (BS)
>	Herbert Carter, Holbeach, accounts (HD65/64)
>	Clarke estate, Markby (Misc Don 157, Higgins 12/3)
>	Dixon estate (DIXON)
>	Dudding of Garthorpe
>	Edlington and Thimbleby cropping records (Misc Dep 265)
>	Heneage estate (HEN)
>	Higgins collection (HIG)
>	Monson estate (MON)
>	Nelthorpe estate (NEL)

Scorer Farm
Taylor, Glover & Hill (2TGH)
Thimbleby deposit
West of Dunholme (also microfilm copy at Museum of
English Rural Life)
Yarborough estate (YARB)

Museum of English Rural Life, Reading
Bridge End Farm, Horbling (FR LIN5)
Fen House Farm, Dorrington (FR LIN3)
Nocton Rise Farm (FR LIN P323)

Public Record Office
Agricultural Returns, parish summaries (MAF68)

Official Publications

Agricultural Returns (later Agricultural Statistics), annually from 1866
Census Returns, 1831–1951
Report on the Decline of the Agricultural Population in Great Britain, Cd. 3273
    (1906)
*Royal Commission on the Employment of Children, Young Persons and Women in
    Agriculture*, Reports and Evidence on Lincolnshire by Edward
    Stanhope, PP, 1867–8(4068), 1868–9(4202)
*Royal Commission on Labour: the agricultural labourer, vol. 1, part 6, Report on
    Lincolnshire*, by Edward Wilkinson, [C6894] (1893)
Royal Commission on the Depressed Condition of the Agricultural Interest, PP, xv,
    xvi (1881), xiv (1882) [The Richmond Commission]: minutes of
    evidence, reports, reports on Lincolnshire by S. B. L. Druce, assistant
    commissioner
Royal Commission on Agriculture, PP, xvi (1894), xvi (1895), xvi (1896):
    minutes of evidence, reports, reports on Lincolnshire by A. Wilson
    Fox; Isle of Axholme by R. Hunter Pringle, assistant commissioners
Royal Commission on Agriculture (1919)
Select Committee on Agriculture (1833)

Select Committee of the House of Lords on the Improvement of Land (1873)
Select Committee on Allotments and Small Holdings, PP, xii (1889), xvii (1890)
Wages and Conditions of Employment in Agriculture. General Report, Cmd 24,
PP, xxii (1919)

Newspapers and magazines

Agricultural Gazette
Bell's Weekly Messenger
Farmer and Stockbreeder
Farmer's Magazine
Farmers' Weekly
Journal of the Board (later *Ministry*) *of Agriculture*
Lincoln, Rutland and Stamford Mercury
Lincolnshire Chronicle
London Gazette
Mark Lane Express

Books and Articles

The Agrarian History of England and Wales, vol. VI, 1750–1850, ed. G. E.
Mingay (Cambridge, 1989)
The Agrarian History of England and Wales, vol. VII, 1850–1914, ed. E. J. T.
Collins (Cambridge, 2000)
The Agrarian History of England and Wales, vol. VIII, 1914–1939, Edith
Whetham (Cambridge, 1978)
Anon, 'Some Lincolnshire Contractors', *Steaming,* vol. 18 (1975)
pp. 70–80.
Armstrong, Alan, *Farmworkers: a social and economic history 1770–1980*
(London, 1988)
Ashby, A. W., 'Bulb Growing in South Lincolnshire', *JRASE,* v. 76
(1915) pp. 110–30
Barnwell, P. S. and C. Giles, *English Farmsteads 1750–1914* (London,
1997)
Baumber, Peter and Dennis Mills, ed., *Kirkby Green and Scopwick: historical
sketches of two Lincolnshire parishes* (Lincoln, 1993)

Bear, W. E., 'The Survival in Farming', *JRASE*, v. 52 (1891) pp. 257-75

Bear, W. E., *A Study of Small Holdings* (London, 1893)

Bear, W. E., 'Flower and Fruit Farming in England', *JRASE*, v. 59 (1898) pp. 286–316, 512–55

Beastall, T. W., *A North Country Estate: the Lumleys and Saundersons as landowners 1600–1900* (London, 1975)

Beastall, T. W., *Agricultural Revolution in Lincolnshire*, History of Lincolnshire v. 8 (Lincoln, 1978)

Beckett, J. V., *The Aristocracy in England 1660–1914* (London, 1986)

Beckett, J. V., 'Lincolnshire and the East Midlands: a historian's perspective', *Agriculture and Lincolnshire History and Archaeology*, v. 27 (1992) pp. 23–6

Bellerby, J. R., *Industry Relative Income* (London, 1956)

Bennett, S. & N., *An Historical Atlas of Lincolnshire* (Lincoln, 1993)

Bensusan, S. L., *Latter Day Rural England* (London, 1928)

Bonnett, H., *Saga of the Steam Plough* (London, 1965)

Bowie, G. G. S., 'Northern Wolds and Wessex Downlands: contrasts in sheep husbandry and farming practice, 1770–1850', *AgHR*, v. 38 (1990) pp. 117–26

Bracey, H. W., *History of Seed Crushing in Great Britain* (London, 1960)

Brassey, Thomas, 'Agriculture in England and the United States', *JRSS*, v. 42 (1879) pp. 751–64

Bridges, A. and H. Whitby, *Studies in Power Farming: I. Mechanized Corn-growing* (Oxford, 1936)

Brigden, R. D., Farming in partnership: the Leckford estate and the pursuit of profit in inter-war agriculture, PhD thesis, University of Reading (2000)

British Yearbook of Agriculture 1908–9 (London, 1908)

Brook, A. S., 'Farm Buildings of North Kesteven: two examples', *Journal of the Historic Farm Buildings Group*, v. 9 (1995), pp. 12–24

Burke, John, 'Breeding and Management of Horses on a Farm', *JRASE*, v. 5 (1844) pp. 508–46

Burnett, John, *Plenty and Want* (London, 1966)

Bygott, J., *Eastern England* (London, 1923)

Cadle, C., 'The Farming Customs and Covenants of England', *JRASE*, v. 29 (1868) pp. 144–75

Caird, James, *English Agriculture in 1850–51* (London, 1852)

Caird, James, 'General View of British Agriculture', *JRASE,* v. 39 (1878) pp. 271–333

Cannadine, D.,*The Decline and Fall of the British Aristocracy* (London, 1998)

Carslaw, R. McG. and P. E. Graves, 'Farm Organization on the Black Fens of the Isle of Ely', *JRASE,* v. 98 (1937) pp. 35–53

Carslaw, R. McG. and P. E. Graves, 'Farm Organization on the Silty Soils of Holland, Lincolnshire', *JRASE,* vol. 99 (1938) pp. 54–76

Carter, E. S., 'The Agriculture of Lincolnshire', *JRASE,* v. 131 (1970) pp. 56–68

Cherrington, John, *On the Smell of an Oily Rag* (London, 1979)

Chivers, Keith, *The Shire Horse: a history of the breed, the society and the men* (London, 1976)

Clarke, J. A., 'On the Great Level of the Fens, including the Fens of South Lincolnshire', *JRASE,* v. 8 (1847) pp. 80–133

Clarke, J. A., 'On the Farming of Lincolnshire', *JRASE,* v. 12 (1851) pp. 259–414

Clarke, J. A., 'Practical Agriculture', *JRASE,* v. 39 (1878) pp. 445–642

Clifford, Frederick, 'The Agricultural Holdings (England) Act, 1883', *JRASE*, v. 45 (1884), pp. 1–77

Collins, G. E., 'Agriculture', *Victoria County History, Lincolnshire*, v. 2 (1906) pp. 397–415

Collins, G. E., 'Lincolnshire Red Shorthorns', *JRASE,* v. 75 (1914), pp. 33–40

Collins, G. E., 'From Fen to Farm, Heath to Husbandry', *Lincolnshire Magazine,* v.1 (1934)

Cooke, F. I., 'Report on the Farm Prize Competition in Nottinghamshire and Lincolnshire in 1888, class I', *JRASE,* v. 49 (1888) pp. 508–65

Cooper, A. F., *British Agricultural Policy, 1912–36: a study in Conservative politics* (Manchester, 1989)

Cory, V., 'The Development of Farming in the Isle of Axholme', *JRASE,* v. 147 (1986) pp. 54–60

Cox, G., P. Lowe and M. Winter, 'The Origins and Early Development of the National Farmers' Union', *Agricultural History Review*, v. 39 (1991) pp. 30–47

Crust, Linda, 'William Paddison: marsh farmer and survivor of the agricultural depression, 1873–96', *Agricultural History Review*, v. 43 (1995) pp. 193–204

Darby, H. C., *The Draining of the Fens* (Cambrdige, 2nd ed. 1956)

Davies, C., 'The Mechanization of Lincolnshire Farms', *Journal of the Ministry of Agriculture*, v. 54 (1947) pp. 168–70

Davies, John, 'The End of the Great Estates and the rise of Freehold Farming in Wales', *Welsh Historical Review*, v. 7 (1974) pp. 188–212

Denton, J. Bailey, *The Farm Homesteads of England* (London, 1864 ed.)

Dewey, Peter E., 'British Farming Profits and Government Policy during the First World War', *EcHR*, 2nd ser., v. 37 (1984) pp. 373–90

Dunbabin, J. P. D., 'The "Revolt of the Field"; the agricultural labourers' movement in the 1970s', *Past and Present*, v. 26 (1963) pp. 68-97

Eagle, E. C., 'Some Light on the Beginnings of the Lincolnshire Bulb Industry', *Lincolnshire Historian*, no. 6 (Autumn 1950) pp. 220–9

Edwards, K. C., 'Lincolnshire', in J. Mitchell (ed.), *Great Britain: geographical essays* (Cambridge, 1962) pp. 308–29

Ernle, Lord, *English Farming Past and Present* (London, 6th ed. 1961)

Everley, Lord, 'The Decline in the number of Agricultural Labourers in Great Britain', *JRSS*, v. 70 (1907) pp. 267–306

Fell, H. R., 'Two Notable Lincolnshire Farmers', *JRASE*, v. 152 (1991) pp. 36–46

Fenton, Michael, *Farmers and Farming in Lindsey 1900–1914* (London, 1978)

Fream, *The Complete Grazier* (London, 1893 ed.)

Fricker, B. J., 'The Agriculture of Gloucestershire', *Journal of the Bath and West of England Society*, 6th ser., v. 14 (1939–40) pp. 16–21

Fuller, G. Joan, 'The Development of Drainage, Agriculture and Settlement in the Fens of South Eat Lincolnshire during the Nineteenth Century', *East Midland Geographer*, v. 7 (1957) pp. 3–15

Fussell, G. E., *The Farmer's Tools* (London, 1952)

Gresswell, Fred, *Bright Boots* (London, 1956)

Grigg, D. B., *The Agricultural Revolution in South Lincolnshire* (Cambridge, 1966)

Grigg, D. B., 'The Development of Tenant Right in South Lincolnshire', *Lincolnshire Historian*, v. 2, no. 9 (1962) pp. 41–8

Hall, Adrian, *Fenland Worker–Peasants: the economy of smallholders at Rippingale, Lincolnshire 1791–1871* (Supplement to *Agricultural History Review*, 1992)

Hall, A., 'A Lincolnshire Horseman: work and class', *Oral History*, v. 5 (1977) pp. 88–96

Hall, A. D., *A Pilgrimage of British Farming* (London, 1913)

Hammond, R. J., *Food and Agriculture in Britain 1939–45* (London, 1954)

Haresign, S. R., Agricultural Change and Rural Society on the Lincolnshire Fenlands and Isle of Axholme, 1870–1914, PhD thesis, University of East Anglia, 1980

Haresign, S. R., 'Small Farms and Allotments as a Cure for Rural Depopulation on the Lincolnshire Fenland 1870–1914', *Lincolnshire History and Archaeology*, v. 18 (1983) pp. 27–36.

Harvey, Nigel, *A History of Farm Buildings in England and Wales* (Newton Abbot, 1970)

Hasbach, W., *A History of the English Agricultural Labourer* (London, 1908)

Heath, Richard, *The English Peasant* (London, 1893)

Hill, Sir Francis, *Victorian Lincoln* (Cambridge, 1974)

Hogg, W. H., 'The Farm Prize Competition', *JRASE,* v. 68 (1907) pp. 166–90

Holderness, B. A., Rural Society in South East Lindsey, unpublished PhD thesis, University of Nottingham, 1968

Holderness, B. A., 'Landlord's Capital Formation in East Anglia, 1750–1870', *EcHR,* 2 ser, v. 25 (1972) pp. 434–47

Holderness, B. A., 'The Origins of High Farming', in *Land Labour and Agriculture 1700–1920,* ed. B. A. Holderness and M. E. Turner (1991) pp. 149–64

Holderness, B. A., 'Agriculture' in *Twentieth Century Lincolnshire*, ed. Dennis R. Mills (Lincoln, 1989) pp. 37–73

Horn, Pamela, *Rural Life in England in the First World War* (London, 1984)

Howard, C. E., 'Lincoln Longwools', *Lincolnshire Magazine*, v. 2 (1934)

Hunt, Ruby, 'Portrait of a Village: Kirton', *Lincolnshire Life* (February 1969)

Jebb, L., *The Small Holdings of England* (London, 1907)

Jenkins, H. M., 'Farm Reports 3. Aylesby, Riby and Rothwell Farms, near Grimsby, Lincolnshire, in the occupation of Mr William Torr', *JRASE*, v. 30 (1869) pp. 415–42

Johnson, A., Enclosure and the Changing Agricultural Landscape of Lindsey from the Sixteenth to the Nineteenth Century, University of Liverpool MA, 1957

Jones, E. L., *Seasons and Prices* (London 1964)

Kain, R. J. P. and H. C. Prince, *The Tithe Surveys of England and Wales* (London, 1985)

Keary, H. W., 'On the Management of Barley', *JRASE*, v. 10 (1849) pp. 453–62

Kelsey, Victor, 'The Lincolnshire Floods, Spring 1947', *Journal of the Ministry of Agriculture*, v. 54 (1947) pp. 175–8

Kightly, Charles, *Country Voices: life and lore in farm and village* (London, 1984)

Kitchen, Fred, *The Farming Front* (London 1943)

Knox, Allan, 'The East Midland Counties', in *Regional Types of British Farming*, ed. J. P. Maxton (1936), pp. 95–111

Lavergne, Leonce de, *The Rural Economy of England, Scotland and Ireland* (London, 1855)

Layton, W. T. and G. Crowther, *An Introduction to the Study of Prices* (London, 3rd ed. 1938)

Leak, G. W., 'The Bulb Growing Industry' *Lincolnshire Magazine*, v. 1 (1934)

Levy, H., *Large and Small Holdings* (London, 1911)

Londonderry, Edith, Marchioness of, *Henry Chaplin, a memoir* (London, 1926)

Longstaffe, G. B., 'Rural Depopulation', *JRSS*, v. 56 (1893)

McCrone, Gavin, *The Economics of Subsidising Agriculture* (London, 1962)

MacDonald, W., 'On the Relative Profits to the Farmer from Horse, Cattle and Sheep Breeding, Rearing and Feeding in the United Kingdom', *JRASE*, v. 37 (1876) pp. 1–109

McHardy, D. N., *Power Farming for Crops and Stock* (London, 1938)

McIntosh, T. P., *The Potato* (London, 1927)

Makings, S. M., *Lincoln Wold Farming* (Loughborough, 1939)

Malden, W. J., *British Sheep and Shepherding* [1890s]

Martin, John, *The Development of Modern Agriculture: British farming since 1931* (London, 2000)

Matthews, A. H. H., *Fifty Years of Agricultural Politics* (London, 1915)

Mills, Dennis R., 'The Small Farm with special reference to Victorian Lincolnshire', *Lincolnshire Past and Present*, no. 24 (1996) pp. 7–11

Mills, Dennis R., ed., *Twentieth Century Lincolnshire*, History of Lincolnshire v. 12 (Lincoln, 1989)

Mills, Dennis R., 'The Regions of Kesteven devised for the purpose of Agricultural History', *Reports and Papers of the Lincolnshire Architectural and Archaeological Society*, v. 7 (1957) pp. 60–82

Ministry of Agriculture, *National Farm Survey of England and Wales (1941–43): a summary report* (1946)

Ministry of Agriculture, Fisheries and Food, *A Century of Agricultural Statistics: Great Britain 1866–1966* (1968)

Mitchell, B. R. and P. Deane, *Abstract of British Historical Statistics* (Cambridge, 1962)

Mitchell, B. R. and H.G. Jones, *Second Abstract of British Historical Statistics* (Cambridge, 1971)

Moore-Colver, R. J., 'Kids in Corn: school harvest camps and farm labour supply in England, 1940–50', *AgHR*, v. 52 (2004) pp. 183–206

Morgan, Raine, The Root Crop in English Agriculture, 1650–1870, PhD thesis, University of Reading, 1978

Morton, J. C., 'The Past Agricultural Year', *JRASE*, v. 41 (1880) pp. 210–49

Murray, K. A. H., *Agriculture, History of the Second World War* (London, 1955)

Mutch, Alistair, 'Farmers' Organizations and Agricultural Depression in Lancashire, 1890–1900', *AgHR*, v. 31 (1983) pp. 26–36

Nelson, G. K., *To Be a Farmer's Boy* (London, 1991)

NFU Yearbook (1926)

Obelkevitch, James, *Religion and Rural Society in South Lindsey 1825–1875* (London, 1976)

Offer, Avner, 'Farm Tenure and Land Values in England c1750–1950', *EcHR*, v. 44 (1991) pp. 1–20

Ogle, W. 'The Alleged Depopulation of the Rural Districts', *JRSS*, v. 52 (1889)

Olney, R. J., *Lincolnshire Politics 1832–1885* (Oxford, 1973)

Olney, R. J. (ed.), *Labouring Life on the Lincolnshire Wolds* (Sleaford, 1975)

Olney, R. J., *Rural Society and County Government in Nineteenth-century Lincolnshire*, History of Lincolnshire v. 10 (Lincoln, 1979)

Olsen, Mancur, *The Economics of Wartime Shortage* (London, 1963)

Orwin, C. S. and E. H. Whetham, *History of British Agriculture 1846–1914* (London, 1964)

Page, John, 'The Sources of Supply of the Manchester Fruit and Vegetable Markets, *JRASE*, vol. 41 (1880) pp. 475–85

Page, J. O., 'Lincolnshire Bulb Flowers', *Journal of the Ministry of Agriculture*, v. 54 (1947) pp. 165–7

Parker, C. T., 'Sir John Henry Thorold, Bart.', *JRASE*, vol. 83 (1922) pp. 1–3

Perkins, J. A., 'Tenure, Tenant Right and Agricultural Progress in Lindsey 1780–1850', *AgHR*, v. 23 (1975) pp. 1–23

Perkins, J. A., 'Harvest Technology and Labour Supply in Lincolnshire and the East Riding of Yorkshire 1750–1850, part I', *Tools and Tillage*, v. 3 (1976) pp. 47–58

Perkins, J. A., *Sheep Farming in Eighteenth and Nineteenth Century Lincolnshire* (Sleaford, 1977)

Perkins, J. A., 'Allotments in Nineteenth-Century Lincolnshire', *Lincolnshire History and Archaeology*, v. 18 (1983) pp. 21–25

Perry, P. J., *British Agriculture 1875–1914* (London, 1973)

Perry, P. J., 'Where was the "Great Agricultural Depression"? A geography of agricultural bankruptcy in late Victorian England and Wales', *AgHR*, v. 20 (1972), reprinted in P. J. Perry (ed.), *British Agriculture 1875–1914* (1973) pp. 129–148

Phillips, A. D. M., *The Underdraining of Farmland in England during the Nineteenth Century* (London, 1989)

Phillips, A. D. M., 'Landlord Investment in Farm Buildings in the English Midlands in the Mid Nineteenth Century', in *Land Labour and Agriculture 1700–1920*, ed. B. A. Holderness and M. E. Turner (1991) pp. 191–210

Pratt, E. A., *The Transition in Agriculture* (London, 1906)

Prewett, F. J., *Progress in English Farming Systems I: milk production on arable land* (London, 1929)

Proctor, Jim, 'Cole Brothers, Roxholme, Sleaford', *Steaming*, v. 18 (1975) pp. 109–11

Pusey, Philip, 'The Improvement of Peaty Ground', *JRASE*, v. 2 (1841) pp. 400–16

Pusey, Philip, 'On the Progress of Agricultural Knowledge during the last Four Years', *JRASE*, v. 3 (1842) pp. 169–217

Pusey, Philip, 'On the Agricultural Improvements of Lincolnshire', *JRASE*, v. 4 (1843) pp. 287–316

Rawding, Charles K., *Binbrook 1900–1939* (Binbrook, 1991)

Rawding, Charles K., *The Lincolnshire Wolds in the Nineteenth Century* (Lincoln, 2001)

Redmore, Ken, 'The Early Days of Steam–powered Threshing', *Lincolnshire Past & Present*, 53 (Autumn 2003) pp. 7–8

Rider Haggard, H., *Rural England* (London, 1902)

Robinson, G. M., *Agricultural Change* (London, 1988)

Robinson, H. G., 'Company Farming and Direct Marketing', *Country Life*, vol. 62, 3 December 1927, pp. 851–3

Ruddock, J. G. and R. E. Pearson, *The Railway History of Lincoln* (Lincoln, 1974)

Russell, E. & R. C., *Making New Landscapes in North Lincolnshire* (Lincoln, 1983)

Russell, E. & R. C., *Parliamentary Enclosure and New Lincolnshire Landscapes* (Lincoln, 1987)

Russell, Sir John, *The Farm and the Nation* (London, 1933)

Russell, Rex, *The 'Revolt of the Field' in Lincolnshire* (Lincoln, 1956)

Russell, Rex, *Cottagers and Cows 1880–1892* (London, 1987)

Saloman, R. N., *The History and Social Influence of the Potato* (London, rev. ed. 1985)

Saunders, Gordon, 'The Claying of the Fen Lands', *Journal of the Ministry of Agriculture*, v. 48 (1942) pp. 42–3

Scola, Roger, *Feeding the Victorian City: the food supply of Manchester 1770–1870* (Manchester, 1992)

Scott Hall, H., *Farming by Fiat,* advertising pamphlet for Fiat tractors (MERL, TR MRL P2/B51)

Sheail, John, 'The role of the war agricultural executive committees in the food production campaign of 1915–1918 in England and Wales', *Agricultural Administration*, v. 1 (1974) pp. 141–54

Skehel, M., *A Taste of Lincoln Red* (Lincoln, 1995)

Smith, G., *The Land of Britain, part 69, the Fens* (Land Utilization Survey, London, 1937)

Smith, J. H. and P. R. Richardson, *Farming in the Lincolnshire Limestone Areas 1936 to 1947* (Nottingham, 1950)

Squarey, E. P., ' Farm Capital', *JRASE*, v. 39 (1878) pp. 425–44

Stamp, L. Dudley, *Land Utilization Survey of England, parts 76–77* (London, 1942)

Stirton, Thomas, 'Report on the Farm Prize Competition in Nottinghamshire and Lincolnshire, classes 2 and 3', *JRASE*, v.50 (1889) pp. 34–91

Steele, David I. A., *A Lincolnshire Village: the parish of Corby Glen in its historical context* (London, 1979)

Steele, Mary, *Lincolnshire: land, longwools and legends* (Lincoln, 1996)

Stovin, J., *Journals of a Methodist Farmer, 1871–1875* (London, 1982)

Straw, Alan, 'The Ancholme Levels North of Brigg: a history of drainage and its effect on land utilization', *East Midland Geographer,* no. 3 (June 1955) pp. 37–41

Straw, Alan, *The Soils of Lincolnshire* (Lincoln, 1969)

Street, A. G., *Farming England* (London, 1937)

Sturmey, S. G., 'Owner Farming in England and Wales 1900–1950', in W. E. Minchinton, ed. *Essays in Agrarian History*, v. 2 (London, 1968) pp. 281–306

Symons, G. J., 'Recent British Weather', *JRASE*, v. 44 (1883) pp. 411–21

Tariff Commission v.3 Report of the Agricultural Committee (London, 1906)

Thirsk, Joan, *English Peasant Farming* (Cambridge, 1957)

Thompson, F. M. L., 'Agriculture since 1870', *VCH Wiltshire*, vol. 4 (1959) pp. 92–114

Thompson, F. M. L., *English Landed Society in the Nineteenth Century* (London, 1963) pp. 62–77

Thompson, F. M. L., 'The Second Agricultural Revolution', *EcHR,* 2 ser. v.21 (1968)

Thompson, F. M. L., 'Rural Society and Agricultural Change in
   Nineteenth–century Britain', in *Agrarian Organization in the century of
   Industrialization: Europe, Russia and North America,* ed. G. Grantham
   and C. S. Leonard (*Research in Economic History,* Supplement 5, part A,
   1989) pp. 187–202
Thompson, F. M. L., 'English Landed Society in the Twentieth Century
   I', *Transactions of the Royal Historical Society* Fifth series, v. 40 (1990)
   pp. 1–24
Thompson, F. M. L., 'An Anatomy of English Agriculture 1870–1914',
   in *Land Labour and Agriculture 1700–1920,* ed. B. A. Holderness and
   M. E. Turner (London, 1991) pp. 211–40
Tiffin, Tom, *The Origin of the Farmers' Union* (1949)
[Torr] 'The Late William Torr: a compilation from many sources',
   JRASE, v. 36 (1875) pp. 303–9
Trow-Smith, R., *A History of British Livestock Husbandry 1700–1900* (1959)
Turner, M. E., 'Output and Prices in UK Agriculture 1867–1914', *AgHR,*
   v. 40 (1992) pp. 38–51
Turner, M. E., J. V. Beckett and B. Afton, *Agricultural Rent in England
   1690–1914* (Cambridge, 1997)
Turner, M. E., J. V. Beckett and B. Afton, *Farm Production in England
   1700–1914* (Cambridge, 2001)
University of Cambridge Department of Agriculture, *Landownership in the
   Eastern Counties 1941* (1941)
Wade-Martins, Susanna and Tom Williamson, *Roots of Change (Agricultural
   History Review,* supplement series 2, 1999)
Wallace, J. C., 'Fenland Farming', *Agricultural Progress,* v. 11 (1934)
   pp. 52–65
Wallace, J. C., 'Notable Farming Enterprises: an up-to-date farming and
   horticultural enterprise', *JRASE,* v. 96 (1935) pp. 100–8
Wallace, J. C., 'The Development of Potato-growing in Lincolnshire',
   JRASE, v. 115 (1954) pp. 60–8
Ward, Sadie, *War in the Countryside* (London, 1988)
Watson, J. A. S., *Rural Britain Today and Tomorrow* (London, 1934)
Waugh, James, 'Narcissus Cultivation', *Journal of the Board of Agriculture,* v.
   15 (1908–9) pp. 897–909

Wells, G. B. and A. Mann, 'Farming in Kesteven and Lindsey', *Journal of the Ministry of Agriculture*, v. 54 (1947) pp. 153–8

Wells, G. B., 'Some Aspects of East Midland Agriculture: 5 Lincolnshire (Kesteven)', *JRASE*, v. 115 (1954) pp. 16–19

Wheeler, W. H., *History of the Fens of South Lincolnshire* (London, 1896)

Whetham, Edith H., 'The Mechanization of British Farming, 1910–1945', *Journal of Agricultural Economics*, v. 21 (1970) pp. 317–31

Whetham, Edith H., *see also The Agrarian History of England and Wales, vol. VIII*

Whitehead, Charles, 'Fifty Years of Fruit Farming', *JRASE*, v. 50 (1889) pp. 156–80

Williams, G. M., 'On the Tenant's Rights to Unexhausted Improvements According to the Custom of North Lincolnshire', *JRASE*, v. 6 (1845) pp. 44–6

Williams, H. T., 'Changes in the Productivity of Labour in British Agriculture, *Journal of the Agricultural Economics Society*, v. 10 (1954) pp. 332–55

Wilson Fox, A., 'Agricultural Wages in England and Wales during the last half century', *JRSS*, v. 66 (1903), reprinted in W. E. Minchinton (ed.), *Essays in Agrarian History* (London, 1968) v. 2, pp. 121–98

Woodhead, Len, *A Lincolnshire Lad Looks Back* (Driffield, 2003)

Wright, Neil R., *Lincolnshire Towns and Industry 1700–1914*, History of Lincolnshire v. 11 (Lincoln, 1982)

Wright, S. J., 'Farm Implements and Machinery', *JRASE*, v. 102 (1941) pp. 34-44

Wrightson, John, 'The Agricultural Lessons of the Eighties', *JRASE*, v. 51 (1890) pp. 275–88

Young, Arthur, *General View of the Agriculture of Lincolnshire* (London, 1799)

Young, Arthur, *General View of the Agriculture of Lincolnshire* (London, 1813)

INDEX